Auto Body Repair and Refinishing

Third Edition

Auto Body Repair and Refinishing

Third Edition

John W. Hogg

McGRAW-HILL RYERSON LIMITED

Toronto Montreal New York Auckland Bogotá Cairo Caracas Hamburg
Lisbon London Madrid Mexico Milan New Delhi Panama Paris
San Juan São Paulo Singapore Sydney Tokyo

Auto Body Repair and Refinishing, Third Edition
Copyright © McGraw-Hill Ryerson Limited, 1988, 1978
Copyright © McGraw-Hill Company of Canada Limited, 1969
All rights reserved. No part of this publication may be re-
produced, stored in a retrieval system, or transmitted, in any
form, or by any means, mechanical, electronic, photocopy-
ing, recording or otherwise, without the prior written per-
mission of McGraw-Hill Ryerson Limited.

ISBN 0-07-548869-8

4 5 6 7 8 9 0 D 7 6 5 4 3 2 1

Printed and bound in Canada

Technical illustrations for third edition by Denis Trower

Canadian Cataloguing in Publication Data

Hogg, John W., date —
   Auto body repair and refinishing

ISBN 0-07-548869-8

1. Automobiles — Bodies — Maintenance and repair.
2. Automobiles — Painting.   I. Title.

TL255.H63 1988   629.2'6   C87-093372-8

CONTENTS

Preface vii

Introduction viii

Chapter One: Automobile Construction 1

Chapter Two: Hand Tools 35

Chapter Three: Fasteners 53

Chapter Four: Sheet Metal Damage and Repair 65

Chapter Five: Body Fillers 107

Chapter Six: Plastics and Fibreglass 121

Chapter Seven: Oxy-Acetylene Processes 144

Chapter Eight: Electric Welding 168

Chapter Nine: Expansion, Contraction, Heat Distortion,
        and Shrinking 190

Chapter Ten: Panel-Forming Techniques 206

Chapter Eleven: Fitting Methods 220

Chapter Twelve: Conventional Frame and Unitized Body Design 247

Chapter Thirteen: Frame Straightening: Suspension
        and Steering Systems 270

Chapter Fourteen: Surface Preparation 298

Chapter Fifteen: Refinishing Materials 312

Chapter Sixteen: Spray Equipment 332

Chapter Seventeen: Paint Preparation and Spraying Procedures 351

Chapter Eighteen: Automotive Electricity 371

PREFACE

Auto Body Repair and Refinishing has been written for the auto body student, the apprentice, and, to some extent, the journeyman.

All aspects of the auto body trade are covered. It is hoped that the student will learn about both the theoretical and the practical aspects of the many skills needed in the trade when studying from this text.

The book is written from the standpoint of *how* things are done in the repair shop, *in what order,* and *why,* keeping in mind the pitfalls the student may encounter in the shop. Each chapter contains all the up-to-date information for that specific area of theory or repair. Those areas with which students often have difficulty are explained in greater detail.

This third edition has been considerably revised. Most vehicles made today have unibody construction. In the seventies, the majority of vehicles had a separate frame with a body mounted on it. As well, many changes to vehicles are due to the use of lightweight, high-strength steels and, increasingly, plastics.

Cars, vans, and small trucks have all been downsized. Certainly much has changed since the publication of the second edition in 1978; these changes are well addressed in this third edition.

The use of high-strength, lighter steel has required new welding methods, since heating must be minimized in order to retain the steel's strength. GMAW (gas metal arc welding) or MIG (metal inert gas) has been expanded on in this edition.

The new unibody construction demands new straightening techniques and equipment required to retain strength. Those chapters on frame straightening have been much expanded on. Since front-wheel drive is more prevalent, sections on steering and suspension affected by collision and repair have been given new attention.

INTRODUCTION

CAREERS

The auto body trade encompasses the servicing and repair of the body and other related mechanical components of automobiles, trucks, and buses. The repairer's responsibilities consist of servicing, diagnosing, and repairing damaged or corroded vehicles, both new and used. The repair person must be able to comprehend the extent of the damage and formulate the method and sequence of repair, as well as actually complete the necessary repairs. After the repairs are complete, the correct paint preparation, finish painting, final assembly, and clean-up operations are performed.

The auto body student will be a person who can accept the challenge of having to apply logic and reasoning to the repair procedures, and who enjoys working with his or her hands to actually complete the necessary work.

As each make of vehicle is somewhat different in design and construction, so too is every accident and the damage sustained. The auto body repairer must also be willing to learn about new materials, products, tools, and repair processes. The vehicle design and the materials used are continually changing. New metals, many types of plastics, electronic controls, and computers are examples of the ever-changing technology that must be diagnosed and repaired. The repairer must be able to understand, repair, and weld metals; bond or weld plastics; remove and replace glass; disconnect, check, and replace electrical, sheet metal, and mechanical parts and components; as well as repair upholstered seats; etc. Understanding and operating the specialized straightening equipment needed to straighten and align the damaged body is most important. All of these procedures might be necessary in the repair of a single accident-damaged vehicle.

The refinishing operations themselves are so complex that many people specialize in the surface preparation and final refinishing of the vehicle. A refinisher must be knowledgeable in the many different paint products, their purpose and their application, and is likely to have a special "artistic touch." The auto body repairer may be a combination body repair person as well as a painter. However, most people tend to specialize in either one area of the trade or the other. The great variety of auto body job operations offers the repair person a long list of related work opportunities.

Specialities in the auto body trade include:

- painting
- glass installation
- interior and upholstery repair
- wheel alignment
- metal fabrication
- fibreglass and plastic work
- specialized vehicle building or antique and classic vehicle restorations

Other opportunities for people with an auto body background include:

- estimator
- insurance appraiser
- manufacturer's sales representative
- jobs in the parts supply industry
- auto assembly jobs

METRICATION

Automboile manufacturers across North America are still in the long process of changing to SI metric tools, supplies, and measurements. SI (Système Internationale) is a simplified metric system that is being adopted world wide. The auto body repair student must expect to live and work in an SI world.

Many SI quantity units may be multiplied or divided by factors of ten to multiples. These multiples and sub-multiples have prefix names which attach to the quantity unit, as well as accepted SI symbols. Common prefix names, their symbols, and meanings are:

Giga	G	one billion
Mega	M	one million
kilo	k	one thousand
hecto	h	one hundred
deca	da	ten
deci	d	one tenth

centi	c	one hundredth
milli	m	one thousandth
micro	μ	one millionth
nano	n	one billionth

Quantities commonly measured in automotive work and their SI units and symbols are given in the following chart.

Students should be familiar with these units and their symbols. Although SI units and proper SI style are used throughout this text, many automobiles still on the road are built to imperial standards with imperial supplies and tools. Also some supplies and materials used in auto body repair procedures are not yet available in metric sizes. In some areas standards still have not been decided.

Students must therefore have a working knowledge of those imperial supplies and materials which they may need to use. In cases where both metric and imperial materials may be encountered, coverage has been given to both. Sometimes only imperial supplies or standards exist.

Quantity	Unit	Symbol
length	metre	m
area	square metre, square centimetre square millimetre	m^2, cm^2, mm^2
volume or capacity	cubic metre, cubic decimetre or litre cubic centimetre	m^3, dm^3 or L, cm^3
mass	gram	g
time	second (minute, hour)	s (min,h)
force	newton	N
pressure	pascal	Pa
temperature	degree Celsius	°C
electrical potential	volt	V
electrical current	ampere	A
electrical resistance	ohm	Ω
frequency	hertz	Hz
energy or work	joule	J
power	watt	W
torque	newton-metre	N • m

DEFINITIONS

Base Units

metre The metre is equivalent to the length of 1 650 763.73 wave lengths of radiation of the krypton-86 atom, in transition between levels $2p_{10}$ and $5d_5$, when measured in a uum. In everyday language, this is equivalent to about half the height of an average door.

kilogram The kilogram is equal to the mass of the international prototype of the kilogram, kept in a special vault in France. 1000 mL of pure water has a mass of 1 kg.

second The second equals 9 192 631 770 periods of radiation of the transition between two hyperfine levels of the ground state of the caesium-133 atom.

Kelvin The Kelvin measures temperature. On this scale absolute zero is 1/273.16 of the freezing point of water, zero is the freezing point, and 100°K is the point at which water boils. The degree Celsius is used instead of the degree Kelvin for everyday use. The Celsius scale is exactly the same as the Kelvin scale, except that the Celsius uses "below zero" readings below the freezing point of water.

ampere The ampere is the unvarying electrical current flowing through two conductors positioned one metre apart in a vacuum which will produce between the conductors a force of 2×10^{-7} N/m of length. The conductors must be extremely thin, straight, and parallel.

Derived Units

newton The newton is the force which will give a 1 kg mass an acceleration of one metre per second squared.

joule A joule is the work done or energy expended when the surface on which a force of one newton is applied moves a distance of one metre in the direction of the force.

watt One watt equals the power of one joule per second.

ohm The ohm is the electrical resistance present between two points on a conductor when a potential of one volt, present between these two points, produces a current of one ampere. The conductor must not generate any of its own electricity.

pascal The pascal is the pressure created by a force of one newton applied over an area of one square metre.

hertz The hertz is the frequency of any periodic phenomenon of which the periodic time is one second.

volt The volt is the difference of electrical potential or pressure between two points of a conductor which carries a constant current of one ampere when the power spent between the two points equals one watt.

SAFETY

When working on a motor vehicle, you should be safety conscious at all times. You should never take unnecessary chances.

- Never go under any raised vehicle without first placing proper holding stands under it. Make sure that the stands are in a correct position so that there is no chance of the vehicle falling.

- Never weld or bring a flame close to inflammable paints, paint solvents, or their containers. Similarly, welding flames and gasoline do not mix.

- Always have both a water-type and a foam smothering-type fire extinguisher handy when you are welding around a vehicle. The water-type extinguisher should be used on upholstery, dust, and small underseal fires. The smothering-type extinguisher should always be used for gasoline and oil fires.

- Never run the engine of a vehicle in a closed building without venting the exhaust. Deadly carbon monoxide fumes given off through the exhaust are colourless and odourless. They give no warning before striking.

- Always be safety conscious. It might save your life.

Auto Body Repair and Refinishing

Third Edition

1 AUTOMOBILE CONSTRUCTION

1-1 History
1-2 Modern Vehicle Design
1-3 Panels
1-4 Body Parts Identification
1-5 Front End Assembly
1-6 Radiators
1-7 Doors
1-8 Interior Hardware and Trim
1-9 Seat Construction
1-10 Exterior Trim
1-11 Glass

1-1 HISTORY

The first automobiles were developed from the early horsedrawn carriage. The body was little more than a single seat, and very little safety or protection from the weather was given to the occupants (Figure 1-1A). What little body there was was made of solid wood panels in a "slab" side design, like a wooden box. The bodies were gradually made larger and more stylish. Canvas tops and glass windshields were added (Figure 1-1B, C) and, finally, completely closed-in bodies with glass side windows appeared.

These larger, more stylish body styles necessitated a change in construction design (Figure 1-1D). They would have been square-looking and far too heavy if made with a slab design. Instead, a body "skeleton" was made from a wooden framework, as illustrated in Figure 1-2. Thin plywood type wooden panels were nailed to the body skeleton. This outer panel covering was gradually replaced with sheet metal panels formed to the wooden body framework and nailed in place.

This type of body construction continued to be used by some vehicle manufacturers until the mid-1930s. Other manufacturers had already switched to complete steel constructed bodies by the late 1920s.

The wooden body "skeleton" frame was slow and difficult to make. Each part was individually cut and then fitted to form the

1

Courtesy Collections of Greenfield Village and the Henry Ford Museum, Dearborn, Michigan

Figure 1-1A 1901 Stanhope Steam Car — note the wood slab type body pattern

Courtesy of Ford of Canada Archives.

Figure 1-1C Note the completely closed-in body with glass side windows

Courtesy of Ford of Canada Archives.

Figure 1-1B 1909 Ford "Model T" Touring Car

Courtesy Collections of Greenfield Village and the Henry Ford Museum, Dearborn, Michigan

Figure 1-1D 1937 Cord Convertible — note the all-steel body and large high-crowned panels

complete body frame. Since they were handmade, any one part from one body might not fit another.

The first metal panels were also handmade or, at best, made by simple sheet metal forming machines. Because of this, their shapes had to be kept relatively flat in at least one direction. As the demand for and use of automobiles increased, faster and more econom-ical methods had to be found to produce larger, fancier-shaped bodies and fenders. During this period of automotive production, the manufacturers gradually changed their manufacturing technique from that of handmade body frames, outer panels, and fenders to machine-made, mass-produced parts. The vehicles gradually became more stylish. The bodies, the outer panels, and

Figure 1-2 Wooden framework of the early automobile body

fenders all increased in size and had greater curves and crowns incorporated into their shapes.

Metal Stamping

New methods were developed to form flat metal sheets into any desirable shape. The flat metal sheets were **stamped** to shape by special **dies** held in large **presses.** Dies are carefully machined from solid pieces of steel. They are made as a set (male and

Figure 1-3 Huge stamping press

Courtesy Educational Affairs Department, Ford Motor Company

female) and must fit together, leaving just enough room between them for the sheet metal.

The flat sheet of metal is placed between the two dies, which are held in alignment and brought together by the pressure from a huge hydraulic press (Figure 1-3). The tremendous force from the press and the close fit of the dies forces the sheet metal to take the shape of the dies.

At first only relatively simple curves were stamped. As the stamping technology further developed, higher crowned and larger panels were made. Eventually, these new stamping processes brought about the evolution of the all-steel body. The heavy wooden skeleton, or frame, of the body was replaced with many steel stampings.

These steel stampings could be made quickly and accurately. Each stamping was identical in both size and shape. The various stampings and body-forming contour panels were assembled and held in specially designed jigs and fixtures to be welded together to form the all-steel body. The **jigs** and **fixtures** are holding frameworks specifically designed to clamp the stampings in correct alignment throughout the welding process, so that each body produced is identical in both size and shape.

Robots are now used to do the spot welding in some areas of the body. They are programmed to put the same number of spot welds in exactly the same positions on every body welded as they move along the assembly line. Automobile bodies are still made of steel, although many manufacturers are using more **fibreglass** and **plastic** materials in non-structural areas. Fibreglass and plastic are discussed in Chapter 6.

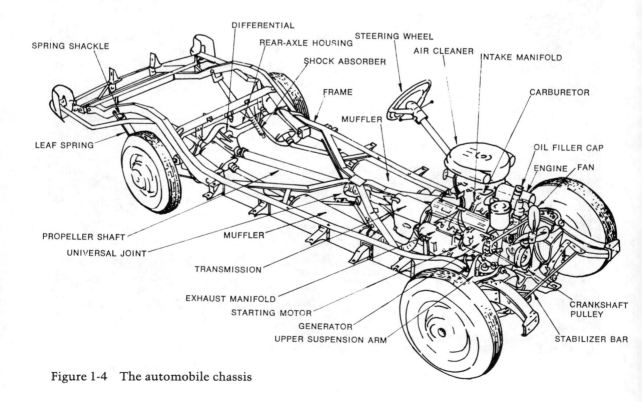

Figure 1-4   The automobile chassis

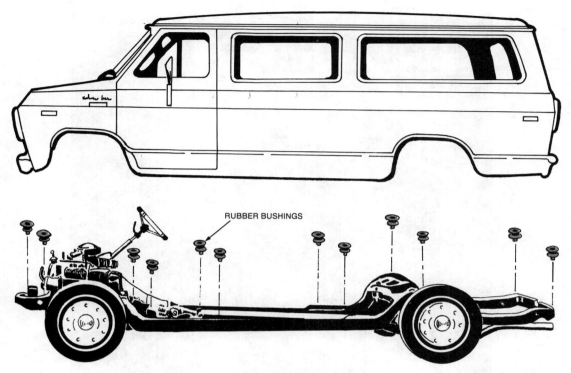

RUBBER BUSHINGS

Figure 1-5A   Conventional body to chassis mounting locations

1-2 MODERN VEHICLE DESIGN

The method of assembling automobiles has not changed very much since the assembly line was introduced. But the structural design of vehicles has changed greatly. There are two basic designs for cars today: **conventional** and **unitized.**

Conventional Design

In this type of design a heavy, rigid frame supports and aligns the engine, power train, and running gear. These three units, along with the frame, make up the vehicle's **chassis** (Figure 1-4). The heavy frame can be considered the vehicle's "backbone" since it provides support for all the chassis parts, the body, the front end assembly, and the bumpers.

The **body** is a weatherproof enclosure which provides comfort and safety for the driver and passengers. It is made of many stamped steel panels welded together and reinforced.

The **front end assembly** consists of the fenders, the hood, and the inner panels. These parts are all bolted together, and on a conventional vehicle the assembly is in turn bolted to the chassis frame in strategic locations (Figure 1-5A, B). At these locations, or **body mounts,** thick rubber bushings are inserted to prevent road noises, squeaks, and

Ford of Canada Photo

Figure 1-5B   Mounting a conventional body on the assembly line

rattles from reaching the passenger compartment.

Most vehicles of conventional design have rear-wheel drive. The extra frame strength helps absorb the greater pushing forces from the rear wheels. Larger, heavier vehicles such as vans, pick-ups, and trucks are usually of conventional design.

Unitized Design

In unitized or "unicoup" design, the entire body frame rails, and front end assembly inner panels are welded together and reinforced to produce a strong, one-piece body. There is no separate frame. They are de-

signed either as front- or rear-wheel drive vehicles.

Unitized bodies are today's most popular design, particularly for passenger vehicles. Sturdy U-shaped rails are welded to the body's rear section to reinforce that area and strengthen the rear suspension mountings. Even heavier box-section rails are welded to the front floor section at the cowl. These front rails, the inner wheelhouse panels (aprons), the radiator support, and the firewall are all welded together to make a rugged, twist-resistant front section.

The centre section of a unitized body shell has no frame members. The shell's lower-body strength comes instead from the box-shaped rocker panels and the stamped, shaped floor panel. These are illustrated in Figure 1-6. Each fold or bend in the floor panel adds strength to the centre section. The boxed pillars, headers, rails, and inner and outer panels are welded together, which further adds to the vehicle's strength.

Finally, the windshield and rear window are both bonded to the body. This also adds strength to the overall shell.

The body and box-section members support the engine, power train, and running gear assemblies. The lower reinforcing rails carry the weight of the driving, breaking, and suspension systems and distributes the road stress evenly through the body.

Vehicle design is covered in greater detail in Chapter 12.

1-3 PANELS

Auto bodies are made of many sheet metal stampings that are welded together into a solid unit. The basic body structure of all automobiles consists of pillars or posts, headers, rails, and outer and inner panels.

Panel Strength

Each panel stamping is designed to add strength and rigidity to the assembled unit.

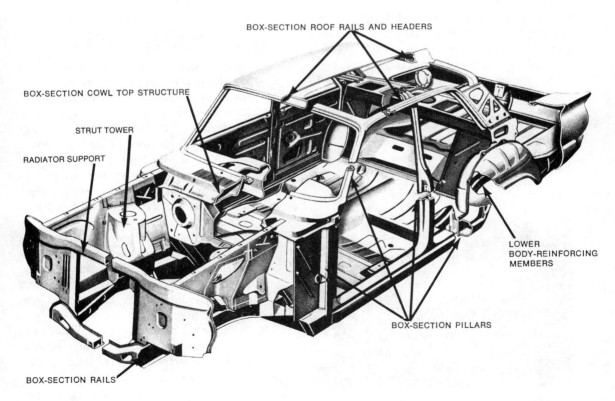

BOX-SECTION ROOF RAILS AND HEADERS

BOX-SECTION COWL TOP STRUCTURE

STRUT TOWER

RADIATOR SUPPORT

LOWER BODY-REINFORCING MEMBERS

BOX-SECTION PILLARS

BOX-SECTION RAILS

Figure 1-6   Unitized body construction

Courtesy Ford Motor Company of Canada, Limited

The amount of strength in any stamping depends on the metal's thickness, size, and shape. Generally, a large panel would not be as strong as a similarly shaped smaller panel, and an outer fender panel would be made from thinner metal than a main pillar or frame rail.

However, the most important factor determining a panel's strength is its shape. Whenever metal is forced to change shape by bending or stamping, the reshaped areas are made stronger. This may be illustrated by bending a piece of wire and then trying to straighten it. It is much harder to bend back, and the metal is said to have become **work hardened.** Likewise, flat sheet metal is very soft and flexible. After being pressed into a shaped panel it has greater resistance to further bending.

Crowns, Flanges, Pressed Ridges, and Channels. The curved shapes pressed into panels are referred to as crowns, flanges, and pressed ridges and channels (Figure 1-7). Each one is purposely designed to add strength to the body. The degree of crown in an area of panel can vary from a high (very curved) crown, to a low crown, to a reversed crown (Figure 1-8). Any area of a panel having crowns crossing at right angles to each other is said to be a compound crown (double curve).

Figure 1-8   Various crowns

Inner and Outer Panels

The outer panels are the ones you see by looking at the outside of the vehicle. They give the body its contour. Every outer panel will have some crown in it. It is almost always a compound crown, with a very slight crown running from front to back and a vertical shape anywhere from a very high to a very low crown. Flanges of various shapes are found along the fender wheel openings. Ridges and channels are often pressed into hoods and deck lids to strengthen them.

The inner panels reinforce the body shell and provide mounting locations for the various interior trim panels and other connecting assemblies. They are also strengthened by the many ridges, folds, bends, and ribs pressed into them.

Both the inner reinforcing panels and the outer box-forming contour panels are spot welded to box-shaped pillars, headers, and rails, which form the main frame, or skeleton, of the body. These boxed shapes provide maximum strength to mass ratio.

Figure 1-7   Pressed ridges and channels

1-4 BODY PARTS IDENTIFICATION

Whether the vehicle is of unitized or conventional design, the names of the various body parts and their reinforcements remain basically the same.

Floor Pan Assembly

The floor of the body is usually assembled first and the various pillars, rails, and panels are joined to it to form the complete body. Figure 1-9 illustrates the **floor pan assembly** to which the other body panels are added. The floor pan is made of three different stamped sheet metal panels. Each of the three panels is shaped to fit over the various suspension assemblies, giving the automobile a lower profile and providing more room for the occupants of the vehicle.

To reinforce the floor pan, **capping strips** (extra channels or box-shaped strips

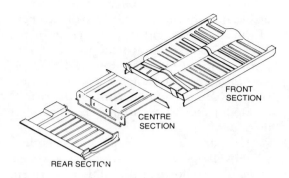

Figure 1-9   Floor pan assembly

of metal) are spot welded to it at various locations. Channels, ridges, and folds are pressed into each of the panels to add rigidity and to prevent excessive vibrations. The rocker panels and rear wheelhouse inner panels are then welded to the floor. Note that there is both an inner and an outer rocker panel which, when welded together, form a closed box-shaped enclosure along each side of the floor pan (Figure 1-10). This

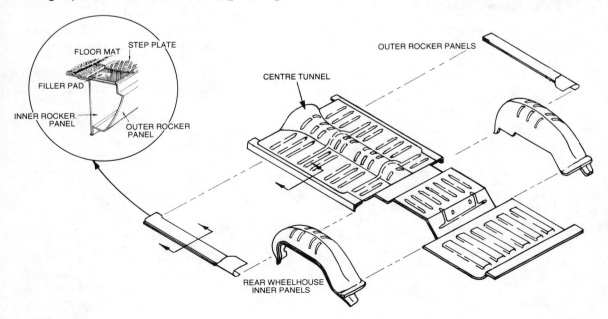

Figure 1-10   Wheelhouse and rocker panels added to floor panels

box shape contributes greatly to the strength of the floor pan and centre section of the body. This is especially necessary with unitized designed vehicles. Unitized vehicles also have the additional lower frame rails spot welded to the underside of the rear of the floor panel. Conventional vehicle bodies do not.

The rear wheelhouse panels provide a wheelwell opening in which the rear wheels move up and down as the vehicle is driven. The panel encloses the top of the wheels and stops any objects, such as stones, that are thrown up by the tires. Its compounded, high-crowned shape greatly increases the strength of the floor panel centre and rear section.

The raised shape of the **centre drive tunnel** contributes to the longitudinal strength of the centre floor area. Even front-wheel drive and space frame bodies have a similar raised centre area.

Front Cowl Assembly

Figure 1-11 illustrates the **front cowl assembly** of a conventional type body, which is built up from many similar panel stampings. The various parts of the cowl are:

1. The **fire wall,** which is heavily insulated on the inside to prevent the engine noise from penetrating the body enclosure

2. The **reinforced hinge pillars,** to which are fastened the front door hinges and the cowl side panels just in front of the pillars

3. The **windshield opening frame,** consisting of two box-shaped pillars and a boxed top header

4. The **top outer cowl panel,** which is vented on some vehicles to allow fresh air to enter the vehicle

5. The **dash,** or instrument panel, which contains the special instruments necessary to operate the vehicle.

On some vehicles, the instrument panel is a steel stamping, welded to the cowl and pillars, increasing the strength through that area of the vehicle. However, on most vehicles it is likely to be made of plastics and is bolted to the cowl. A steel channel or box-shaped reinforcement is used behind it, connected from one pillar to the other, to

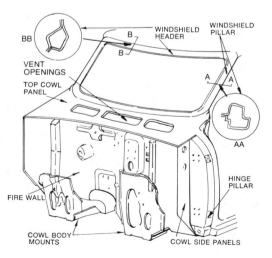
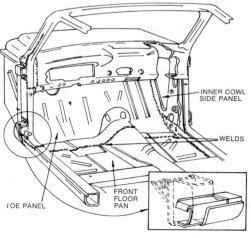

Figure 1-11   Front cowl assembly — conventional type vehicle

strengthen the cowl area in the event of a broadside collision.

The cowl assembly also supports the steering column, the windshield-wiper assembly, and the heater-defroster units. The lower cowl assembly is welded to the top of the rocker panels and floor pan.

Quarter Panels

The outer contour-forming rear quarter panels for both four-door and two-door vehicles are spot welded at the front to their pillar and along the bottom to the inner wheelhouse panel, the floor pan, and the rear of the rocker panels. When the vehicle is designed to have a separate enclosed trunk area, the two quarter panels are joined above the trunk-lid opening to the rear window or upper deck lid panel and the inner parcel

shelf panel. Below the deck-lid opening the rear quarters are joined to the lower deck-lid panel which is welded to the rear of the floor panel.

Reinforcing braces or a solid bulkhead panel are added from the parcel shelf to the floor panel. These braces or the panel reinforces the rear section of the body, providing support for the rear seat back and separating the trunk area from the passenger compartment (Figure 1-12).

Roof Assembly

If the vehicle is to be a four-door sedan, the **centre pillars** and **roof rails** are then added to the assembly (Figure 1-13). The centre pillars support the rear door and its hinges and the front-door striker catch. The roof rails are welded to the windshield head-

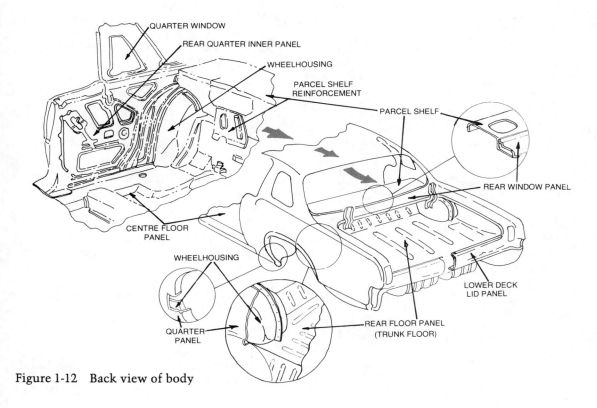

Figure 1-12   Back view of body

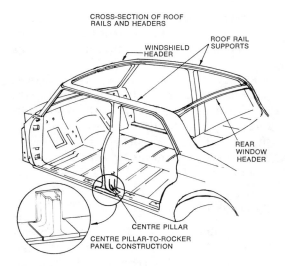

CROSS-SECTION OF ROOF
RAILS AND HEADERS

WINDSHIELD
HEADER

ROOF RAIL
SUPPORTS

REAR
WINDOW
HEADER

CENTRE PILLAR

CENTRE PILLAR-TO-ROCKER
PANEL CONSTRUCTION

Figure 1-13   Centre post and roof rail construction (four-door sedan)

ers at the front and to the rear quarter inner and outer panels at the rear. The rear window header is added to the roof rails to provide the rear window opening.

Figure 1-14 illustrates the addition of the **roof panel** and **drip mouldings** to the four-door sedan body. The roof panel is spot welded to the side roof rails, the windshield, and the rear window headers. The drip mouldings are U-shaped channels spot welded to the roof side rails. They catch any water runoff from the roof and direct it to the back of the vehicle. Not all vehicles have drip mouldings. Some have the top of the door frame extending into the roof, with a channel built into the door opening to catch any water runoff. Note that both the centre pillars and the roof rails are boxed to provide maximum strength to the body.

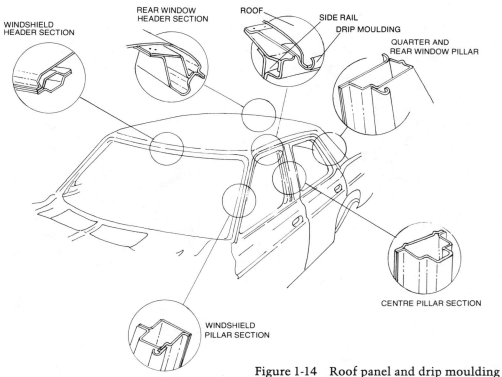

WINDSHIELD
HEADER SECTION

REAR WINDOW
HEADER SECTION

ROOF

SIDE RAIL
DRIP MOULDING

QUARTER AND
REAR WINDOW PILLAR

CENTRE PILLAR SECTION

WINDSHIELD
PILLAR SECTION

Figure 1-14   Roof panel and drip moulding construction

Deck Lid

The **deck lid** is often referred to as the trunk lid because it provides a cover for the trunk compartment. The deck lid is constructed of an outer contour-forming panel which flanges over the edges of an inner reinforcing panel (Figure 1-15). The inner panel provides the mounting location for the lid hinges and lock. Pressed ridges and channels in the inner panel provide added strength to the lid. The metal of the inner panel between the pressed ridges and channels is removed to lighten the lid, making it easier to open. A rubber weatherstrip seals the opening when the lid is closed to prevent water or dust from entering the compartment. It is cemented to a formed, U-shaped channel around the edge of the deck-lid opening. The lid is attached to the body by two hinges that that are counterbalanced by torsion bar springs or gas support shocks. The torsion bars and/or shocks assist in opening the lid and holding it in the open position (Figure 1-16). The lid is held closed by a lock and striker catch (Figure 1-17). The lock is mounted to the inner deck-lid reinforcing panel, and the catch to the lower deck-lid panel. A key cylinder mounted in the outer

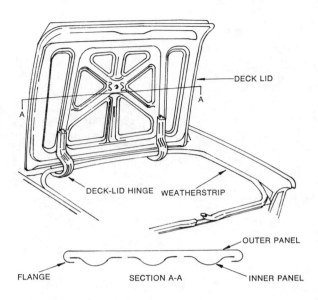

Figure 1-15   Deck lid construction

deck-lid panel activates the lock. The lock and striker catch must be adjusted so that the lid can be opened without exerting excessive pressure on the key cylinder and closed without slamming the lid. When the lid is closed, it must also be sufficiently compressed against the rubber weatherstrip so that neither dust nor water can enter the

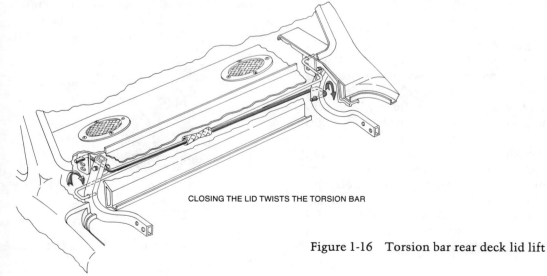

CLOSING THE LID TWISTS THE TORSION BAR

Figure 1-16   Torsion bar rear deck lid lift

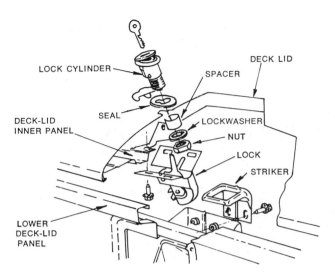

Figure 1-17   Deck-lid lock and striker catch

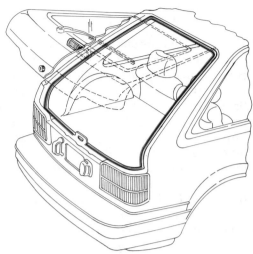

Figure 1-18   Hatch back vehicle back end

compartment. The deck-lid lock and striker adjustments are explained in greater detail in Chapter 11.

> Do not attempt to remove the torsion bars or gas shocks without checking the correct procedure in the vehicle manual.

Some vehicles do not have a separate trunk compartment and lid. The trunk bulkhead panel, the parcel shelf and upper deck panels are eliminated. The backs of the rear seats can be folded forward, providing a rather large cargo area. Access to the rear cargo area is through a much larger rear door, which is hinged from a reinforced roof header. The rear window is mounted into the door. The door is similar to the standard deck lid with an inner and outer panel. On some vehicles, the complete door is glass. A pair of gas shocks is used to help lift and hold the door open. This type of vehicle is known as a **hatch back** design (Figure 1-18).

Hood

The **hood** is constructed in the same manner as the deck lid. The outer panel is formed to blend with the contour of the body and fenders. The inner panel acts as a reinforcement and provides mounting locations for the hinges and hood lock. The hood may be hinged from either the cowl or the radiator support. Some hinges used are of a rather simple design, their only purpose being to hinge the hood. Others are designed for coil

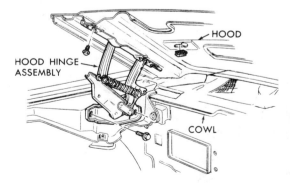

Figure 1-19   Coil spring hood hinge assembly

Figure 1-20 Hood lock and safety catch

Bumpers

The front and rear **bumpers** are designed to protect the front and rear of the vehicle from damage caused by light collisions at speeds up to 8 km/h. Various materials and designs are used by the different vehicle manufacturers in meeting the requirements of an 8 km/h impact absorbing bumper.

A high-strength impact bar is bolted to two impacting energy absorbers which in turn are bolted to the body. The impact bar can have either an outer chromed steel or polished aluminum bumper bolted to it, or it can be covered with an impact absorbing urethane pad.

The absorbing devices are hydraulic shocks. They work on the principle of oil being forced from one chamber through a very small hole or orifice into another chamber. As the oil is forced into the second chamber, it displaces a floating piston which

springs or torsion bars which counterbalance the hood, holding it up when opened (Figure 1-19). Hood hinges not using a counterbalance mechanism are propped open by a simple metal rod.

Most vehicles have some type of safety hook or stop either designed as part of the hinge or as a separate "bolt-on" item to the hood or cowl in the hinge area. Their purpose is to catch against the cowl or hood to stop the hood from being forced back into and possibly through the windshield in a front-end collision. The hood is held closed by a hood lock and catch, both of which are usually adjustable to provide proper hood alignment and closing. A separate safety catch is also used on a front opening hood. The safety catch prevents the hood from flying open while the vehicle is moving, should the main lock fail to hold (Figure 1-20).

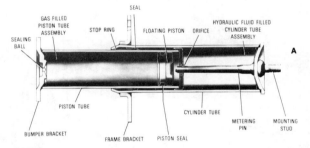

Courtesy General Motors Corp.

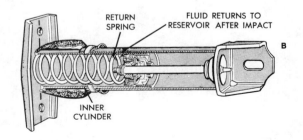

Figure 1-21A, B Energy absorbers: hydraulic and coil spring

moves to compress a gas in the opposite end of the piston tube (Figure 1-21A). After the impact, the compressed gas forces the floating piston back and the oil back through the orifice and the unit itself back to its normal position. A similar hydraulic absorber uses a coil spring instead of the compressed gas principle to return the unit back to its normal length (Figure 1-21B).

Damaged energy absorbing devices can be dangerous. Use caution when removing damaged absorbers. Do not take them apart, puncture, or apply heat or fire before first checking the manufacturer's recommendations.

1-5 FRONT END ASSEMBLY

The front sections of unitized (or unicoup) and conventional vehicles are constructed very differently from each other.

Conventional. The conventional vehicle **front end assembly** consists of those sheet metal panels which are the contour-forming panels of the front of the vehicle. When assembled, the various panels form the engine compartment opening of the front of the vehicle. All of the panels are bolted to each other, to the body, and to the frame of the vehicle (Figure 1-22).

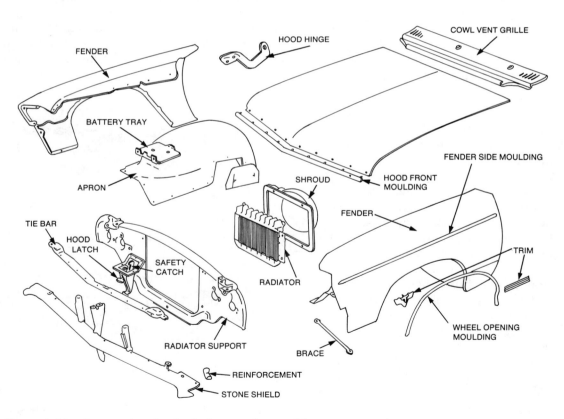

Figure 1-22   Conventional vehicle front end assembly

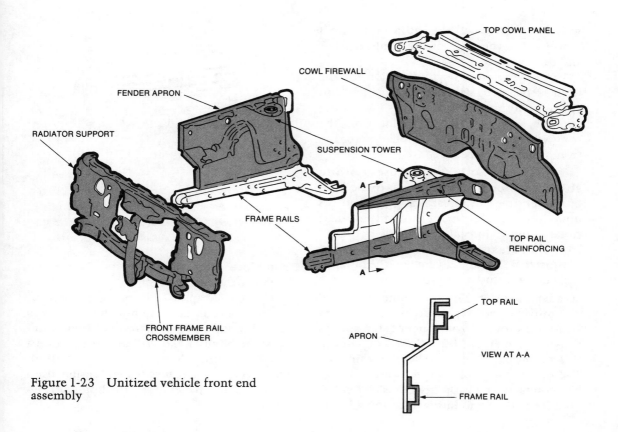

Figure 1-23   Unitized vehicle front end assembly

The **radiator support** connects and supports the two front fenders and the radiator. The support itself is bolted to each frame rail. The **front fenders** are usually bolted to the cowl at the rear and to the radiator support at the front.

The **inner splash apron** used on conventional vehicles is a highly crowned, stamped metal panel or plastic shield. Their main purpose is to fit under the fender and over the wheel to stop any throw-off. They are bolted to the cowl section of the body, the frame rails, the edge of the fender, and the radiator support.

Unitized. The unitized front section is an all-welded unit. It is stronger and more twist resistant. This is especially important for front-wheel drive vehicles, as the front sec-

tion must be able to withstand additional torquing forces from the front wheels. These torque forces are transferred from the wheels through the front section to the rest of the body.

The front frame side rails are made from thinner gauge metals than the frame used on a conventional vehicle. They are box shaped and made from high-strength steel. They are welded to the front lower cowl area and to the floor panel. The plastic inner fender shield used for the conventional vehicle is replaced by a larger, stronger inner wheelhouse panel often called a **fender apron** and a **suspension tower.** Both are made of special high-strength steel. The tower is welded to the apron which is welded to the frame side rails and to the hinge pillar-firewall area of the cowl. The **radiator support** is welded to the ends of the fender aprons and the frame members.

The towers provide the location for the front suspension, MacPherson Strut, and coil spring. The apron, as well as providing strength, offers splash protection from the front wheel and a mounting location for the front fender (Figure 1-23).

Stone Shield. Both designs use a **stone shield** or **filler panel.** This bolts to the front of the fenders and radiator support and fits under or up to the bumper to prevent small stones from flying into the grille and radiator. They are usually made of soft, flexible plastics that fold and give when the bumper and energy absorber are forced in.

Header Panel or Tie Bar. Some front end assemblies are designed with a **front header panel** and front fender extensions as illustrated in Figure 1-24. Others do not use this header panel design. They use a **tie bar.** The header panel or, in some cases, the tie bar, connects to the top front of each fender. They provide a mounting location for the

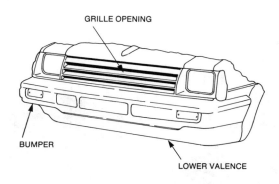

Figure 1-25A   Bumper grille and lower valence arrangement

hood-lock catch and grille, and help to tie together the two fenders.

The **grille,** apart from being decorative, provides a ventilated opening for cool air to pass through to the radiator. On some vehicles, the bumper and grill are designed as a one-piece unit. No stone shield is used. Other vehicles, because of their design, use a lower valence panel under the bumper (Figure 1-25A, B).

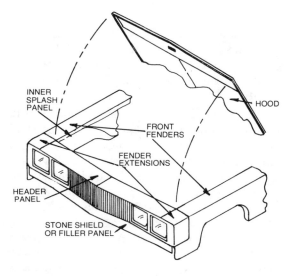

Figure 1-24   Header panel and fender extensions

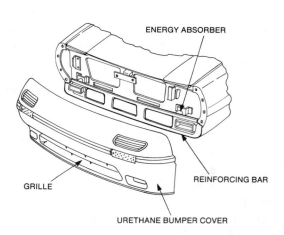

Figure 1-25B   Urethane bumper cover and grille arrangement

1-6 RADIATORS

The **radiator** is bolted to the radiator support. Its purpose is to cool the engine by absorbing the heat from the coolant that is pumped by the water pump from the engine through the radiator. The radiator heat is dissipated into the cool air passing through the radiator.

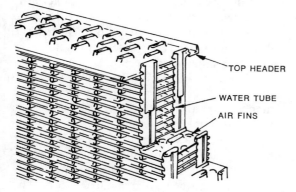

Figure 1-26   Radiator cross section

The radiator consists of rows of small rectangular tubes which are either soldered (if copper) or bonded (if plastic) to layers of thin fins placed at right angles to the tubes, about 3 mm apart. The ends of the tubes are soldered or bonded into headers and a tank is joined to each header (Figure 1-26). A fan draws fresh air through the radiator to create a faster heat transfer from the radiator to the air. Some fans are driven by a fan belt. Others are driven by a small electric motor and have a thermostat mounted in the radiator which controls the fan motor so it runs only when it is needed.

The radiator **shroud** connects to the radiator and surrounds the fan. It serves a two-fold purpose: to offer protection from the fan and to enclose the area around the fan so that the fan must draw more air through the radiator, thus increasing the cooling performance.

A radiator can be positioned in the vehicle in either a vertical or a horizontal position. When it is vertically mounted, it is referred to as the **down-flow type.** A horizontally mounted radiator is known as the **cross-flow type.** It fits lower, enabling the designers to lower the hood to achieve a more aerodynamic vehicle. With either type, the coolant is pumped into one of the tanks at the top inlet. The coolant flows through the tubes and leaves the radiator through the lower outlet starting another cycle.

Radiator Pressure Cap

A special double sealing pressure cap (Figure 1-27) is used to hold a certain pressure on the coolant which is greater than that of the atmosphere. A **pressure valve** built into the cap is spring-loaded and holds a pre-set pressure on the coolant. It allows air or excess coolant to escape if the pressure in the radiator becomes too high. A small **vacuum valve** is also built into the cap to allow air in when necessary.

It is most important that the correct pressure cap be used with the radiator. Using a cap with a pressure higher than recommended could split the seams of the radiator. Using a cap with a lower pressure than recommended could result in the engine overheating.

Alternative Cooling System

Some vehicles use a rather different arrangement. They have a separate non-pressurized reservoir tank mounted near the radiator. It is usually made of transparent plastic and has markings indicating full and low fluid levels. An overflow hose connects the reservoir to the filler neck of the radiator.

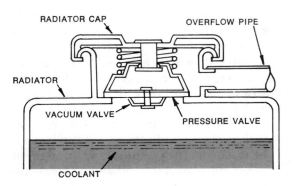

Figure 1-27   Radiator pressure

The radiator is filled with coolant and no expansion area is left in the tank. As the coolant heats and expands, the pressure cap maintains pressure by allowing some of the coolant to leave the radiator through the overflow hose into the reservoir. Upon engine shut-down, and as the temperature of the coolant decreases, the vacuum valve opens to allow the coolant to return to the radiator from the reservoir.

The advantage of this system is that the coolant system is kept full of liquid, thus enabling greater cooling capacity. As an additional safety precaution, it is not necessary to remove the radiator cap to check or add to the coolant level. This is done at the non-pressurized reservoir.

Coolant

The **coolant** used is ethylene glycol usually mixed with an equal quantity of water. This mixture is recommended for use even in warm climates where there is no danger of freezing.

When replacing the coolant in the pressurized system, a slight expansion area should be left at the top of the tank. If there is a reservoir system, competely fill the radiator and fill the reservoir to the level indicated.

1-7 DOORS

Automobile doors are constructed of two panels, as are the hood and deck lid. The outer panel is shaped to conform to the outer body contour, while the inner door shell provides the reinforcing strength and mounting locations for the door hardware and interior trim panels.

Although the inner door shell is actually made from one stamping, it is divided into two sections for classification purposes: the door frame which comprises the thickness of the door, and the inner panel.

They form a box-type unit with room on the inside for fitting and operating the door mechanisms and the window glass. Holes are stamped out in the inner panel to provide access for adjusting, removing, and replacing the various door and window mechanisms. Vehicle manufacturers must install a heavy corrugated steel beam in the door. The beam is fastened to each end of the door frame against the outer door panel. Its purpose is to offer greater protection to the occupants in the event of a broadside collision (Figure 1-28). This beam is made from a very special high-strength, lightweight steel. Should it become bent from collison damage, the manufacturers recommend that the beam should never be straightened either in its cold state or by first heating it. In either case, the strength is removed from the beam. Either the beam or the complete door must be replaced.

If the outer panel is steel, its outer flange is crimped over the edge of the door frame and spot welded to the inner panel. On some vehicles it is actually bonded with a special adhesive before the flange is crimped, instead of being spot welded. Other outer panels are made of plastic materials that are bolted and bonded to the steel door frame.

Most doors include an upper window frame above the belt line. Others do not. The

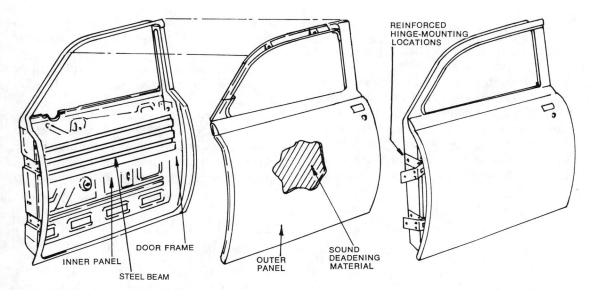

Figure 1-28   Door construction

upper door frame surrounds the glass in the "up" position to provide support to the glass and to provide a seal between the frame and the glass.

The doors are hung from concealed hinges that are bolted to the pillar and the inner door panel or frame. The hinge-mounting locations are reinforced with extra, formed metal shapes. In most cases, working allowance is provided at the hinge-mounting locations to permit proper door fitting. On some vehicles the door hinge is actually welded to both the hinge pillar and the door frame. The hinge pin must be driven out to remove the door, and there is no provision for door adjustment at the hinges.

A "hold-open" mechanism, or **check stop,** is usually built into one of the hinges to hold the door open in a fixed position while a person enters or leaves the car. A rubber weatherstrip is fastened to the body opening to seal the door against the body opening when the door is closed (Figure 1-29).

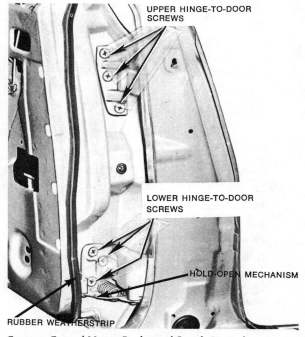

Courtesy General Motors Products of Canada Limited

Figure 1-29   Rear door hinge attachment

Door Hardware

The **door lock** is a mechanical mechanism which locks into the striker catch on the pillar of the body to hold the door securely closed. The striker catch can be adjusted vertically and in and out to line it up with the door lock (Figure 1-30). The main part of the lock mechanism is inside the door and only a very small part of the lock can be seen through the opening in the door frame. The lock is held in position by machine screws through both the inner panel and the door frame.

The lock mechanism may be released by either the inner or the outer door handle. The outer door handle, located at the back of the door over the lock mechanism, is connected directly to the door lock. The inside handle, however, is always positioned in the centre of the door, and a remote-control mechanism is used to join it to the lock (Figure 1-31).

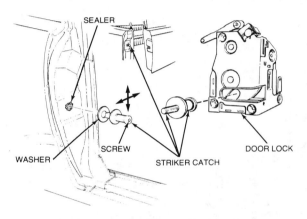

Figure 1-30   Door lock — striker catch

Front Door Lock Cylinder Assembly

The **door lock cylinder** is usually directly under the outer door handle, although on a special spring-steel clip on the inside of the outer panel (Figure 1-32).

The doors can also be locked from the inside by pushing down a plunger that protrudes through the top of the inner door panel or by pushing the inner door handle ahead or in, depending on the design.

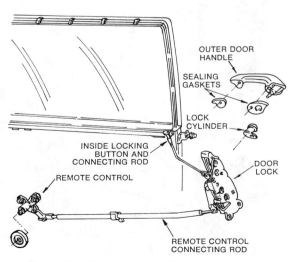

Figure 1-31   Door lock mechanism

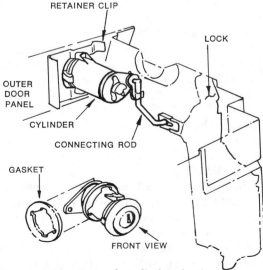

Figure 1-32   Front door lock cylinder

Door Glass Mechanisms

The glass areas of the doors can be either one- or two-piece glass sections. If it is two-piece, the smaller section may open and is called the **ventilator glass.** On some vehicles, the smaller glass is "fixed" into position, its purpose being to square up one end of the window opening which then provides the correct shape for the main glass so that it can be moved up and down.

The larger door glass is separated from the vent glass by division bar. With vehicles not using a ventilator assembly, the door glass is a one-piece design. In either case, the up and down movement of the door glass is controlled by either an electrically driven or a manually operated **window regulator.** There are two very different types: the **arm type** (Figure 1-33) and the **flex** or **tape drive type.**

With either type, the regulator is bolted to the inner door panel. The manual ones are operated by the window regulator handle. A small electric motor is used to drive the regulator for "power" windows. The arm type regulator works on the leverage principle with a very small gear driving a much larger gear, allowing the window to be easily lifted up. A roller on the end of the regulator arm

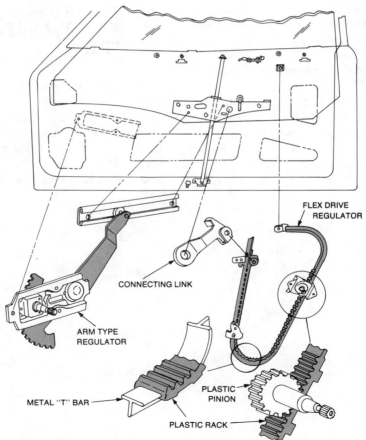

FLEX DRIVE
REGULATOR

CONNECTING LINK

ARM TYPE
REGULATOR

METAL "T" BAR

PLASTIC
PINION

PLASTIC RACK

Figure 1-33 Types of window regulators

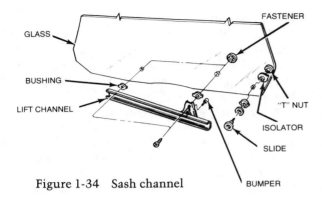

Figure 1-34   Sash channel

fits into a C-shaped lift channel. This channel bolts directly to the door glass (Figure 1-34). The tape or flexible drive regulator consists of a plastic tape with either slots or teeth that mesh into the teeth of a small gear turned by the window regulator handle. With the flex drive type, the end of the tape is connected directly to a lift plate bolted to the glass.

Doors which have an upper door frame use a fabric-covered, U-shaped channel for the window to move up and down in. It is called a **window run channel.** It provides a seal around the glass edge and the door frame to make a sealed weather-tight opening (Figure 1-35).

A relatively new concept is glass which is said to be **flush mounted.** It is mounted flush with the outer surface of the door frame and is sealed in an insulating rubber with an outer lip that folds over the edge of the glass. This design is said to prevent wind whistle and noises.

With the half door type, the glass seals against the weatherstrip around the body door opening. Slotted holes at the mounting locations of both the window regulators, the window run channels, and the glass track allow adjustments to be made to the fit of the windows.

1-8 INTERIOR HARDWARE AND TRIM

Interior hardware refers to such things as inner door and window handles, rocker panel step plates, and any other parts of the interior that serve either a functional or a purely decorative purpose. The **trim parts** are considered to be the upholstery panels and covers that enhance the interior of the

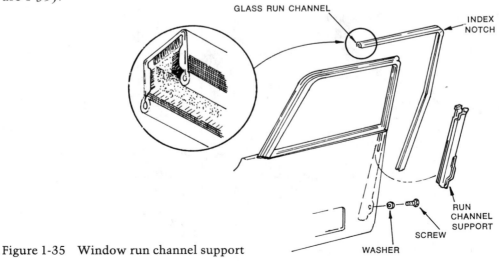

Figure 1-35   Window run channel support

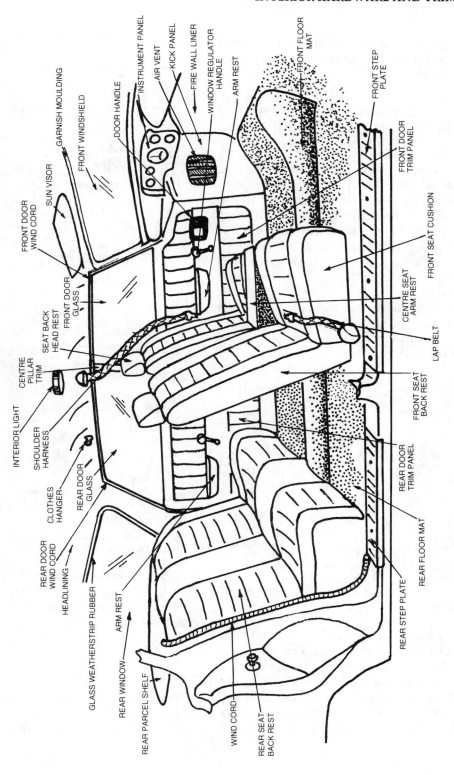

Figure 1-36   Interior hardware and trim

automobile. Figure 1-36 shows the names and locations of the varous interior hardware and trim parts.

Door Interior Hardware and Trim

The inside door handles have a crank or a lever design; window regulator handles are always of the crank type. The handles connect directly to the remote-control shaft and the window regulator shaft. The cranking handles can be mounted onto their respective shafts in any number of positions, since there are matching splines both on the ends of the shafts and on the inside of the handle openings.

The lever-design handles come in several styles. They are usually built into the door armrest or trim panel as a safety precaution against passenger injury.

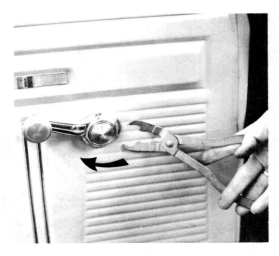

Photos by B. Robinson

Figure 1-38 Handle horseshoe clip removal (using two types of tools)

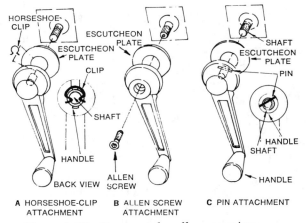

A HORSESHOE-CLIP ATTACHMENT **B** ALLEN SCREW ATTACHMENT **C** PIN ATTACHMENT

Figure 1-37 Common handle-mounting methods

Different methods are used to hold the crank handles onto the shaft. The more common fasteners are a horseshoe-shaped retaining clip or an Allen set screw (Figure 1-37). The horseshoe clip is removed from the handle with one of two specially designed tools, illustrated in Figure 1-38.

The **escutcheon plate** is a round, anti-wear washer that is mounted between the handles and the trim panel. It prevents the handles from wearing into the door panel as they are turned.

Door and Quarter Panel Trim

The trim panels for both doors and quarter panels consist of a hard fibreboard which is covered with the trim material. On some models there is padding between the trim covering and the backing board. Some manufacturers use a moulded fibreglass or plastic trim panel.

The trim panels are fastened to the inner door and quarter panels by either one or a combination of the following: metal screws, metal spring clips, plastic retaining clips (Figure 1-39). The heads of the metal spring clips and plastic retainers connect to the trim panel and their bayonet ends snap into matching holes in the inner panels.

These special trim fasteners are removed by sliding a "vee" notched tool or screwdriver between the inner door panel and the trim pad to carefully pry out the trim retainers.

The prying tool must be kept as close to the clip as possible to prevent the fasteners from pulling out of the trim pad. The pads are replaced by lining up the clips with the holes in the inner panel and then tapping the pad over the fasteners to drive them in. The palm of the hand is used to drive in the fasteners, never a hammer, because the hard tool could mark the pad covering.

Coil springs or a donut-shaped ring of foam rubber are mounted over the window regulator shafts between the inner panel and the trim pad. The coil springs or foam hold the trim panel tight against the escutcheon plate and the escutcheon plate against the handle. The larger end of the coil spring is always placed against the trim pad.

A heavy paper or plastic cover is glued to the inner door panels. It acts as an insulator pad and prevents the water that runs down the window glasses from coming through the inner-panel inspection openings onto the trim pad.

Garnish Mouldings

Garnish mouldings are metal or plastic finishing trim frames that fit around the inside of the window openings and along edges to hide a seam or unfinished edge found in the interior. These mouldings are not used on the doors of some models because the door frame and trim pad have been designed to take their place.

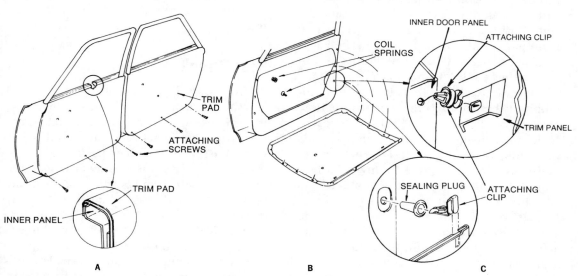

Figure 1-39 Door trim pad removal

Headlinings

The **headlining** is the trim material which is used to cover the underside of the roof panel.

Centre Pillar Trim

The **centre pillar trim** is either a plastic panel, a fibreboard panel covered with trim material, or a metal painted panel. It is fastened to the centre pillar with spring clips, similar to those used on the door pad, or with metal screws.

Kick Panel

The **kick panel** is a plastic, fibreboard, or metal panel that fits under the dash from the front hinge pillar to the fire wall.

1-9 SEAT CONSTRUCTION

Front Seats

Front seats can be of either the single bucket-seat construction or the full bench-type design. Both types are constructed from two main parts: the seat cushions and the backrest. The bench seat has a full width cushion with either a solid or split backrest.

The seat backrest in a two-door automobile is hinged to swing forward to allow access into the back seat. They also have a lock mechanism as part of the hinge. This prevents the seat backrest from moving ahead should the vehicle be involved in a front-end collision. Some manufacturers provide a recliner mechanism in their bucket and split backrest seats to allow the backrest to move backward. The backrest on a four-door model is solidly bolted to the seat cushion and cannot be moved.

The backrests of some seats are purposely built very high to offer protection to the front seat occupants from whiplash when in a rear collision. Other backrests have adjustable head restraint cushions for the same purpose.

The front seats are constructed of an outer metal frame, springs, foam rubber, and outer upholstery cover. The springs on some seats have been replaced with either a solid foam slab or a stretched rubber **insert**. The insert is a flat piece of rubber stretched and fastened to the seat frame. It has "give" similar to a spring. A moulded foam cushion sits on the rubber insert. The outer upholstery cover is pulled tightly over the foam and is fastened to the seat frame.

Rear Seats

The rear seat cushion and backrest are of the same basic construction as the front, except that a much lighter seat frame is used for the immovable seat. The backrest is usually bolted in place and the seat cushion is held in position by metal tabs protruding from the floor pan. With a hatch back design, a split bench-type seat is used so the seat backrests can be folded ahead to enlarge the cargo area.

Seat Track Mechanisms

All front seats, regardless of style, are bolted to a seat track mechanism. This mechanism, in turn, is bolted to a reinforced area in the floor pan. These track mechanisms allow the complete seat to be moved back and forth to position the driver the correct distance from the steering wheel and pedals. The track may be either manually controlled or electrically driven.

Electrically operated track mechanisms that only move the seat back and forth are referred to as two-position seat tracks. Others designed to move the seat up and down, as well, are called four-position tracks.

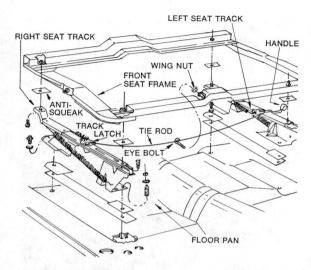

Figure 1-40   Manual front seat mechanism

When either the front or the back of the seat can be moved up or down separately, the tracks are then called six-position seat tracks.

The forward movement of the manually operated track is controlled by a coil spring; the backward movement is controlled by the seat occupant's pushing back on the seat. A locking lever at the bottom of the seat on the driver's side locks the track mechanism in the various positions. The right seat track is controlled by either a wire or a rod connected to the left seat-track release lever (Figure 1-40).

1-10 EXTERIOR TRIM

The exterior trim are those items placed on the outside of the body. Sometimes their only purpose is to accentuate the lines of the vehicle, but they may serve a functional purpose as well. Side mouldings, belt mouldings, rocker panel mouldings, vehicle name scripts, emblems, mirrors, and windshield reveal mouldings are all considered exterior trim items. The side trim mouldings, as an example, serve two purposes: functional and decorative. They accentuate the lines of the vehicle as well as protect the painted surfaces from being marked by other vehicle doors in parking lots, etc.

The exterior trim items are made from a variety of materials, such as white metal, stainless steel, plastic and aluminum. **White metal** is a mixture of zinc and small amounts of aluminum. It is first cast in moulds, and then chrome plated. Stainless steel, plastic, and aluminum mouldings are either extruded or stamped into shape and then finely polished. The methods used to secure the exterior mouldings to their respective panels are covered in Chapter 3.

1-11 GLASS

Specially designed **safety glass** is used in all automobile, truck, and bus windows. Safety glass differs from ordinary, house window glass in that when it breaks it will not shatter into sharp, jagged pieces that could seriously cut the vehicle's occupants. The glass used for front and rear windshields must be finely ground and polished to provide clear undistorted vision through all the angles at which the windows are mounted.

Side window glasses are not held to such close optical tolerances. They are usually mounted in a near vertical position which prevents distortion. These are two different types of safety glasses used in most vehicles: **laminated safety glass,** and **tempered safety glass.**

Laminated Safety Glass

This type of glass consists of two layers of glass bonded together with an inner layer of vinyl transparent plastic (Figure 1-41). The

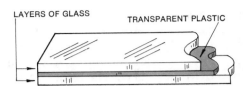

Figure 1-41   Cross-section of laminated safety glass

two layers of glass are bonded to the inner plastic layer by means of both heat and pressure. When the window is fractured, the centre layer of plastic holds the fragments of glass together. The glass tends to break into blunt rectangular pieces which cannot scatter or fly to cut, maim, or injure the occupants of the car. The plastic inner layer also absorbs force by ballooning outward when the glass is impacted from within the vehicle.

A recent development is the addition of a two-layer plastic laminate applied to the inside surface of the windshield. It is designed to further prevent facial cuts to the occupants and prevent any glass splinters from entering the passenger compartment when the glass is badly impacted from the outside.

Tempered Safety Glass

Tempered glass is made from a single piece of heat-treated or case-hardened glass. This glass is cut to its correct shape, heated until it becomes soft, and then blasted with cold air which rapidly cools and shrinks its outer surface. Considerable tension is created between the soft inner glass and its hard outer

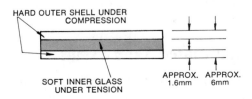

Figure 1-42   Cross-section of tempered glass

skin (Figure 1-42). This tension makes the glass four to five times harder than ordinary glass. After the glass has been tempered, it remains flexible and resists extremes of heat and cold. When it breaks, the complete glass crumbles into harmless, granular-like particles resembling crushed rock salt (Figure 1-43).

Figure 1-43   Granular particles of broken tempered glass

Glass Breakage

Tempered glass is more vulnerable to breakage from piercing blows which puncture its compressed outer skin. A blow from a baseball might have no effect on a tempered glass window, while a sharp pebble thrown up by a passing vehicle could shatter it. The same baseball might crack a laminated window, as shown in Figure 1-44, but a pebble would probably put only a star-like chip in it. Usually only the immediate area hit breaks. The surrounding glass can still be seen through. Once the glass has been tempered, it cannot be cut, ground, or polished since it will break if the hard outer skin is marked.

Laminated glass must be used in the front windows of all vehicles, whereas either tempered or laminated glass may be used in the

Courtesy Ford Motor Company of Canada, Limited

Figure 1-44   Cracked laminated glass

side and rear windows. However, tempered glass is more commonly used in these locations, especially for door glasses, because it will withstand more vibration and the jars which occur in closing the doors. Tempered glass is not suitable for use in the front windshield because the complete glass breaks into granular-like particles which cannot be seen through (Figure 1-45).

Courtesy Ford Motor Company of Canada, Limited

Figure 1-45   Shattered tempered glass

Most glasses are marked either **tempered** or **laminated** by the manufacturer, along with an optical rating, such as **AS1** or **AS2**

A LAMINATED WINDSHIELD MARKING

B TEMPERED SIDE GLASS MARKING

A. Courtesy Ford Motor Company of Canada, Limited
B. "Armourplate"ᴿ Courtesy Duplate Canada Limited

Figure 1-46   Typical safety glass markings
(A) Laminated windshield marking
(B) Tempered side glass marking

(Figure 1-46). An optical rating of AS1 indicates that the glass is suitable for use anywhere in the vehicle. Glass rated as AS2 can be used anywhere in the vehicle except in specific windshield locations where a curved glass is used.

Windshield and Rear Window Glass Mountings

Windshield and rear window glasses are held in their respective body openings by either a rubber weatherstrip, or a self-curing butyl or urethane adhesive caulking compound that adheres to both the glass and the window-opening pinchweld flange. The butyl material remains somewhat more pliable after curing than the urethane materials. When stationary glass is bonded with the urethane materials, the glass actually adds additional strength to the overall unitized body shell.

The style of the rubber weatherstrip varies with the different vehicle manufacturers. Some weatherstrips are designed to allow the glass to be removed without taking the weatherstrip from the glass opening frame. With other designs, both weatherstrip and glass must be removed or installed in the opening together. Figure 1-47 illustrates a typical windshield mounting.

Windows that are held in the body opening with the self-curing, adhesive caulking compound are often referred to as **sealant-bound.** The glass itself rests on small, rubber blocks that are spaced around the glass opening frame. A bead of the caulking compound is applied to the pinchweld frame and the glass is then placed in the opening. The caulking compound is in a soft state when it is applied, but soon after it has been exposed to the air it begins to cure. Because of the fast curing characteristic of the compound, the glass must be installed as quickly as possible after the sealant has been applied. Figure

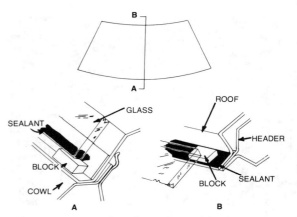

Figure 1-48   Sealant-bound windshield mounting

1-48 illustrates a sealant-bound glass design. When a sealant-bound glass has to be removed, it is cut loose from the compound with a knife or fine wire. An electrically heated knife is needed to cut the much tougher urethane caulking materials.

Reveal Mouldings

The windshield and rear window reveal mouldings are exterior trim mouldings that cover the edge of the glass and window opening. They are held in place by either the

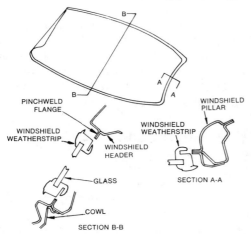

Figure 1-47   Windshield and weatherstrip mounting

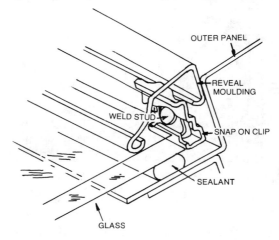

Figure 1-49   Typical reveal-moulding fastenings

rubber weatherstrip or specially designed clips which are fastened to the pinchweld frame before the glass is installed (Figure 1-49). After the glass has been installed, the mouldings are snapped over the edge of the clips. Another method uses plastic T-shaped moulding that drives into the space between the edge of the glass and the opening. No clips are needed. The barb type ridges on the moulding hold it in place.

REVIEW QUESTIONS

1. a) Explain how the first automobile bodies were constructed.
    b) Why did this type of body design not prove satisfactory?
2. a) List the next two basic changes from the first body construction design.
    b) Briefly list one disadvantage of each.
3. Briefly explain "dies" as used in making sheet metal panels.
4. What is the advantage of stamping the sheet metal automobile panels?
5. a) How are the various body panels held in place while the bodies are being assembled?
    b) What is the advantage of using this method of assembly?
6. a) What two types of structural design are employed in the building of today's automobiles?
    b) Briefly explain their differences.
7. a) Briefly explain the purpose of the body mounts used with the conventional type vehicles.
    b) Why are the body mounts insulated with rubber?
8. Why are conventional vehicles rear-wheel driven?
9. Explain how the rear section of a unitized vehicle is strengthened.
10. List the four main parts that are welded together to form the front section of the unitized vehicle.
11. How is the front and rear of a unitized vehicle designed to protect the passengers when it is involved in a collision?
12. List the four types of panels that form the main structure of the body.
13. List the three factors that determine panel strength.
14. Which of the factors determining panel strengh is the most important and why?
15. What functions do the inner and outer panels of the body perform?
16. List the various shapes that are pressed into the outer panels to strengthen them.
17. Explain how the floor panels are strengthened.
18. Why are the rocker panels constructed in the boxed form?
19. a) List the panels which are part of the cowl assembly.
    b) Indicate the panels that would comprise the windshield frame.
20. List three panels that join together the two quarter panels.
21. a) Which pillar present in a four-door sedan is not used in a two-door vehicle?
    b) Why must this pillar be used with a four-door vehicle?
22. a) Where are the drip mouldings located?
    b) What is their purpose?
23. Briefly explain how a hatch back vehicle differs from a trunk-type vehicle.
24. What is the purpose of the hood lock safety catch?
25. Explain the purposes of the impact absorbing devices used to connect the bumpers to the vehicle.
26. Briefly explain the purposes of the splash panel used with the conven-

tional vehicle and the wheelhouse panel used with the unitized vehicles.

27. Where is the suspension tower located and what is its purpose?

28. a) Explain the purposes of the radiator used with liquid-cooled vehicles.
    b) Why must the correct radiator pressure cap be used to pressurize the coolant?

29. To what part of the body are the front door hinges connected?

30. What is the purpose of the corrugated steel beam in the door?

31. a) To what part does the door lock connect to hold the door closed?
    b) Can this part be adjusted? If so, how and for what purpose is it necessary to adjust it?

32. What mechanism is used to connect the inner door handle to the door lock?

33. How is the up-and-down movement of the door glass controlled?

34. a) What is the name of the channel in which the door glass slides up and down?

    b) What other purpose does this channel serve?

35. What is the purpose of the escutcheon plate?

36. a) Name the mechanism that controls the movement of the front seat.
    b) How is the mechanism on the passenger's side of the vehicle operated?

37. a) What two types of glass are used in motor vehicles?
    b) Explain how they differ in construction.
    c) Which type is used in the windshield? Why?
    d) Which type is usually used for door glasses? Why?

38. a) List and explain the two methods used to secure the windshield and rear window glasses in the body openings.
    b) How are the windshield and rear window reveal mouldings held in place?

2 HAND TOOLS

2-1   Screwdrivers
2-2   Wrenches
2-3   Pliers
2-4   Hacksaws
2-5   Files
2-6   Cold Chisels
2-7   Punches
2-8   Snips
2-9   Twist Drills
2-10   Hammers
2-11   Dollies and Spoons
2-12   Body Working Files

Mechanics are often judged by the quality and condition of their tools. It is with these tools that the mechanic earns a living. So it is important that the right tool be selected for each job and that the tools be kept in good repair. This prevents damage to the parts being worked on, and also speeds up the work.

2-1 SCREWDRIVERS

Standard Screwdrivers. These straight-blade screwdrivers are used to tighten and loosen screws and stove bolts. They vary in size and shape according to their use. Screw-driver sizes are determined by the combined length of shank and blade. The blade's width and thickness are proportional to the shank's length and diameter (Figure 2-1). There are

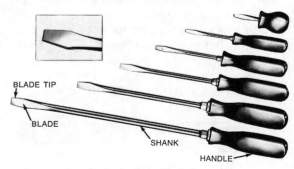

BLADE TIP

BLADE

SHANK

HANDLE

Courtesy Snap-on Tools of Canada, Ltd.

Figure 2-1   Standard tip screwdrivers

35

some specially designed screwdrivers which don't follow this rule. They may have extra-long or extra-short shanks, and extra-thick or extra-thin blades.

It is important that the correct size of blade be used for any given screw, and that the blade be ground correctly. Otherwise the screw slot could sustain damage or the screw itself could fail to turn.

Phillips Screwdrivers. These have a special tip to fit cross-slot, or Phillips, screws. Since these slots vary in depth, width, and thickness, it is important that the correct size screwdriver be used. There are four sizes of Phillips screwdrivers which are marked #1 (smallest) to #4 (largest). Of these, #2 is the most common (Figure 2-2).

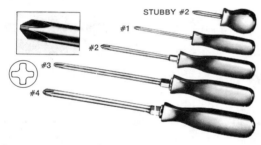

Courtesy Snap-on Tools of Canada, Ltd.

Figure 2-2   Phillips tip screwdrivers

Pozidrive Screwdrivers. These are very similar to the Phillips type, and are even sized the same, but they are not interchangeable. Their tips give a tighter, more positive connection between driver and screw. Their handles are red, to distinguish them from Phillips screwdrivers. Screw heads will have four small identifying marks on them to indi-

Figure 2-3   Pozidrive tip screwdriver

cate they require this type of screwdriver (Figure 2-3).

Torx Screwdrivers. This type has a six-point shaped tip. It is a deep seating drive and holds well. This makes it especially handy for use with power-driving tools. Torx sizes are identified by number: T15, T20, T25, T30, T40, and T50 are some of the sizes. The larger sizes fit striker catches and seatbelt anchor bolts (Figure 2-4).

Figure 2-4   Torx screwdriver

Loosening Tight or Rusted Screws

A screw's head will often plug with dirt or rust and should always be cleaned with a sharp instrument before attempts are made to loosen it. A tight or rusted screw can often be loosened by inserting the screwdriver into the screw head and hitting it with a hammer.

When turning a tight screw, one hand should be held over the end of the handle and the other hand used to turn the driver. As the screw is turned, the pressure exerted against the end of the screwdriver keeps it in the screw slot. For normal screw turning, one hand should be held down close to the screw to keep the tip of the blade in the screw slot. If the blade slips, damage to the surrounding painted surface could result.

Impact Driver Set. These are used for loosening frozen bolts and screws. Each set includes a number of bit drivers. The bit is inserted in the screwhead, and the end of the impacter is hit with a hammer. The hammering forces the impacter to twist at the same time as the bit is being forced into the screwhead. The inward driving force prevents the bit from slipping, while the sudden twist loosens the screw. The handle of the driver can be adjusted to set the impact wrench to move clockwise or counter-clockwise (Figure 2-5).

Offset Screwdrivers. These are used in tight spaces. They have two blades: one parallel to the handle, the other at right angles to it (Figure 2-6).

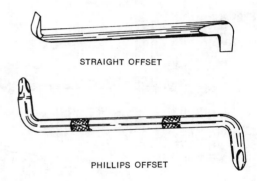

STRAIGHT OFFSET

PHILLIPS OFFSET

Figure 2-6   Offset screwdrivers

2-2 WRENCHES

Wrenches are made so that the length of each is in proportion to the size of the nut or bolt on which it is used. Special wrenches of different shapes and lengths are available for special jobs (Figure 2-7).

Since each type of wrench is designed for a particular type of job, it should be used only for the work to which it is best adapted. Following this rule will result in faster work habits, fewer damaged parts, and less chance of personal injury to the operator.

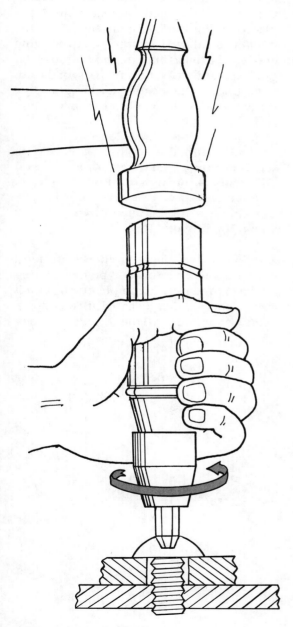

Figure 2-5   Impact driver

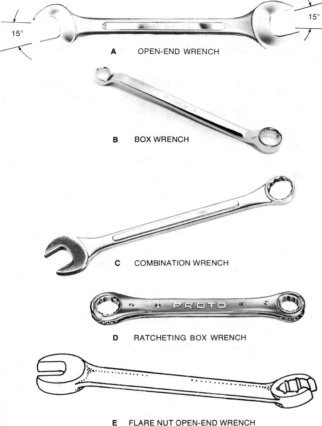

A   OPEN-END WRENCH

B   BOX WRENCH

C   COMBINATION WRENCH

D   RATCHETING BOX WRENCH

E   FLARE NUT OPEN-END WRENCH

A. Manufactured by S-K Wayne Tool Company
B, E. Courtesy Snap-on Tools of Canada, Ltd.
C, D. Courtesy Proto Tools of Canada, Ltd.

Figure 2-7   A–E Wrenches

The size of the wrench, listed either in millimetres or inches, indicates the diameter or distance across the socket or wrench opening. The wrench size therefore is the same as the bolt head or nut size but not of the bolt itself, which is always smaller (Figure 2-8).

Wrench sets are available with openings ranging from 6 through 26 mm in diameter increasing in size by 1 mm steps. When the sets are based on imperial measure the widths increase by increments of 1/16 in.

Open-End Wrenches. This type is usually made with the jaw at a 15° angle to the body of the wrench. This angle allows the wrench to be used in small confined areas because the wrench is turned over each time it is placed on the work. The offset angle of the wrench head will let the wrench swing enough after it has been turned over so that it can be placed on the next two flats of the nut or bolt head. Open-end wrenches grab only the two sides of the bolt head or nut and may slip.

Always pull the wrench toward you when turning a fastener. This way you will avoid skinning your knuckles if the wrench slips. For this reason, this type of wrench is usually used when no other wrench will work.

Box Wrenches. These wrenches are most often used when a socket-type wrench cannot be used. This type completely surrounds the fastener, which means that twisting leverage is applied to **all** the corners and sides.

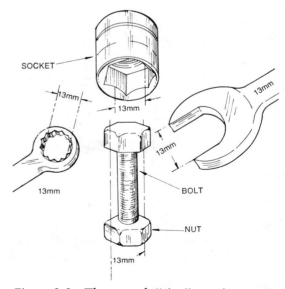

Figure 2-8   The wrench "size" opening

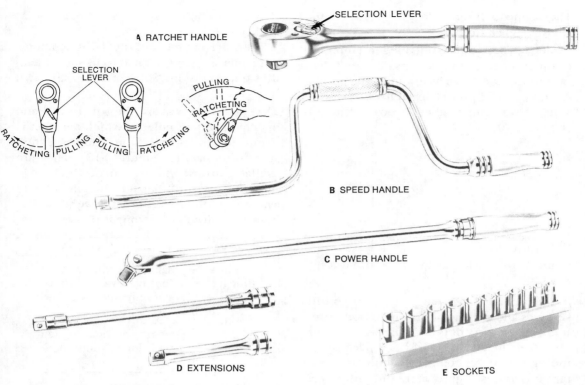

Figure 2-9 Socket handles and extensions

Courtesy Snap-on Tools of Canada, Ltd.

Combination Wrench. This wrench is a combination of an open-end and boxed-in wrench. Both ends are usually the same size.

Ratcheting Box Wrenches. These wrenches are similar to box wrenches except that they may be ratcheted back for another turn without removing the wrench from the bolt. Turning the wrench over reverses the direction of the ratchet and the turn of the bolt.

Flare Nut Wrench. These wrinkles are designed for use on soft flare nuts such as on brake lines. The cut-out at the end of the wrench allows the wrench to fit over the line. It can then be fitted onto the nut. A much better holding and turning torque can be applied without the nut collapsing as it would if an open-end wrench when used.

Socket Wrench Sets

Socket wrench sets consist of a variety of sockets, handles, and attachments. Every socket can be combined with different handles or extensions, each having a specific purpose (Figure 2-9).

The ratchet handle may be used to either tighten or loosen the work by adjusting the selection lever on the ratchet. Power handles are used when leverage and strength are required. The hinged, socket-receiving end permits the operator to work the tool in different positions, thus avoiding obstructions. A speed handle is used when speed but very little leverage is required.

Extension Bars. These lengthen the distance from the handle drive to the socket.

They come in different lengths. Some extensions are even flexible.

Sockets. These can be obtained in a number of different sizes and designs. The end that fits over the work can have a single (6-point) or double (12-point) broach design, the same as box and ratcheting box wrenches (Figure 2-10).

6-POINT SOCKET
SINGLE BROACH

12-POINT SOCKET
DOUBLE BROACH

Figure 2-10   Single and double-brooch design sockets

The 6-point design takes a firm grip on all six sides and corners of the nut or bolt head. It is used on rusty nuts and bolts and brass or other soft metal nuts and bolts because of their greater wall contact. Its one disadvantage is that it is slightly more difficult to get on and off because of the close fit to the nut or bolt head.

The 12-point socket grips only the corners of the nut or bolt head. This design is easier to get on and off than the 6-point. It can also be repositioned on the nut by moving the handle a shorter distance than is possible with the 6-point socket. The disadvantage of the 12-point design is that it sometimes slips off or strips the nut corners on rusty or worn fasteners.

Deeper sockets can be obtained for working with nuts which have been threaded further down a bolt than the length of a regular socket.

There are a number of special attachments which have been designed to fit socket handles and extensions. Some of these are shown in Figure 2-11.

Drives. The drives are the square end and matching square hole by which a socket is connected to its extension, and the extension to its handle (Figure 2-12). They are available in different sizes, all of which are in imperial measure. Socket wrench sets are available with four different drive sizes. The bigger the drive, the stronger the tool.

Drive	Uses
1/4 in. (midget)	lights jobs, e.g., grilles, door hardware, mouldings, clip nuts
3/8 in.	medium work, e.g., removing or replacing fenders, doors, hoods, deck lids
1/2 in. (standard)	heavy work finishing jobs started with 3/8 in. drive
3/4 in. (heavy-duty)	heavy vehicles and machinery where large sockets and high torques are required

Torque Wrenches

Torque wrenches are designed to measure the amount of twisting force being applied to a fastener. The amount of torque is deter-

UNIVERSAL JOINT   HEX-HEAD SOCKET

SCREWDRIVER SOCKETS   RATCHET ADAPTOR FOR USE WITH A POWER BAR

Figure 2-11   Socket set special attachments

Courtesy Snap-on Tools of Canada, Ltd.

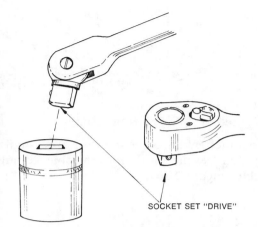

Figure 2-12   Socket drive

mined by multiplying the force being applied by the length of the wrench (that is,
force times leverage). Torque can be expressed in Newton metres (N · m) or pound-
feet.

Some torque wrenches have a built-in
gauge and needle which indicates the force
being applied. Others have a handle which
must be set to the required torque — when
that amount of force is attained, an audible
"click" is heard and a release of tension in
the handle occurs (Figure 2-13).

Torque wrenches are recommended for
some fasteners which must be tightened to
an exact amount. If these fasteners are over-
or under-tightened they could fail creating a
hazard.

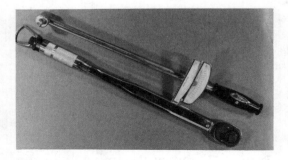

Figure 2-13   Torque wrench

Hex Key Wrenches

These are used to turn special hex drive set
screws (Figure 2-14). They are hex (six-
sided) shaped, and can be obtained in metric
or imperial.

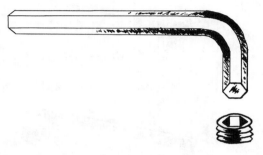

Figure 2-14   Hex key wrench and set screw

2-3 PLIERS

Pliers are designed for gripping work, and
for cutting material such as wire or cotter
pins. In body work, pliers are often used to
straighten inaccessible flanges.

There are many special types of pliers
available, as illustrated in Figure 2-15.

Combination Pliers. These are the most
common type. They are usually equipped
with a slip joint which allows the pliers to be
opened out for gripping large objects or
closed for gripping small objects or for cutting. The ends of the jaws are designed to
firmly grip flat items. The centre section is
designed to grip round items, such as, bolts
or rods. The rear portion is the cutting area.

Diagonal Cutting Pliers. These are designed with the cutting jaws at an angle to
obtain both leverage and a close grip for
pulling and cutting cotter pins.

Body Trimmers' Pliers. These pliers are
used for closing the prongs of the metal lock

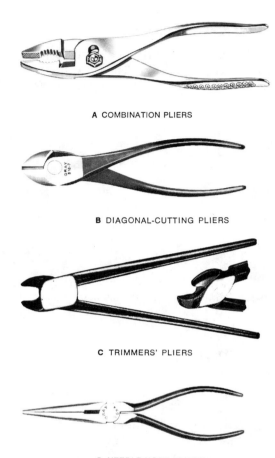

A COMBINATION PLIERS

B DIAGONAL-CUTTING PLIERS

C TRIMMERS' PLIERS

D NEEDLE-NOSE PLIERS

A. Courtesy Snap-on Tools of Canada, Ltd.
B, C, D. Courtesy Gray Tool Co. of Canada Ltd.

Figure 2-15   A–D Pliers

rings that fasten the seat upholstery coverings to the seat frames.

Needle Nose Pliers. These have long, narrow jaws. They are used to grab or hold items that are hard to reach. Their jaws are easily bent so they should be used with caution. They can also be used for cutting light-gauge wire.

Vise Grips and Clamps. Vise grips and clamps are used to hold panels in correct alignment while they are being welded. The end screws in the clamps and grips provide

VISE GRIP
WELDING TOOL

VISE GRIP
BENDING TOOL

VISE GRIPS

VISE GRIP
"C" CLAMP

Courtesy Snap-on Tools of Canada, Ltd.

Figure 2-16   Vise grips and clamps

for quick jaw adjustment. Closing the handle pressurizes the jaws against the object being held (Figure 2-16).

2-4 HACKSAWS

Hacksaws have an adjustable frame to hold different length blades. Hacksaw blades are available in 20, 25, and 30 cm lengths with either fine or coarse teeth. The degree of coarseness is determined by the size of each tooth, expressed in millimetres. For example, a coarse tooth blade has 1.8 mm teeth, a fine tooth blade has 0.8 mm teeth. The standard or general purpose blade would have a 1–1.4 mm tooth size. The blade is installed with the teeth pointing away from the operator.

If possible, two teeth should be kept in contact with the work at all times. With light metal, a fine-toothed blade is recommended. If a fine-toothed blade is not used, cutting

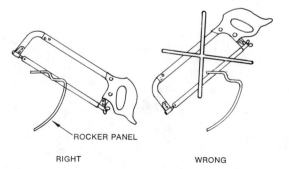

ROCKER PANEL

RIGHT

WRONG

Figure 2-17   Cutting sheet metal with a hacksaw

will be difficult and the blade teeth will break. Thin metal can be cut more easily when the saw is held at an angle to the metal, as shown in Figure 2-17.

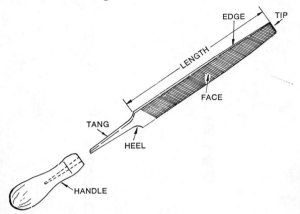

Figure 2-18   File terminology

2-5 FILES

Files are hand-held cutting tools. They are used to remove small amounts of metal and to produce smooth, finished surfaces (Figure 2-18). They are highly tempered, that is, they are very brittle, and are easily broken if misused. A file should always be fitted with a handle so that the "tang" does not run into the palm of the user's hand.

Files are manufactured in a variety of shapes and sizes (Figure 2-19) and have five

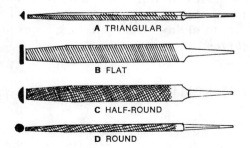

Figure 2-19   Types of files

grades of coarseness: smooth, second-cut, bastard, coarse-cut (Figure 2-20), and body file. Each of the grades except the body file can be found on either a double-cut or a single-cut file. A single-cut file has one row of parallel teeth cut the length of the file, while a double-cut file has two sets of teeth which cross one another.

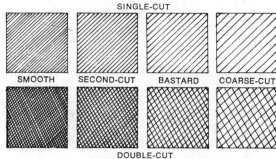

Figure 2-20   File cuts

2-6 COLD CHISELS

Cold Chisels. These are used to cut metal, break spot welds, and split nuts. They are made in various lengths and sizes. Some are made specifically for cutting sheet metal panels.

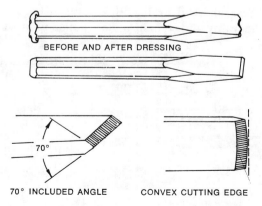

Figure 2-21   Correct grinding of a chisel head

The head of the chisel should be kept properly ground. After much use it tends to become "mushroomed." If this is not corrected, chips could fly off and injure the user.

Flat chisels. These are ground to have an included angle of 60° to 70° and a slightly convex cutting edge. These features prevent the corners from digging into the surfaces being chiselled (Figure 2-21).

2-7 PUNCHES

The standard types of punches used are: centre punch, starter punch, pin punch, drift or taper punch, and ice pick or scratch awl. Each type of punch is designed for a specific task (Figure 2-22).

Centre Punch. This is used to mark the centre of a hole to be drilled.

Starter Punch. This has a long, gentle taper and a flat end, and is used to begin driving out a pin.

Pin Punch. This is thinner than the starter punch and is used to finish driving out a pin (Figure 2-23).

Drift or Taper Punch. This is used when aligning parts in assembly work.

Scratch Awl or Ice Pick. This is used for marking and punching holes in sheet metal.

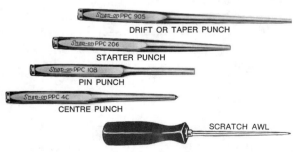

Courtesy Snap-on Tools of Canada, Ltd.

Figure 2-22   Punches

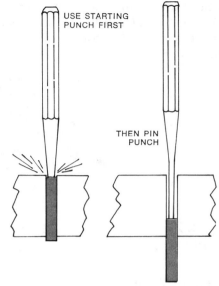

Figure 2-23   Using starter and pin punches

A metal furrow on the blade helps to prevent pressure from pushing the handle down over the blade.

Air Hammers

Air hammers and tools are used to cut body panels, split spot welds, punch out pins, and shear rivets and bolts. The air pressure that operates this tool forces a piston at up to 3500 blows per minute against the end of the tool. Several different tools are used for the above operations.

Caution should be observed when using the air hammer. The operator should always wear safety glasses and gloves.

2-8 SNIPS

Hand Snips. There are different types of hand snips for cutting straight lines, curved lines, and irregular shapes in sheet metal.

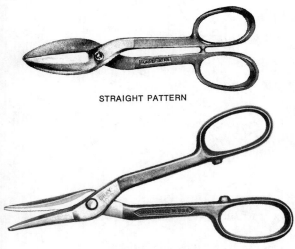

STRAIGHT PATTERN

COMBINATION CIRCLE PATTERN

A HAND SNIPS

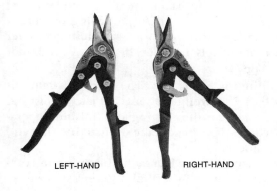

LEFT-HAND   RIGHT-HAND

A. Courtesy Gray Tool Co. of Canada Ltd.
B. Photo by B. Robinson

Figure 2-24   Snips

They are classified by their overall length and by the type of work for which they are designed.

Aviation Snips. Aviation snips are used to cut tough metals. There are three types available, each designed to provide a different cut. One type cuts to the left, another to the right, and the third straight ahead. All three snips use the compound-lever principle (Figure 2-24).

2-9 TWIST DRILLS

Twist drills have three main sections: the shank, the body, and the point.

The **point** is the cone-shaped end which does the actual cutting. Normally, the included angle of a point is 118°. **Dead centre** is the chisel-shaped portion of the drill.

The **lips** are the cutting edges. They must be of equal length and be at the same angle, usually 59°. This angle keeps the drill running true so that it will not cut a hole larger than its own diameter (Figure 2-25A and Figure 2-25B).

Lip clearance is the clearance ground on the point of the drill from the cutting lip back to the heel. The lip clearance allows the sharp cutting edges of the drill to cut into the metal without interference. When sharpening a drill, it is important to make the lips, or cutting edges, of equal length and to leave a lip clearance of 12° to 15°.

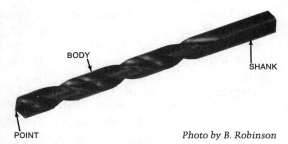

BODY

SHANK

POINT   *Photo by B. Robinson*

Figure 2-25A   Twist drill

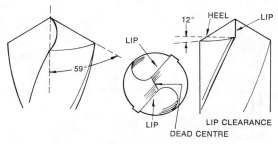

59°

12°   HEEL   LIP

LIP

LIP

DEAD CENTRE

LIP CLEARANCE

Figure 2-25B   Drill point

2-10 HAMMERS

Automobile body designs are constantly changing and no two collisions are ever exactly the same. The repair person always has a somewhat different type and area of damage to repair. Because of these variables, a selection of hammers, dollies, spoons, pries, and files are necessary for use in straightening the damaged metal. Techniques for using the following tools will be covered in detail in Chapter 4.

The size of a hammer is determined by the mass of its head. The mass of available body hammers varies from 200 g to over 1000 g. Body hammers are usually double hammers in that they have a working face on each end of the hammer head. The hammer can be used for two or more different operations.

A variety of styles of hammers are necessary for use on the different types of damage. A good hammer must be properly balanced so that it is easy to handle and does not tend to twist in your hand each time the metal is struck. Body hammers are divided into two different categories: **bumping** and **dinging**.

Bumping Hammers. Bumping hammers are quite heavy, with masses ranging from ap-

BUMPING HAMMER

DINGING HAMMER — SHORT SHANK

Courtesy Gray Tool Co. of Canada Ltd.

Figure 2-26 Bumping and dinging hammers

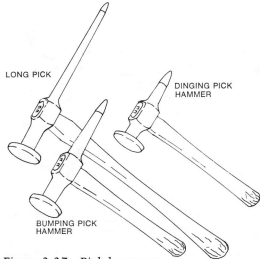

LONG PICK

DINGING PICK HAMMER

BUMPING PICK HAMMER

Figure 2-27 Pick hammers

proximately 400 g to 1200 g. The face of the head usually has a slight crown. Bumping hammers are used for roughing out badly damaged areas, and for straightening heavier inner panels, bumpers, frame rails, and floor pans, etc.

Dinging Hammers. The dinging hammer is lighter in weight (about 200 g to 350 g) and is used for the dinging and finishing operations. The head face is usually flat and smooth.

Each of these hammers (bumping and dinging) comes in several different styles (Figure 2-26).

Pick Hammers. A pick hammer has a round surface on one end of the head and a pick on the other. The pick end is used for picking up small dents and pimples.

The **bumping pick hammer** is heavy and has a higher-crowned face and a blunter pick than the dinging hammer. The lighter **dinging pick hammer** is used in finishing operations.

The **long-pick hammer** is used for picking awkwardly located areas where a long reach is required. The handle is usually longer than that on an ordinary hammer (Figure 2-27).

Round- and Square-Faced Hammers. The bumping hammer of this type has a wider head, a higher-crowned face, and a larger shank than the dinging hammer. The square face is used for bumping in corners and along the edge of a right angle bend or body joint. When a round face is used in these areas, ring marks are usually left in the metal. The round face is used for most general work.

Cross-Peen Hammers. This type of hammer has a chisel-like pick and is used for working sharp corners and for reshaping beads (Figure 2-28).

Always make sure the hammer head is tight on its handle to prevent the head from flying off.

A hammer's head can often be tightened to its handle by soaking it in water or anti-freeze. This makes the wood swell, which tightens the joint. If this doesn't work, try driving a wedge into the wood where it connects to the head.

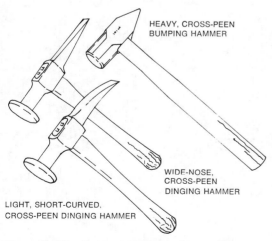

HEAVY, CROSS-PEEN BUMPING HAMMER

WIDE-NOSE, CROSS-PEEN DINGING HAMMER

LIGHT, SHORT-CURVED, CROSS-PEEN DINGING HAMMER

Figure 2-28　Cross-peen bumping and dinging hammers

Installing a New Hammer Handle

Whenever it is necessary to install a new hammer handle, use a handle similar in size and length to the original, to maintain the correct balance and handling characteristics.

Place the hammer head on the tapered end of the handle. Hold the head on if it is a poor fit and drive the back end of the handle against a solid object, such as, a bench or floor. Remove the head and grind or file off any high spots which prevent the hammer head from fitting onto the tapered end of the handle. Continue to repeat these two steps until the head fits the handle correctly. The bottom of the hammer head should fit the handle tightly, with no gap showing between the handle and head opening (Figure 2-29A, B, C).

When the correct fit has been obtained, press the head on (Figure 2-29) or use the driving method (Figure 2-30) to force the handle tightly into the head.

Use a flat blade screwdriver to spread the wedge slot in the end of the handle and then drive in the wooden wedge. Cut the end of the handle and wooden wedge off within 2 or 3 mm from the end of the head. Cut one or two slots in each end of the handle across the wooden wedge and drive in the steel wedges. Grind the end smooth (Figure 2-31A, B, C).

2-11 DOLLIES AND SPOONS

Dollies

Dollies are heavy solid pieces of steel with smooth, polished surfaces or faces. They are often called **hand anvils.** They are used to back up or provide support under the

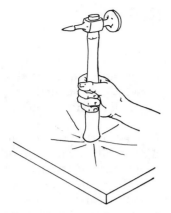

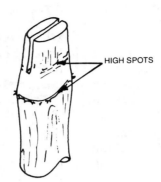

Figure 2-29   A. Drive the handle against a solid object

B. Grind or file off the high spots

C. The handle should fit the head tightly

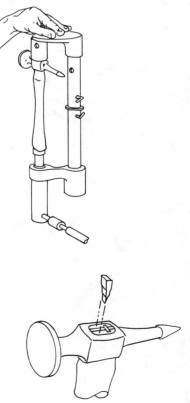

Figure 2-30   Using a hydraulic body jack set-up to press the head tightly onto the handle

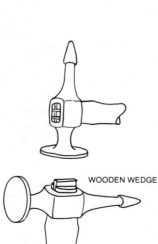

Figure 2-31
A. Spreading the wedge slot in the end of the handle

B. Drive in the wooden wedge

C. Install the steel wedges across the wooden wedge

damaged metal while the area is being straightened back to its original size and shape.

In most cases, the shape of the dolly's face must be close to that of the metal being worked on. This means it is necessary for a body shop to have a large selection of dollies of different shapes and configurations to fit the different contours of the metal. Figure 2-32 shows some of the different dollies available.

Figure 2-33   Spoons   *Photo by B. Robinson*

BAR DOLLY BLOCK   BUDD DOLLY BLOCK

TOE DOLLY BLOCK   HEEL DOLLY BLOCK

WEDGE DOLLY BLOCK   GENERAL-PURPOSE
                         DOLLY BLOCK

Courtesy Gray Tool Co. of Canada Ltd.

Figure 2-32   Dollies

Spoons

Spoons, also called hand anvils, are sometimes used where dollies will not fit to support the metal. They are also used to pry up low spots and to spring-hammer ridges or creases left in a panel from a snap bump (Figure 2-33).

A snap bump occurs when an area of metal is pushed in. When the pressure is released, the metal snaps back to its original position. A slight convex ridge or crease is often left around the edge of the area that had popped in. This slight ridge or crease can be removed by holding a flat-faced spoon against the crease and driving it with a hammer (Figure 2-34).

The large flat area of the spoon spreads the force of the blow out along the crease. The area is driven down to its proper position, with very little or no marking of the painted surface.

Masking tape or a light coating of grease or oil is sometimes used on the spoon or on the painted surface to prevent damage to the paint. Some body mechanics make spoons for special jobs from used spring leaves.

> The faces of hammers, dollies, and spoons should be kept clean and polished to avoid marking the metal when a blow is struck.

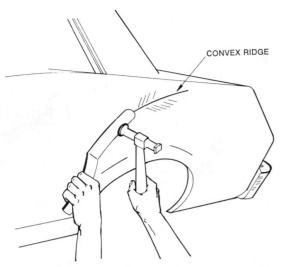

CONVEX RIDGE

Figure 2-34 Spring hammering a convex ridge

Pry Bars

These are used to pry out damaged areas which cannot be reached with a dolly. Different length pry bars are available. They can also be made from discarded screwdrivers or deck lid torsion bar springs (Figure 2-35).

Often it is possible to punch a hole in the bottom of a door in order to pry up a small crease. Considerable time can be saved this way, since the door's inner panels do not have to be removed.

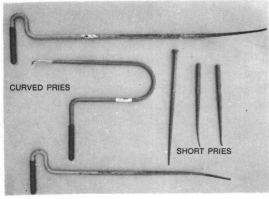

CURVED PRIES

SHORT PRIES

Figure 2-35 Pry bars   *Photo by B. Robinson*

2-12 BODY WORKING FILES

Body files are used to file smooth (**metal finish**) damaged areas of metal after they have been "bumped" back into shape. The body file smoothes the surface and produces a scratch pattern that indicates the level areas and the high and low spots. The high spots are then tapped down with the flat face of the hammer, and the low spots are picked up with the pick end of the hammer. The area is then refiled to further smooth the surface and create a new scratch pattern. The metal finishing process is time-consuming, highly skilled work. To save time and cost most damaged areas are now bumped level and then filled over with a body filler.

Body fillers can be filed with the body file. However, most repair people prefer to use a **Surform file** to shave off the rough cut and a **board file** to finish smoothing the area.

Construction of Body Files

Body files are usually about 35 mm long, and have cutting teeth on both sides. The teeth

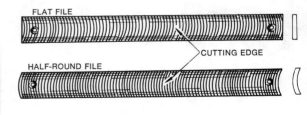

FLAT FILE

CUTTING EDGE

HALF-ROUND FILE

Photo by B. Robinson

Figure 2-36 Body files and handle

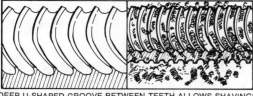

DEEP U-SHAPED GROOVE BETWEEN TEETH ALLOWS SHAVINGS TO ESCAPE AND PREVENTS PLUGGING

Figure 2-37 Enlarged view of file teeth

are set on a curve across the face of the blade (Figure 2-36). There is an unbroken cutting edge on the convex side of each tooth. The file is mounted on a wooden handle with the cutting edge of the teeth pointing away from the holder. The cut is made on the push stroke. When the file is held and pushed at an angle to the direction of travel, the curved teeth still cut at right angles.

The standard body file has approximately 8 teeth per 25 mm. A coarse file with approximately 6.5 teeth per 25 mm is available for use on body fillers. The deep, U-shaped grooves between the teeth allow the ribbon-like shavings from the work to escape without plugging the file (Figure 2-37).

Surform Files

These are used for filing body fillers (Figure 2-38). They come in a variety of sizes and are either half-round or flat. The one most commonly used for plastic fillers is the 250 mm long half-round type. With this file, parallel rows of teeth are set at a 70° angle to the length of the body. Each row consists of a series of small cutting teeth separated by a space. In front of each tooth's cutting edge there is a hole through the blade. These holes, and the space between the teeth, allow the cuttings of body filler to escape. The file can be used with a handle but most body repairers prefer to use it without. The cut is made on the pull stroke rather than the push stroke.

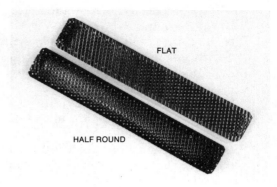

FLAT

HALF ROUND

Figure 2-38 Surform file

Board File

This is similar to a body file, but has an additional flat base to which long narrow sheets of abrasive paper are fastened. Some board files have front and rear clips which hold the abrasive paper to the board. Others are designed to take glue-backed abrasive paper. Board files are used to smooth and level plastic fillers. Filing techniques are discussed in detail in Chapter 4.

REVIEW QUESTIONS

1. List the largest Phillips screwdriver size, the smallest, and the size most commonly used on the automobile.
2. a) What other type of screwdriver is very similar to the Phillips drive?
   b) What are the differences between this type and the Phillips screwdriver?
   c) How does the screw head indicate which of these two types of screwdrivers to use?
3. What two advantages does the torx screwdriver have?
4. a) Why should plugged screw slots

first be cleaned before attempting to loosen the screw?

   b) How can a tight or rusty screw often be loosened?

   c) Explain how to turn a tight or rusty screw.

5. Why are open-end wrenches made with the head openings at a 15° angle to the body of the wrench?

6. Is a box wrench more likely to slip off the nut or bolt head than an open-end wrench? Why, or why not?

7. List and explain the purposes of the various socket handles.

8. List the advantages and disadvantages of 6- and 12-point sockets.

9. What purpose do deep sockets serve?

10. a) What is meant by the "drive" of socket sets?

   b) List the different drive sizes and explain where each would be used.

11. Explain why it is necessary to torque certain fastenings.

12. For what two purposes can combination pliers be used?

13. How can the jaws of vise grips and clamps be adjusted?

14. How is a blade installed in a hacksaw?

15. a) What type of hacksaw blade should be used for cutting thin metal? Why?

   b) How can the cutting of thin metal with a hacksaw be made easier?

16. Explain the difference between a single- and double-cut file.

17. a) What is the difference in design between a pin punch and a starter punch?

   b) Explain the purpose of each.

18. Should a centre punch ever be used to drive or loosen a pin? Explain your answer.

19. Why is it important when sharpening a drill to have the lips, or cutting edges, of equal length?

20. How is the size of a hammer determined?

21. List the differences between a bumping and a dinging hammer.

22. Where are square-faced hammers used?

23. What are the purposes of dollies?

24. What are the purposes of spoons?

25. a) Describe a "snap bump."

   b) How can the slight ridge, or crease, left from a snap bump be removed without marking the paint?

26. What is the purpose of the pry bar?

27. List the uses of the body file.

28. Explain the term "metal finishing."

29. a) On which side of the teeth is the cutting edge of a body file located?

   b) Why are the teeth of the body file curved?

   c) What is the purpose of the U-shaped grooves between the teeth?

30. Compare the construction of Surform blade teeth to that of standard body file teeth.

3

FASTENERS

3-1   Bolts
3-2   Types of Threads
3-3   Screws
3-4   Nuts
3-5   Specialty Fasteners
3-6   Washers, Rivets, and Mouldings

Fasteners are used to connect two or more things. There are many different types. Threaded bolts are the most commonly used fasteners on automobiles, but they are gradually being replaced with newly designed non-threaded self-locking clips. Many of these clips are made of plastic. Specially designed adhesives are also being used instead of fasteners to bond parts together.

The threaded fastenings on newer automobiles are sized in SI metric; however, imperial fasteners are still available. Automobile repairers must be familar with both systems and must be aware of the many types of fasteners.

3-1 BOLTS

Cap Screws. A cap screw has a hexagonal (six-sided) head and a coarse or fine thread.

It is used in a blind or open-threaded hole. When a nut is used with the cap screw, it is called a bolt. However, these terms are not strictly adhered to. A cap screw is often called a bolt even if it is used without a nut (Figure 3-1).

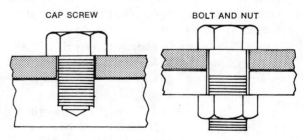

Figure 3-1   Cap screw vs. bolt

Carriage Bolts. A carriage bolt has a round, high crowned head with a square shoulder under the head. Carriage bolts were originally designed for use in fastening wooden

53

Figure 3-2   Carriage bolt

ELLIPTICAL HEAD   ROUND HEAD

Figure 3-3   Bumper bolt

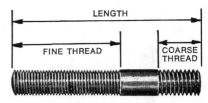

Courtesy J.C. Adams Company Limited

Figure 3-4   Stud

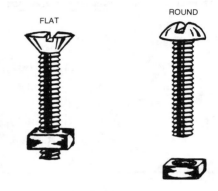

Figure 3-5   Stove bolts

items together. The square shoulder pulled into the wood to prevent the bolt from turning while the nut was tightened or removed (Figure 3-2).

Bumper Bolts. The bumper bolt is a type of carriage bolt (Figure 3-3). The bolt head is either chrome plated or has a thin chromed cap. The square shoulder fits into a square hole in the bumper to prevent the bolt from turning. The crowned chrome head of the bolt provides a smooth "finished" look to the bumper face bar.

Studs. These have no heads and are threaded at both ends. Their threads can be fine or coarse at either or both ends (Figure 3-4).

Stove Bolts. Stove bolts are not commonly used in automobile construction, but they are often used with various automotive-related items (Figure 3-5). Traditionally a square nut was used with a stove bolt. Hex nuts are also available. The nut fits the thread loosely to permit rapid assembly. Stove bolts have flat- or round-shaped heads with a slotted drive for use with standard screwdrivers.

A stove bolt is very similar to some types of machine screws.

Bolt Sizes

Bolts are sized in both SI metric and the imperial system. The size of the fastener is determined by its diameter which is measured loosely across the threads. A metric fastener is measured in millimetres and the imperial fastener in sixteenths of an inch. Common metric sizes are M5, M6, M7, M8, M10, M12 (the M stands for metric). Common imperial fastener sizes are 1/4 in., 5/16 in., 3/8 in., and 1/2 in.

A fastener's length is measured from the tip to just underneath the head (Figure 3-6). An 8 mm bolt that is 25 mm long is referred to as an M8 × 25 mm bolt. Imperial fasteners increase in size by increments of sixteenths of an inch.

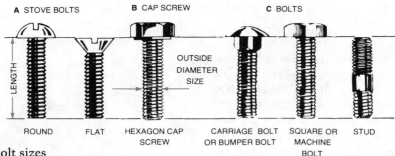

Figure 3-6 Bolt sizes

3-2 TYPES OF THREADS

Fasteners can have two types of threads: **coarse** or **fine.** A coarse thread is deeper, wider, and covers a greater distance of the length of the fastener than a fine thread. The width of each thread, measured from any

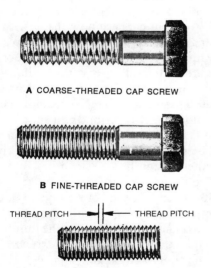

A COARSE-THREADED CAP SCREW

B FINE-THREADED CAP SCREW

THREAD PITCH ⟶ ⟵ THREAD PITCH

A, B. Courtesy J.C. Adams Co.

Figure 3-7 Coarse and fine threads and thread pitch

given point on one thread to the corresponding point on the next, is referred to as the **thread pitch** (Figure 3-7).

Thread Identification Systems

Metric. In this system, bolt size and thread pitch are both expressed in millimetres. The following chart gives the most common metric bolt sizes and their corresponding thread pitches. The larger thread pitch number indicates the coarse or "standard" thread.

Bolt Size	Thread Pitch Size
M5	0.8 0.75
M6	1 0.75
M8	1.25 1
M10	1.5 1.25
M12	1.75 1.5
M14	2 1.5

As the size of the bolt increases, the pitch size also increases. The thread pitch size is not usually listed for coarse metric fasteners. They are assumed to be **coarse,** or of **"standard"** thread, unless otherwise indicated. The size of a typical metric bolt with standard metric thread would be expressed as **M10 × 25 mm** (size × length). A **fine-threaded** bolt of the same size would be expressed as M10 × 1.25 × 25 mm (size × pitch × length).

Imperial. The term "thread pitch" is not usually used with this system. Instead, coarse and fine are expressed in terms of the number of threads per inch a fastener has. For example, a 1/4 in. coarse threaded bolt has 20 threads per inch, and a 1/4 in. fine threaded bolt has 28 threads per inch. In this system, the number of threads per inch decreases as the bolt size increases.

Never substitute a metric fastener for an imperial one, or an imperial for a metric. While the sizes may correspond almost exactly, the threads have different pitches and cannot be interchanged without causing thread damage.

Uses of Coarse and Fine Threads

Coarse threaded fasteners are used in soft or crumbly metals such as aluminum and cast iron. The larger, deeper threads hold better in these metals than do the fine threads. The larger depth and distance between each coarse thread prevents them from filling with rust as quickly and even if they are rusted, they are still easier to get off than rusted fine threaded fasteners. Most fasteners used on automobiles are coarse threaded.

Fine threaded fasteners are used where greater bolt strength and additional accuracy of assembly is required. They tend to tighten tighter, hold better, and will not shake loose quite as easily as coarse threads.

Pipe Thread

This type of thread is self-sealing. The threaded part of the end of the pipe is ta-

pered. The threads tighten together to seal without a gasket or locking device and produce a leak-proof joint (Figure 3-8).

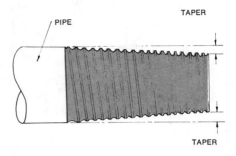

Figure 3-8 Pipe thread

Bolt Strength

Vehicles have been getting smaller and lighter. As a result they are being made with fewer and smaller bolts than before. Most bolts used in cars are now made with high-strength steel, which gives them greater holding strength. Many manufacturers are now recommending that the bolts in their cars — especially those bolts holding safety-related parts such as steering and suspension assemblies — be torqued to a specific tightness. They also recommend that some bolts not be reused and that replacement bolts be of equal strength.

The strength identification system for metric fasteners consists of numbers which are stamped or embossed onto the head of the fastener and nut. The higher the number, the stronger the nut. Most high-strength bolts are in the 8 to 10 range. (Figure 3-9).

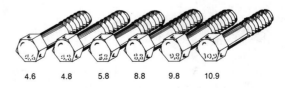

Figure 3-9 Metric bolts — increasing numbers represent increasing strength

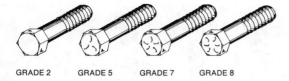

GRADE 2   GRADE 5   GRADE 7   GRADE 8

Figure 3-10   Imperial bolts — increasing numbers represent increasing strength

There is a similar identification system for imperial fasteners, which uses lines embossed on the fasteners' heads. This system identifies grades 2 to 8. The grade is always two higher than the number of lines on the head. For example, a grade 7 bolt would have 5 lines on the head, while a grade 2 bolt would have no lines (Figure 3-10).

3-3 SCREWS

Machine Screws

Machine screws are small fasteners up to 6 mm or 1/4 in. in size. They have a variety of head shapes and can take various types of drives (Figure 3-11).

The round- and flat-headed machine screws look much like stove bolts. The difference is that machine screws have a much closer-fitting thread, for smoother and more accurate assembly.

Machine Screw Sizes. Machine screws are sized the same way as bolts, that is, across the threads for the diameter, and from under the head to the end for length.

Metric machine screws are sized from M1 to M8 and can be from 2 mm to 60 mm in length. They all have coarse threads. Some of the larger screws can be obtained with fine thread, but would rarely be needed.

Imperial screw sizes are identified by a numbering system from #2, the smallest, to #12, the largest, increasing in steps of two. Imperial screws can be obtained in either coarse or fine thread, and as before, the threads are measured in terms of the number of threads per inch. For example, a number 10-24 screw has a #10 diameter and 24 threads per inch, while a number 10-32 screw is a fine thread screw of the same diameter.

Sheet Metal Screws

Metal screws can be obtained with flat, round, oval pan, truss, or hex heads, with standard, Phillips, torx, Pozidrive, or Robertson drive. Figure 3-12 shows a sampling of metal screws drawn to scale.

Metal screws have a sharp point and coarse, deep thread. They are designed to self-thread into either a drilled or punched hole in sheet metal. The drilled hole should be slightly smaller than the diameter of the screw at the bottom of the threads. Metal screws hold better in a punched hole because of the extra metal "punched" out from the hole. However, a punched hole cannot be used on automotive outer panels as the metal tends to dent before the hole is punched through.

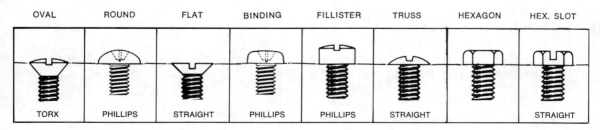

OVAL	ROUND	FLAT	BINDING	FILLISTER	TRUSS	HEXAGON	HEX. SLOT
TORX	PHILLIPS	STRAIGHT	PHILLIPS	PHILLIPS	STRAIGHT		STRAIGHT

Figure 3-11   Machine screw head shapes

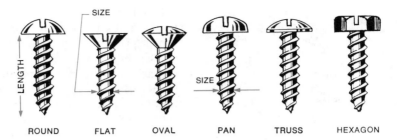

Figure 3-12 Sheet metal head shapes

Sometimes a metal screw hole will become slightly worn or enlarged so that the screw will not fully tighten. A small piece of wire can be placed through the hole for the screw to grab onto as it tightens.

Metal Screw Sizes. These screws are sized the same way as machine screws: an M4 × 25 mm screw would have a diameter of 4 mm and a length of 25 mm. In the imperial system a #8 × 3/4 in. screw has a #8 diameter and is 3/4 in. long.

3-4 NUTS

Common Nuts

Several different types of nuts are used with the various fastenings (Figure 3-13).

The **square nut** is used with stove bolts. It is made with coarse threads only. Square nuts are not often used on the automobile. If they are present, they are not meant to be taken off. The manufacturer often welds square nuts to the body, especially in places where it would be difficult to get a hand or wrench in. These welded nuts are made square so there is spot welding room at the corners. The beginner might think that a wrench is necessary to hold the nut, but it is not.

The other nut styles can be either fine or coarse threaded. The **hex nut** is the most commonly used in the automotive industry.

The **castle**, or **castellated**, and **slotted hex nuts** are made with slotted tops. A cotter pin may be installed in these nuts for locking purposes to prevent the nut from backing off. **Retainer nuts** are used in the assembly of the body sheet-metal parts. They are clipped onto the part and do not have to be held with a wrench when the fastener is added. **Flanged hex nuts** are used with moulding fasteners. The sealant on the flange seals the moulding hole.

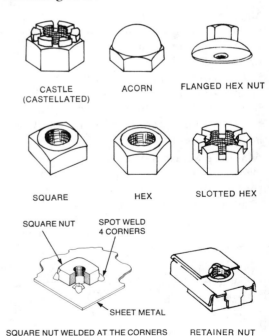

Figure 3-13 Common nuts

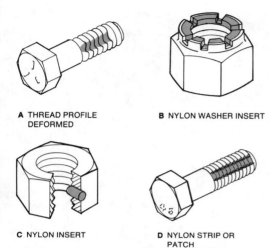

A THREAD PROFILE DEFORMED

B NYLON WASHER INSERT

C NYLON INSERT

D NYLON STRIP OR PATCH

Figure 3-14A–D   Threaded self-locking fasteners

Some fasteners have a self-locking mechanism built into the bolt or the nut. There are various types of self-locking mechanism (Figure 3-14 A-D). The threads may be purposely distorted either in the end of the nut or in a section of the bolt. A nut may have a nylon washer insert in the threads at the top, or a small nylon insert in a hole in the side. Finally, a bolt can have a dry adhesive coating on the threads or a nylon strip inserted into the threads.

> When self-locking fasteners are encountered, they must be carefully inspected for damage or excessive wear. If any is found, they must not be reused.

Head and Nut Sizes

In the imperial system, there is a definite relationship between a fastener's diameter and its head and nut sizes. For all fasteners between 1/4 in. and 7/16 in. in diameter, the head and nut will be 3/16 in. wider. For 1/2 in. bolts the nut and head will be 1/4 in. wider.

With metric fasteners there is no similar rule. The following chart indicates the head sizes of the more common metric bolts. Note that as the bolt size increases, so does the difference in head size to provide a larger head bearing surface for the increased fastener strength.

Fastener Size	Head and Wrench Size	Difference
M5	9 mm	4 mm
M6	10 mm	4 mm
M8	14 mm	6 mm
M10	17 mm	7 mm
M12	19 mm	7 mm
M14	22 mm	8 mm
M16	24 mm	8 mm

3-5 SPECIALTY FASTENERS

A number of automotive manufacturers use specialty fasteners. These vary greatly in size, shape, and use. The following are some of the more common ones:

Tubular-Type Speed Clips. These are used with unthreaded studs or with pins such as

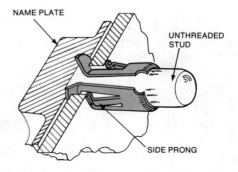

NAME PLATE

UNTHREADED STUD

SIDE PRONG

Figure 3-15   Tubular-type speed clip

those used on vehicle name scripts and emblems. They can be made from steel or plastic. This type of clip is inserted into the hole in a panel so that its side prongs hold the clip in proper position. When the stud is pushed into the clip, the turned-in end of the clip bites the stud and holds it in place (Figure 3-15). Remove the stud by carefully prying it out with a standard screwdriver.

Speed Nuts. Speed nuts are made of heat-treated spring steel. They are designed for use with threaded fasteners. Figure 3-16 illustrates the flat-, J-, and U-shaped speed nuts which are used with threaded sheet metal and machine screws.

The J- and U-shaped types are designed to clip over and lock onto a sheet metal flange. They do not have to be held as the screw is turned.

The flat-types are designed to be pushed onto an unthreaded pin or used as a nut with a threaded screw. When they are used as nuts they have to be held to keep them from turning.

Anchor Insert Nuts. These are made of nylon. (Figure 3-17). They are inserted into a square hole. When the screw is threaded into the insert, the lower lugs are forced outward, tightening the insert in the hole.

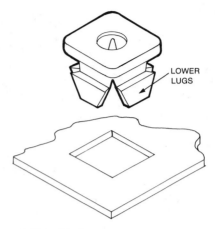

Figure 3-17   Anchor insert nut

Push-in-Trim Clips (Christmas Tree Fasteners). There are many variations. Most types are made of plastic. They are designed to be pushed into the holes of the two parts being fastened. The barbs on the stem spring outward to tightly grab against the hole (Figure 3-18). They are much easier to put in than they are to get out without breaking. Use a vee-notched pry tool that fits under the head when trying to work the clip out.

Plastic Drive Rivets. The body of the rivet is first placed through the holes of the two parts being fastened. The centre pin is either

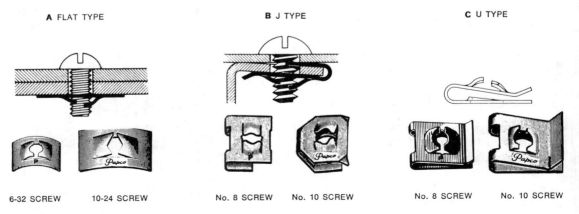

A FLAT TYPE

6-32 SCREW   10-24 SCREW

B J TYPE

No. 8 SCREW   No. 10 SCREW

C U TYPE

No. 8 SCREW   No. 10 SCREW

Figure 3-16   Speed nuts

©H. Paulin & Co. Limited, 1963

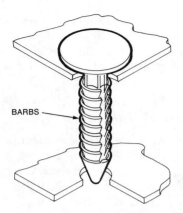

Figure 3-18   Push-in-trim clip (Christmas tree fastener)

pushed or driven into the rivet forcing out the lower tabs of the rivet tightly against the bottom of the hole.

Those centre pins which have a head can be pulled out to remove the clip when separating the two fastened parts (Figure 3-19). But when the centre pin is headless, it must be driven completely through the rivet with a small pin punch.

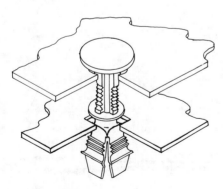

Figure 3-19   Plastic drive rivet

Retaining Link Clip. Retaining clips are used to hold the ends of various rod connectors or arms to such things as door and hood locks and air conditioning controls (Figure 3-20). They can be made of spring steel or plastic material.

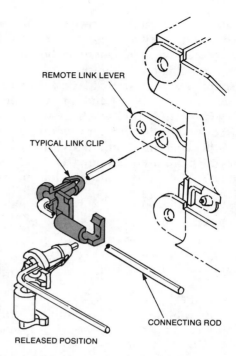

Figure 3-20   Retaining link clip

3-6 WASHERS, RIVETS, AND MOULDINGS

Washers

Flat Washers. These come in different sizes and thicknesses. They are used to cover large holes and to spread the bearing force of a bolt head or nut over a larger area.

Lock Washer. These come in a variety of styles. They are all used to lock a bolt, screw,

| | INTERNAL TYPE   EXTERNAL TYPE |
| **A** SPRING LOCK WASHER | **B** SHAKEPROOF LOCK WASHERS |

©*Courtesy J.C. Adams Company Limited*

Figure 3-21   Lock washers

or nut in place and to prevent them from backing off. They are inserted next to the nut, if there is one, or next to the bolt head if no nut is being used (Figure 3-21).

There are also **spring lock washers** which dig into the nut and into the object being fastened, **fender washers** which have a large outside diameter for covering slotted holes in sheet metal, and **finishing washers** which are used in body trim work. See Figure 3-22 for the positioning of washers.

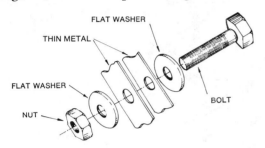

Figure 3-22   Application of washers

Washer Sizes. A washer's size is determined by the diameter of its hole. They can be obtained in metric or imperial. The washer must correspond in size to the bolt it is being used on. For example, a 10 mm washer is used with an M10 bolt (Figure 3-23). In either system, the I.D. (inside diameter) of the washer would actually be slightly larger than its listed size, to allow for an easier fit. A flat washer's O.D. (outside diameter) can vary according to what it is being used for. For

example, a 10 mm standard flat washer could have an O.D. of 20 mm or 30 mm. The 30 mm diameter washer would be better suited for bolting sheet metal panels together.

Hollow Rivets

Hollow rivets are used for fastening small parts together. There is a solid mandrel through the centre of the rivet which resembles a fine finishing nail. After the rivet has been placed in the hole, special **riveting pliers** pull on the mandrel. The mandrel collapses the back of the rivet. When the rivet is set, the mandrel shaft breaks from the head and pulls out (Figure 3-24).

Although they are specially made for "blind" fastenings where there is no access to the other side of the work, rivets are also

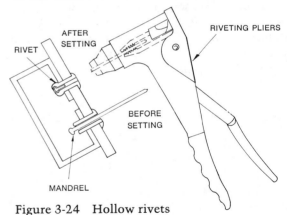

Figure 3-24   Hollow rivets

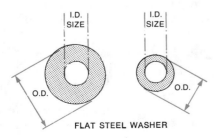

Figure 3-23   The I.D. washer size is the same as the bolt size

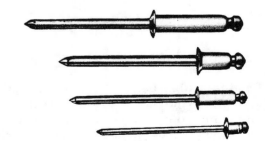

©*Courtesy Spae-Naur Products Limited*

Figure 3-25   Different-size "pop" rivets

used in non-blind applications. The rivets are made in a wide range of sizes and types, in either aluminum, steel, or plastic, some of which are shown in Figure 3-25.

Nut inserts (Figure 3-26) are somewhat similar to rivets, except that the inside of the insert is threaded to take a cap screw or machine screw. They are pulled in or installed in a similar way to hollow (or pop) rivets.

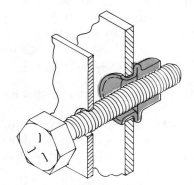

Figure 3-26   Nut insert

Exterior Mouldings

Car exterior mouldings are secured to their panels by the following methods, which can be used alone or in combination (Figure 3-27).

Studs. A stud is threaded into the back of the white metal or plastic casting. The moulding is placed against the body so that the studs protrude through holes in the body. A nut is turned onto the stud from the back of the panel.

Clips. Clips with a threaded stud are locked into the back of the moulding. The moulding is then placed on the panel and a nut is turned onto the clip stud from the back of the panel.

Snap-In Clips. These are fastened to the back of the moulding. The clips then snap into holes in the panel.

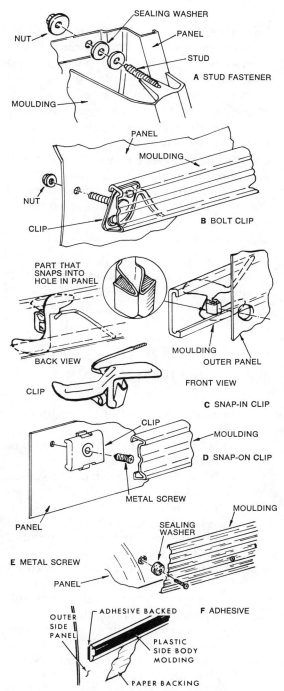

Figure 3-27   Methods of securing exterior moulding

Snap-Over Clips. These clips are tightly secured to the body panels. This can be done with a screw, a pop rivet, or a special pin stud which is welded to the body. The moulding snaps over the clip.

Metal Screws. Mouldings are occasionally secured with metal screws which screw directly into the panels.

Double-Faced Adhesive Tape. Many mouldings are secured to the body with this tape. A protective cover is removed from the tape on the back of the moulding while the moulding is applied to the body.

> There are a number of different clips and fasteners which can be used to secure moulding to a panel, but they all are based on one of the methods outlined above.

REVIEW QUESTIONS

1. a) Neatly draw and label five different types of bolts.
    b) Show where the size and length of each bolt is measured.
2. a) What is the purpose of the square shoulder under the head of a carriage bolt?
    b) Is there any outward difference between a carriage bolt and a bumper bolt?
    c) Why are bumper bolts used to fasten bumper face bars?
3. a) Why is the stove bolt designed with a rather loose fitting thread?
    b) What type of nut is usually used with a stove bolt?
4. List the common metric bolt sizes.
5. Explain the difference between coarse and fine threads.
6. a) Explain how metric threads are designated.
    b) Explain how imperial threads are designated.
7. Why does the thread pitch size automatically increase as the size of the metric fasteners increase?
8. Why are there less threads per inch as the size of the imperial fasteners increase?
9. a) In what type of metals are coarse threads usually used? Why?
    b) List one advantage and one disadvantage of using a coarse thread.
10. How does pipe thread differ from standard thread?
11. Explain the strength identification system for metric fasteners.
12. a) Why is it not necessary to use a metal screw in a threaded hole?
    b) What size hole should be drilled for a metal screw? Explain.
13. Explain two methods used to "self lock" fasteners.
14. List five different types of nuts and briefly explain their purposes.
15. List the head size of the following metric bolts: M6, M10, M16, M12, M8.
16. How may the head size of an imperial bolt be found when the bolt size is known?
17. Briefly explain how the push-on type speed nut works.
18. In what locations are the tubular-type speed clips usually used?
19. a) What is the purpose of a flat washer?
    b) How is the size of a washer determined?
20. Where should the lock washer be placed on the fastener?
21. Explain the snap-in and snap-over methods of attaching exterior mouldings or finish trim.

4 SHEET METAL DAMAGE AND REPAIR

4-1   Sheet Metal Characteristics

4-2   Basic Techniques: Bumping and Metal Finishing Techniques

4-3   Hammering Techniques

4-4   Basic Hammer and Dolly Methods

4-5   Minor Dents

4-6   Methods for Detecting High and Low Spots

4-7   Filing Techniques

4-8   The Grinder

4-9   Sheet Metal Properties

4-10   High-Strength Steel

4-11   Repairing Panel Damage

4-12   Types of Damage

4-13   Body Jacks

4-14   Types of Impact Forces

4-1 SHEET METAL CHARACTERISTICS

Terms commonly used when discussing characteristics of sheet metal are ductility, elasticity, elastic limit, and work hardening.

Ductility. Metal with high ductility is rather soft and flexible. It can be bent, hammered, and pressed into shapes without breaking. Metal with high ductility is easy to stamp into automotive panels because it takes a shape easily and, once bent, holds that shape without a lot of spring-back.

Elasticity. When either a flat piece of metal or a panel is hit, the metal bends out of shape to absorb the force. If the force is not strong, the metal may return on its own to its original shape. Metal with the ability to do this — flex and return to shape — is said to have elasticity (Figure 4-1).

Elastic Limit. When the striking force is strong enough to make a permanent bend in the metal, the metal in the area is said to be bent past its elastic limit. Elastic limit can be defined as the furthest a piece of metal can be bent and still return to its original shape (Figure 4-2).

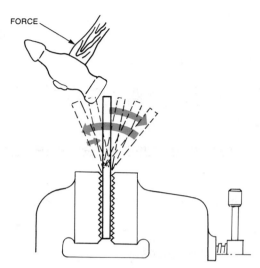

Figure 4-1   Metal having elasticity can be flexed and still return to its original position

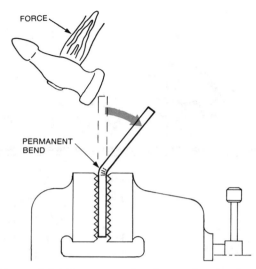

Figure 4-2   Permanent bend past the elastic limit point

Work Hardening: Effects of Bending on Steel

For a sheet metal panel to become damaged, it must go through some type of bending action. Whenever bending takes place in sheet metal, there is a definite physical change in the area of the metal surrounding the bend.

Steel is made up of small granular crystals, or molecules of metal bonded together to form a solid sheet. As a simple explanation, suppose we were able to take small salt or sugar crystals and join them together with some type of glue or bond to form a flat, thin material resembling a sheet of steel. If we were to take this supposed sheet of steel and bend it, we would find that the outer surface was lengthened or stretched, the inner surface shortened, and the centre unchanged (Figure 4-3). The granular crystals on the outer surface would have separated and the bond joining them together would have been stretched. The granular crystals on the underside would have been compressed together.

Whenever any metal is bent past its elastic limit, that is, far enough to strain its crystalline structure, a work hardening condition is created in that area of metal where the bending took place. The farther the metal is bent, the more work hardened the area becomes, and the stronger the metal becomes in the area of the bend. The added

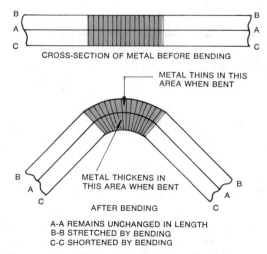

CROSS-SECTION OF METAL BEFORE BENDING

METAL THINS IN THIS AREA WHEN BENT

METAL THICKENS IN THIS AREA WHEN BENT

AFTER BENDING

A-A REMAINS UNCHANGED IN LENGTH
B-B STRETCHED BY BENDING
C-C SHORTENED BY BENDING

Figure 4-3   Change in sheet metal with bending

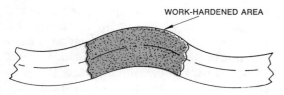

WORK-HARDENED AREA

Figure 4-4   The work hardened area will resist bending

strength caused by work hardening in the bent area produces a resistance to further bending or straightening.

Work hardening can be demonstrated by attempting to straighten a bent piece of metal to its original shape. The bent area is stronger because the bond has been strained and the granular crystals rearranged. Therefore, the metal will not straighten in the bent area. The softer metal on each side of the crease will bend, however (Figure 4-4).

A work hardening condition is created in any piece of metal through bending at any temperature up to a red heat. If the metal is bent at any temperature above a red heat, no work hardening takes place.

When automobile panels are stamped into their shape from a flat sheet of steel they become work hardened in all the reshaped areas. Because the sheet metal has been actually squeezed between the two dies, the molecules have been either forced closer together or forced to flow into a different shape. The amount of change in shape deter-

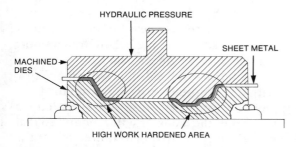

HYDRAULIC PRESSURE

SHEET METAL

MACHINED DIES

HIGH WORK HARDENED AREA

Figure 4-5   Work hardening through stamping

mines the amount of work hardening present in the different areas of the panel (Figure 4-5).

The bends in a dented, or damaged, area take the form of either **ridges** (raised areas) or **channels** (indentations). Since these ridges and channels are work hardened they prevent the damaged area from returning to its original shape.

4-2 BASIC TECHNIQUES: BUMPING AND METAL FINISHING

Bumping

The term **bumping** is often used to describe the procedure of straightening a damaged area and returning it to its original size and shape. The bumping tools, described in Chapter 2, are specially designed hammers, dollies, spoons, and pry bars. They are used to provide a straightening force on the ridges and channels in the damaged metal. (When the damage is too severe for the hammer/dolly force to straighten, hydraulic jack equipment is used. This is discussed later in the chapter.)

The dolly is held tightly behind the damaged area as a backup tool. The hammer blows are directed on the outside of the panel. By skillfully positioning the dolly under the damaged area while hammering the panel in the proper place and with the right amount of force, the damaged area is gradually brought back to its proper position and shape. Skill in correctly using the hammer and dolly must be slowly learned through persistent practice.

Once the area has returned to its correct shape, it is far from being perfectly smooth. The complete area must now either be metal finished or filled over.

Metal Finishing

The process of picking and filing smooth the area is called **metal finishing.** The body file and a small sharp pick hammer are used. A pry bar or a small but heavy bar of metal such as a large cold chisel can be used when the hammer will not fit behind the damaged area.

When the area has been bumped as smooth as possible, the paint is ground off. The body file is then used to file over a part of the area. A very small amount of metal is cut off the surface, but more importantly a **scratch pattern** is made on the level areas of the surface of the metal. Any high spots show up very quickly, and a light tap or two with the flat face of the hammer brings them down. Since there is no scratch pattern over any of the low spots, they can easily be seen. The sharp pick or the pry bar is then used to bring up the low spots. Considerable skill is needed to hit the correct spot to raise it just the right amount. The area is again refiled. If the low spots have been raised enough, they will file out. The metal finishing process of filing/picking is repeated until, by working from one side to the other, the complete damaged area is smooth. Metal finishing is less extensively used now that plastic filler has become acceptable. However, it is still used for smaller areas and in metal finishing operations in the vehicle manufacturing plants.

Body Fillers

Filler is used to fill in "bumped" areas which are then sanded to shape. Solder may be used, but plastic fillers are more common.

Regardless of whether the bumped area is to be metal finished or filled over, it is very important that the damaged area be brought back as close as possible to its original condi-tion. If large channels, low spots, or sharp ridges or creases are left in the panel and filled over, the panel will still have a certain amount of damage stress in it which could cause many problems during the filling procedure, such as poor fit to other panels, incorrect panel shapes, and oil canning (this occurs when a small section of the panel can pop in and out under very little pressure). Excessive fill will be needed to level the area. It is then more prone to cracking and blistering, besides being more costly in that more fill and time are needed to work the area.

4-3 HAMMERING TECHNIQUES

The amount of force that should be exerted on the metal by the hammer blows depends on the extent of the damaged area. The hammer action can be a glancing, slapping type of blow or a forceful direct hit.

The force from the blow is absorbed into the metal and the hammer rebounds, ready to be brought down for the next blow. The amount of force exerted depends on the arm backswing, whether the force is exerted from the shoulder, the arm, or the wrist, and the mass of the hammer.

The majority of the repairer's blows are the glancing, slapping type of blow made from the wrist. When a heavy blow is needed, wrist and arm pressure is used. Only in severe cases is the shoulder and body force used, for example, when straightening a frame or heavy, inner panel.

The wrist is moved in a swinging action with the required force exerted on the hammer downswing. Because of the elasticity in the metal, the hammer will rebound so that very little effort will be required to lift the hammer into position for the next blow. By moving only the wrist in a swinging action,

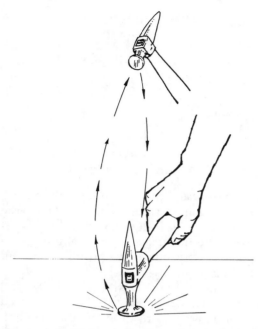

Figure 4-6   Using a glancing, slapping type of blow

and by using the elasticity in the metal to rebound the hammer, as many as 80 blows per minute can be placed on the panel (Figure 4-6).

Types of Hammers

Light Hammers. For most outer-panel bumping operations a light, flat-faced dinging hammer should be used. The outer panels of new vehicles tend to be somewhat thinner and flatter than those found in older ones. These thinner, flatter panels do not need as much hammer force to remove the ridges and channels. Using a hammer which is too heavy and/or pounding the metal too hard can often cause some of the metal to "stretch." The areas of stretched metal make it harder to rework the panel to its original contour. The areas of stretched metal must be shrunk. (Shrinking is covered in Chapter 9.)

Heavy Hammers. A heavy dinging or bumping hammer would be used to repair severely damaged high crown areas, frame rails, inner wheelhousing panels, and other heavier reinforcing panels. Some of the high-strength steel panels need heavier hammer blows to straighten them.

For your own satisfaction, try an experiment with the two types of hammers. Take a light, flat-faced dinging hammer and a heavier high-crowned bumping hammer. Try tapping both of them on a discarded panel. You will find that every hammer blow from the bumping hammer will leave a slight dent in the metal, whereas very few markings will be left on the metal from the dinging hammer, providing it has a flat face. Remember, the object of bumping is to remove dents, not make more.

> Heavy hammer blows will only stretch the metal. For the beginner, the lightest hammer possible should be used. Many body repairers have a tendency to strike the metal too hard.

The secret of metal straightening is to know how to hit the right spot, at the right time, with the right amount of force.

Principle of the Dolly Action

The dolly is held tightly against the underside of the damaged metal to provide lifting support to the low areas. The hammer blows are directed against the outside of the panel at the high spots.

The downward force from the hammer drives down the high spot and then travels through the metal to the dolly. The pressure exerted by the heavy dolly held tightly against the underside of the metal tends to push up (lift) the low areas. A gradual levelling action is created through the continuous hammer blows and dolly lifting action.

The amount of lifting action from the dolly is determined by the amount of arm pressure against the dolly and by the size and shape of the dolly face in relation to the shape of the metal. For example, if a small high-crowned dolly face were used, the amount of lift would be greater in a small area than if a larger, lower-crowned dolly face were used. In this case, the lifting action would be less because the force would be spread over a larger area.

A greater lifting action is also obtained when the hammer blows are closest to the dolly. The further the hammer blows are away from the dolly location, the less the metal is moved. Most of the force is absorbed by the surrounding elastic metal and not transferred to the dolly.

As the ridges and channels are gradually removed there is less tension holding the damage in place. As the tension is removed, the dolly can also be used as a striking tool to drive the dent outward. A combination of dollying, along with an occasional blow from the dolly, gradually removes the damage.

4-4 BASIC HAMMER AND DOLLY METHODS

Hammer Off-Dolly Method

This method is used to **straighten or move** damaged metal. To move the high ridges down and the low channels up, use a dolly block with a face contour approximately like that of the original shape of the metal. The hammer blows are directed along the ridges, driving them down to their original position; the dolly is held tightly with arm pressure against the metal under the channels, forcing them up.

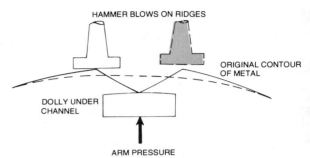

Figure 4-7   Hammer off-dolly blows

In most cases, it is not necessary to mark the undamaged areas of metal. Once the pressure on the ridges and channels is relieved, the undamaged areas should return to their proper shapes and positions without bending (Figure 4-7).

When some of the tension in the ridges and channels has been relieved, the dolly is used as a striking tool to help lift the channel. Lifting the channel also brings up the undamaged elastic metal. The hammer blows are either direct hits from the arm or wrist or glancing hits made from the wrist.

Light, Hammer On-Dolly Method

This method is used to **smooth and level** the small surface irregularities left in the damaged metal after the area has been brought back to its original shape.

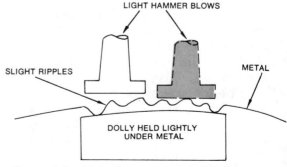

Figure 4-8   Light, hammer on-dolly blows

A dolly with the same face contour as that of the metal is held lightly under the damaged area. The hammer blows are made from the wrist. A flat-faced dinging hammer is used to provide a light, glancing type of blow on the metal over the dolly. Provided that the surface irregularities are not larger than the dolly face, the metal surface is smoothed and leveled, and ready for either metal finishing or filling (Figure 4-8).

Heavy, Hammer On-Dolly Method

Heavy, hammer on-dolly blows are used to **thin and flatten** (stretch) areas of metal in the ridges and channels that are severely folded or buckled. Since there is a greater amount of work hardening in these badly buckled areas, a strong flattening force is needed to reshape the areas. This method should not be used to remove minor damage. It is used only in badly damaged areas.

A dolly having a higher face crown than the surface of the metal is held tightly under the work hardened wrinkles. Medium to heavy hammer blows are concentrated on the metal directly over the dolly (Figure 4-9).

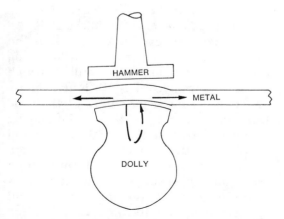

Figure 4-9   Heavy, hammer on-dolly blows

The blows are direct-type blows from either the wrist or arm. The small area of metal between the hammer and dolly is thinned and flattened (stretched).

The force of the hammer blows and the amount of arm pressure exerted against the dolly determines the rate and amount of stretching that will occur in the area.

As the small area of metal is thinned and stretched, it tends to form a bulge or high spot in the area. This is because the surrounding unaffected metal keeps the thinned area from moving outward. Combined with the upward push of the dolly, this tends to force the metal up as it is being thinned. A slight secondary lifting action is created against the metal by the dolly rebound after each blow is struck.

A combination of these three methods is usually used to straighten every damaged area. Since no dents are exactly the same, it is impossible to say which method should be used at any given time in the repair operation. The experienced repairer will automatically know how hard and in which place to hit the metal with the hammer, and how hard and in which place to position the dolly for every blow to be struck.

4-5   MINOR DENTS

Since the ridges and channels of a dent are stronger than the rest of the metal — because of the work hardening — they prevent the dent from springing back to its original shape. The ridges are usually formed around the outside of the dent and the channels in the centre. Between the ridges and channels lie areas of undamaged metal (Figure 4-10).

The undamaged metal between the ridges and channels could be considered elastic metal. In other words, if the molecules in the bent areas were realigned to their original positions, the strain on the channels and

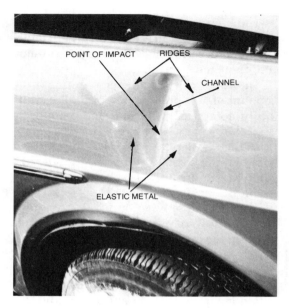

Figure 4-10 Minor dent

ridges would be removed and the elastic metal would return to its proper position.

On a simple dent such as this, the most severe damage is usually at the **point of impact,** the area of metal which was in actual contact with the impact object. This type of dent would be removed by using a combination of the three dollying methods.

Removing the Underseal

The **underseal,** or sound deadener, must be removed from the underside of a panel before the dollying operations begin; otherwise, the force of the hammer and dolly blows will be absorbed by the underseal, and the desired results will not be obtained.

To remove the underseal, heat the outside of the panel with the oxy-acetylene torch, using a large tip and carburizing flame. (Welding is covered in Chapter 7.) Keep the flame well back from the panel, and keep the torch moving. The heat in the metal will soften the underseal so that it can be scraped

off with a putty knife. Do not apply too much heat to the panel. It is not usually necessary to burn the paint.

Procedure to Remove a Minor Dent

The damaged metal in a minor dent is straightened by using the hammer and dolly methods to "roll out" the metal in the reverse order to how it went in. To explain: the point of impact (P.O.I.) was the first area touched by the impact. As the metal was pushed in, a channel was gradually formed out from the top and bottom of the point of impact. This channel is usually deepest next to the P.O.I. and decreases in size toward the outward end of the channel. At the same time as the channels were being pushed in, ridges were being formed around the outer perimeter of the dent, most probably at a right angle from the shallow ends of the channel. The greatest degree of bend in the ridge will be at the end of the channel, gradually decreasing in size toward each end of the ridge. Both the ridges and channels contain work hardening, the amount depending on the degree of bend.

To observe how a dent is formed, push in the side of a soft drink can. The channel is formed out from the P.O.I. The ridges are at right angles to the ends of the channels.

To remove a dent the damage must be rolled outward from the outside, working toward the centre in a reverse order to which the damage went in. The dolly is held tightly under the channel at the outer end where the least degree of bend is. A flat-faced dinging hammer is used to direct light to medium blows at the outer ends of the ridge closest to the dolly (off-dolly blows). The force from the hammer gradually forces down the ends of the ridges while the arm pressure held against the heavy dolly forces the end of the channel upward. The same procedure is then repeated on the other channels and ridges (Figure 4-11).

The repair person gradually works toward the centre or greatest degree of bend in the ridges and both channels. As the pressure is released in the ridges and channels, the surrounding elastic metal tends to move back to its original position. The dolly can also be used as a driving tool to help drive up the channel. However, if the channel does not move when the dolly is hit upward, there is still too much pressure on either or both the ridges and/or channel. More dollying must be done to relieve that tension.

Once the area has been brought back to its basic shape, the light on-dolly method is used to smooth and level the area. It is then ready for either the metal finishing or filling procedure.

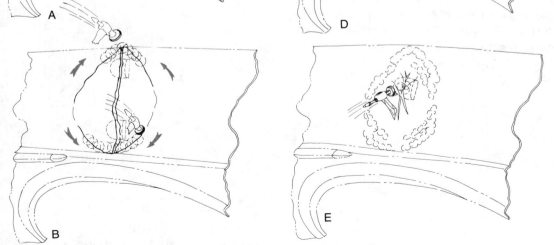

Figure 4-11   Using a hammer and dolly to remove a minor dent

4-6 METHODS FOR DETECTING HIGH AND LOW SPOTS

High and low spots can be detected by sight, by feel, and by using the body file to provide a scratch pattern. The repair person learns through experience to use all three methods to locate the "high" and "low" spots.

Sight Method

It is possible to see small imperfections on a painted or metal surface because paint reflects light. Low spots will reflect the light at a different angle than high spots. When the area is viewed from the proper angle, the low spots will be in shadow and the high spots will be bright.

Feel Method

On bare metal, surface imperfections that cannot be seen can be located by feeling the surface with the hand. To feel for surface imperfections, keep the forearm directly in line with the fingers and parallel to the surface. Hold the hand flat, so that the fingers, palm, and hand-heel are all touching the surface. Keep the hand and wrist relaxed. Move the hand back and forth in the direction in which the fingers are pointing (Figure 4-12).

Figure 4-12   Feeling the metal for surface imperfections

The hand can be made more sensitive by placing a rag between the hand and the metal or by wearing a cotton glove. Many metal repairers rub their hands in the dust on the floor before feeling the metal. The dust absorbs the perspiration on the hand, allowing the hand to slide more easily over the metal.

Filing Method

When the metal in the damaged area has been made as level and as smooth as possible by the dollying methods, the metal is then metal finished or filled over with body filler.

If the area is to be metal finished, the body file is used to provide a scratch pattern over the bumped area (Figure 4-13). The repairer then "picks" up the low spots and refiles the area with the body file. This process is repeated until all the low spots disappear and the area has been filed smooth.

When body filler is used to fill the area, a Surform file is used to shape and level the filler. It is then finish-sanded with sandpaper on a file board. The use of plastic fillers is covered in greater detail in Chapter 5.

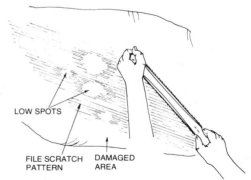

LOW SPOTS

FILE SCRATCH   DAMAGED
PATTERN   AREA

Figure 4-13   File scratch pattern shows up low spots

4-7 FILING TECHNIQUES

The following filing techniques apply when the repairer is holding and pushing the body

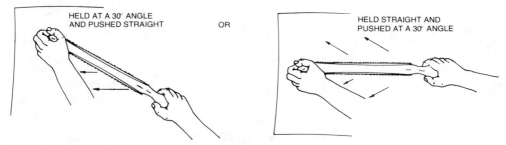

Figure 4-14   Filing techniques on relatively flat panels

file while metal finishing. The same procedures are used for board-sanding plastic fillers, although the angles are not quite so critical. The body file is always used by making the cut while it is on the push. The board file can be used on either the push or pull strokes, or on both. (The Surform filing procedure is different from these; it will be explained in greater detail in Chapter 5.)

The filing should start in the undamaged area on one side and progress across the damaged area to the undamaged metal on the opposite side. Thus, the correct plane can be maintained from the undamaged metal to the damaged area.

If the area is being metal finished, the experienced body repairer usually grinds off the paint before starting to file, because paint is hard to file and tends to dull the file teeth.

The file should be pushed forward by the handle for the cutting stroke. At the same time, the necessary downward pressure is applied to the front of the file holder with the other hand. The front hand steers the file. As long a stroke as possible should be taken. On the return stroke, the file is pulled back over the metal by the handle.

Flat Panels. When filing relatively flat panels, the file is either held at a 30° angle and pushed straight, or held straight and pushed at a 30° angle (Figure 4-14). By using either of these filing techniques, as much surface as possible is covered with each stroke. Because the file teeth are curved, the cutting edges of the teeth are always at right angles to the direction of travel regardless of the file angle, and the correct cut is maintained.

Crowned Panels. On a crowned panel, the file is either held straight and pushed straight along the flattest crown of the panel, or held straight with the length of the flattest crown and pushed to one side at a 30° angle or less (Figure 4-15).

Reverse-Crowned Panels. The half-round, or convex, file is usually held straight and

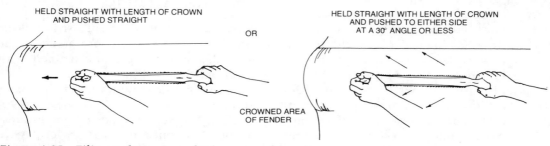

Figure 4-15   Filing techniques on high- crowned panels

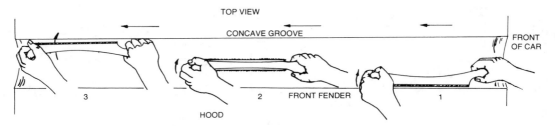

Figure 4-16   Roll the file as it is pushed down the length of the curve

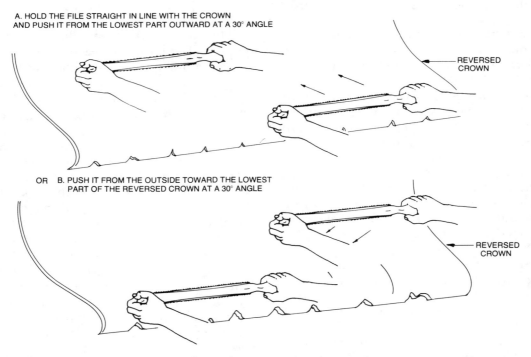

Figure 4-17   Using the half-round file to file in a reverse-crowned area

pushed straight down the length of the curve. It is rolled by the wrist from one side of the blade to the other (Figure 4-16).

On a reverse-crowned panel, the file is held straight in line with the length of the reverse crown and pushed on a slight angle. It may be pushed either from the outside toward the lowest part of the crown, or from the lowest part of the crown toward the outside. The file is rolled from side to side at the same time (Figure 4-17).

Cross and X Filing

These methods of filing are used to make sure that the area is smooth and that the original contour has been maintained in all directions.

In **cross filing,** new scratch pattern marks are filed across the previous ones at a 90° angle. In **X filing,** new scratch marks cross the previous ones at a 45° angle (Figure 4-18). Filing for too long a time in one direction will create ridges or low areas along the entire length of the file stroke. Cross and X filing keep the panel smooth and level in all directions.

When working on the side of the automobile the majority of, and especially the first and final, file scratch patterns should run along the length of the automobile. This practice makes it much harder to see any small waves or irregularities when looking down the length of the car. The scratch patterns will be in line with the line of sight. A good mix is 12 to 15 strokes with the scratch pattern lengthwise, then 6 to 8 strokes crossing those at an X pattern from the bottom, and finally 6 to 8 strokes crossing the original strokes at an X angle from the top. The procedure is then repeated.

If the bumped area is to be filled with plastic filler, it is an excellent idea for the beginner to metal file the area **before** applying the filler. Filing the area provides a scratch pattern that helps the repairer check that there are no real high or low spots in the area. Excessively high spots must be "shrunk down" (Chapter 9). Low spots can be picked or pried up.

Picking Up the Low Spots

The pick hammer is used to bring up the low spots. A blunt pick will raise a larger area of metal per blow, but the raised area is harder to see. A sharp pick will raise a small pimple that is easy to see.

Because beginners usually have trouble seeing the spots they are hitting, they tend to hit the metal too hard. This results in the low spot being driven up too high. When this happens, too much metal is filed away in smoothing the surface so that holes or weak spots occur. It is often better to use several

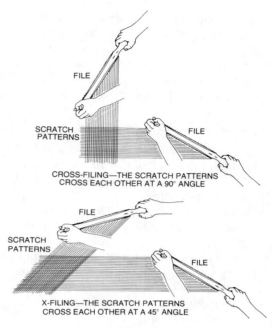

Figure 4-18   Cross and X filing

light blows with a sharp pick because the raised areas are easier to see.

Pry bars, spoons, the corner of a dolly, or a large, heavy cold chisel may be used to pick up the low spots when there is not enough room to use a hammer.

4-8 THE GRINDER

The grinder is used to remove paint and rust, and to grind down and/or clean welds before either metal filing or filling the area with solder or plastic filler.

The grinder is also helpful in providing a scratch pattern which will show up the larger high and low spots as the paint is being removed. The large low spots can then be picked up while any excessively high spots can be tapped down. A file can then be used to continue metal finishing the area or it can be directly filled over. Finally, the grinder is used to lightly buff over any area that has been metal filed smooth. Buffing the area after it has been metal finished removes any deep file scratches and provides a roughened surface to which paint can stick. Grinders are either electrically or air driven (Figure 4-19).

The grinder should not be used to finish-grind either solders or body filler. Fine solder dust can cause lead poisoning. Body fillers are better sanded than ground. The grinder will not smooth and level the metal as the file does because the disc will ride in and out of the high and low spots, cutting the same amount of metal from both areas. The area will be wavy to the touch although it may appear to be smooth and shiny.

When an area is ground for a long time, too much metal is removed, thinning the panel. The thinner metal is more susceptible to heat and could warp from the friction of the disc.

THUMB-TYPE THROTTLE

LEVER-TYPE THROTTLE

AIR GRINDER

ELECTRIC GRINDER

Courtesy Sioux Tools, Inc.

Figure 4-19   Grinders

Grinding Discs

Grinding discs are currently available in two sizes. These sizes are approximately 18 cm and 23 cm in diameter. Flexible backing pads are used under the discs.

Since only the outer part of the disc actually does the cutting, a disc cutter can be used to cut off the worn part. The disc can be used with a smaller backing pad to grind "hard-to-get-at" corners, where a larger disc will not fit. Figure 4-20 illustrates a typical disc cutter.

The grinding disc is available in 16-, 24-, 36-, and 50-grit sizes. The 16-grit disc has the largest, or coarsest, particles while the 50-grit disc has the smallest, or finest. Coarse

Courtesy Sioux Tools, Inc.

Figure 4-20   Abrasive disc cutter

discs are used for rough, or first-cut, work and finer discs are used for final buffing cuts made after the repair work has been completed.

Grinding discs can be of either an open coat or closed coat design. These terms refer to the density with which the grit particles cover the backing paper. On the open coat, the grit is spaced further apart, covering only 50% to 70% of the backing paper. Closed coat papers are completely covered with grit particles.

The open coat discs are more commonly used than the closed coat type, as they do not plug as quickly with paint. The closed coat is better suited for buffing or grinding metal. When they are used over paint, they quickly plug. The plugged disc causes the metal to overheat and the panel to warp.

Grinder Safety Rules

The speed of the portable grinder varies from 4000 to 5000 r/min. Because the disc turns at such a high speed, extreme caution should be exercised when grinding. Important safety rules to follow when using the grinder are:

1. Always wear safety goggles when grinding.
2. Never use a torn or broken disc. A damaged disc will cause the machine to vibrate and a piece of the

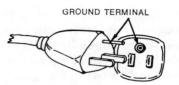

Figure 4-21   Electrical plug ground

disc could fly off and injure someone. The torn disc could catch on the work and twist the grinder out of the hands.

3. Examine the electrical connections and make sure the machine is properly grounded (Figure 4-21). (Many of the newer electrically operated tools, including grinders, do not need the grounded plug. They are insulated against electrical current going through the operator by a plastic housing.)
4. When the grinder is not in use do not leave it lying on the car or bench. Place it on the floor where there is no danger of it falling off and breaking.

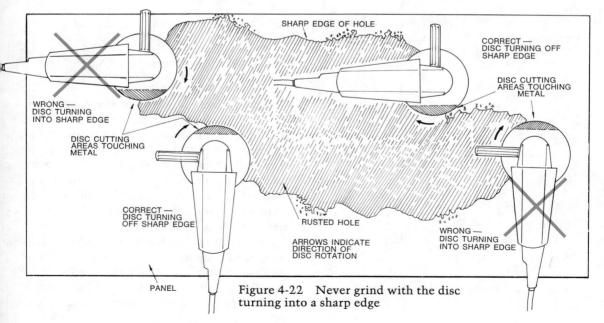

Figure 4-22   Never grind with the disc turning into a sharp edge

5. When grinding around rusty edges, loose bolts, clips, lap joints, or sharp edges be extremely careful to prevent the disc from catching and twisting the grinder away from you. When the grinder must be used over sharp edges and lap joints, move it so that the cutting takes place as the disc turns off the panel or edge, not as it runs into the sharp edge (Figure 4-22).

When using the grinder, the operator should be in a comfortable position. The right hand should be on the rear handle and left hand on the front handle. Regardless of how the grinder is held, only the top or bottom 40 mm to 50 mm of the disc should contact the metal. The sides of the disc are used only when it is impossible to use the top and bottom parts. (Such a situation would occur along the edge of a fender, next to the door.) The grinder should be held so the opposite side of the disc (the one not in contact with the metal) is 10° to 20° out from the metal (Figure 4-23).

Do not exert pressure on the grinder as the weight of the grinder itself provides enough

pressure on flat surfaces. On vertical surfaces, use pressure equal to the weight of the grinder. The speed of the grinder, not the pressure applied, is the main factor in fast cutting. If too much pressure is applied, burning or overheating of the metal may occur, causing a warped, or distorted, surface. Overheating can also be caused by continuously going over an area without allowing the metal to cool, by moving too slowly, or by using a worn or plugged disc.

Uses of the Disc Grinder

The disc grinder is used in basic two ways.

Crosscutting. By using the top or bottom part of the disc and moving from left to right, a crosscutting or double cut is obtained with each grinder pass. This method is used for

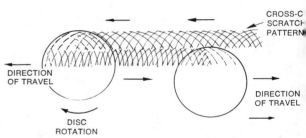

Figure 4-24   Crosscutting method: the grinder is moved from side to side

rough cuttings and removing paint. The abrasive marks will be at X angles to each other. Since the disc turns in a clockwise direction and only the top part of the disc is used, the first half of the disc contact will leave an abrasive scratch pattern on the way up. As the disc rotates, the last half of the disc surface will leave a scratch pattern at an X angle to the first (Figure 4-24).

This method of moving the grinder is also used at the beginning of the metal-finishing process to obtain a scratch pattern over the high spots, providing a guide for further straightening by highlighting the low spots.

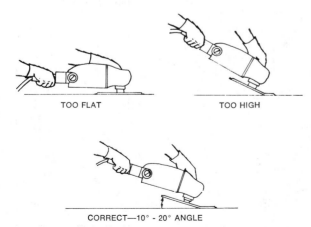

Figure 4-23   The back of the disc should be raised 10° to 20° off the metal

This enables the repairer to locate the large low areas so that they can be brought up before filing. If the area of metal being ground is crowned, move the grinder along the length of the lowest crown if possible, not across the crown.

Buffing. Usually, after an area is filed smooth, the grinder with a fine disc is used to remove deep file scratches and to roughen the area so the primer will bond well to the metal. For this operation the top part of the

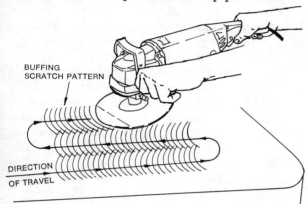

Figure 4-25   Buffing method: the grinder is moved up and down

disc is used again. The grinder is moved up and down on the panel with each cut slightly overlapping the last. The abrasive marks will cross the grinder direction of travel at right angles (Figure 4-25). Wherever possible, the

grinder strokes should follow the highest crown of the area.

The buffing method also helps to feather-edge the paint on the sides, whereas the crosscutting method leaves a very sharp paint edge.

The grinding disc can be cut into octagon, hexagon, or square shapes to clean damaged areas and welds before filing. The corners will cut down into the low spots and clean them (Figure 4-26).

When using this type of disc, care should be exercised because the sharp corners catch easily and the grinder could be flipped from the operator's hands.

4-9 SHEET METAL PROPERTIES

When engineers are designing a vehicle they must consider its strength. They could use thick and/or very strong types of steel, either of which would make the vehicle almost dent proof. However, they also must consider passenger safety. The entire vehicle, but especially its front and rear sections, must be designed to be strong enough to support the loads yet flexible enough so that

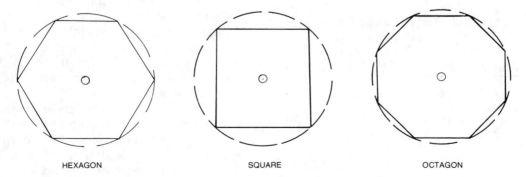

Figure 4-26   Hexagon, octagon, or square-cut disc shapes

the metal folds, bends, and crushes if it is involved in an accident.

A vehicle must absorb the damaging forces from an accident, thus keeping the passenger compartment intact and the passengers relatively safe from serious injury. The thickness and the type of sheet metal used, the shape of the panels, and the design of the vehicle as a whole are all engineered to add to the vehicle's strength and passenger safety.

Sheet Metal Thickness

Thickness may be expressed using either the inch gauge system or metric measurement. The thickness of sheet metal used in the body varies depending on the amount of strength needed in a particular location. For example, the fender or hood need not be as thick as the boxed hinge pillars or other structural supporting members.

The gauge system is a series of numbers — each one corresponds to an inch size, expressed in thousandths. The smaller the gauge number, the thicker the metal. Steels measured in metric are expressed in millimetres. The thickness of the metals used for automotive vehicles varies from 16 to 24 gauge. The following chart lists the most common metal thicknesses and their corresponding metric sizes.

METAL THICKNESS CHART

Gauge	Inches	Fractions of an Inch	SI Metric
16	0.0625	1/16	1.59 mm
18	0.0500		1.25 mm
20	0.0375		0.95 mm
22	0.0312	1/32	0.79 mm
24	0.0250		0.64 mm

Twenty gauge steel is the most common size used. Note that 20 gauge is very close to forty thousandths of an inch or 1 mm. Twenty-two is thinner at a little over 0.75 mm. Eighteen gauge is thicker than 20 at 1.25 mm.

Sheet Metal Strength

The strength of a metal can be controlled by adding certain materials to the metal. When a non-ferrous metal such as nickel is alloyed into steel, the resulting steel is made soft and pliable. When carbon is added to steel, a much stronger, stiffer type of metal is produced. Tool steel, for example, has a very high carbon content. These steels are very strong and can bend very little before breaking. Spring steels, which have less carbon content, are also strong yet can flex and return to their original shape without breaking.

The common steel used for automotive purposes is the low-carbon alloy-type steel. Being soft and pliable, this type of steel has a high degree of **ductility**, that is, it can be bent, pressed, or hammered into shape in its cold form without breaking. It can easily be stamped into the complex shapes of automobile panels. The strength of the panel is obtained by the thickness of the metal and the shapes pressured into the panels.

There is a definite change in its characteristics of sheet metal after it has been stamped into shape. The molecules on both the upper and lower surfaces are compressed closer together, or forced to flow into a different position than they were before stamping.

This forced change in molecule alignment is accomplished by the stamping press exerting extreme pressure on the metal between the male and female dies. The low-carbon steel takes the shape of the dies with very little "spring back." Rearranging the mole-

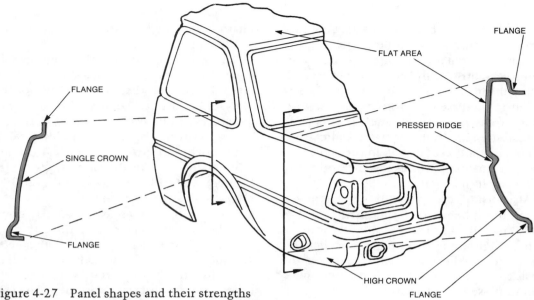

Figure 4-27   Panel shapes and their strengths

cules makes the panel "set" or stay in its pressed shape. Because the molecules have been realigned and their bonds have been strained, the stamped areas are work hardened and strengthened. The degree of work hardening in the panel depends on the amount of change in shape. For example, a flange pressed ridge or high crown area contains more work hardening than there is in a single crown or flat area of metal (Figure 4-27). The added work hardening in the panel not only makes it stronger but also makes it more resistant to further bending when a force is exerted upon it. The added strength in the panel also makes it more elastic, in that it has a greater ability to return to its original shape after being struck by an object.

4-10 HIGH-STRENGTH STEEL

There is a limit to the amount of additional strength that can be added to a panel through the stamping process. In order to make the vehicle lighter yet still strong, vehicle manufacturers are now using various types of high-strength steel. Steel manufacturers have found that the strength of a steel can be further increased by using special heat treating processes and/or by adding various chemical additives to the steel during its manufacture. The biggest advantage in using any high-strength steel is that more strength can be obtained with thinner material. Being able to use thinner material also means less weight per vehicle and better fuel consumption.

There are three main types of high-strength steel generally used in automotive manufacture. They are **high-tensile strength steel (HSS), high-strength low-alloy steel (HSLA), and Martensitic steel.** These stronger steels are used mainly in structural panels such as frame rails, inner wheelhouse aprons, strut towers, bumper reinforcements, radiator supports, and hinge pillars.

The high-strength steel (HSS) is made stronger than the original low-carbon steel by putting the steel through a specific heat treatment process as it is being made.

High-strength low-alloy (HSLA) steel contains very little alloy metal, or none at all. Alloy metals are added to mild low-carbon steels to increase their softness or ductility. High-strength low-alloy steel gets its additional strength from special chemical elements that are added to it and from certain heat treatment processes that are applied to it during its manufacture.

Martensitic steel is a super–high-strength steel. It can be up to 10 times stronger than mild steel. It is used only in special locations where high strength to weight is needed, for example, in the door guard beam on the inside of the door, where it provides maximum passenger protection from a side hit against the vehicle.

Disadvantages to High-Strength Steel

There are several disadvantages to high-strength steels. Their additional strength makes them somewhat harder to stamp into shape. The metal does not tend to flow as smoothly, so the stampings often have slight wrinkles in them. They also tend to spring back somewhat after stamping, as the high-strength steel has more resistance to bending. Although the panels have more resistance to bending from an accident, it is also somewhat harder to bring them back into position during the straightening process and to make them stay there.

The buckles in a severely damaged ordinary low-carbon steel panel can be heated to a light red colour to relieve the stress as the panel is being straightened, but high-strength steels are very heat-sensitive and only limited heat can be applied to them. Martensitic steel is so temperature sensitive that no heat can be used during any repair operation. Some manufacturers recommend

that no attempt be made to straighten this type of steel.

The other high-strength steels can be heated. The amount of heat that should be used depends on the characteristics of that particular steel. To learn which temperatures can be used, check the particular manufacturer's recommendations. Some types can be heated to 350°C (700°F); others up to 500°C (900°F), that is, to a blue colour); and still others to 650°C (1200°F), that is, to a slight red colour.

None of the high-strength steels should ever be heated for more than three minutes at a time. Whenever a high-strength steel is heated for a longer period, or to a temperature higher than recommended, the high-strength characteristics in the heated area are lost. The structure might not be able to support the normal road stresses or damaging collision forces should the vehicle ever be involved in another collision.

Special temperature-indicating crayons can be used which indicate the correct heat. The crayons are available in different heat ranges and are similar to a marking pencil (Figure 4-28). A mark is made across the area to be heated. The crayon material will either change colour or melt when the heat range of the crayon is reached.

High-strength steels must be MIG welded. (MIG welding is covered in Chapter 8.) The

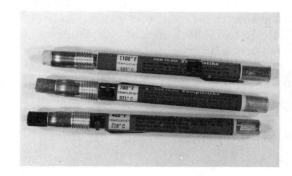

Figure 4-28   Heat sensitive crayons

oxy-acetylene process adds too much heat over too large an area and would reduce the area's strength. Since high-strength steels have extra carbon content, they can be more prone to corrosion problems. Stress cracking problems can occur in yield stress areas caused by accident damage that has not been completely removed. Any kinks or buckles not removed from a damaged panel could crack if there was any excessive movement or stress on them.

Yield and Tensile Strength

Two terms that are used to define a steel's strength are **yield strength** (or stress) and **tensile strength** (or stress).

Yield strength refers to the amount of force per unit of area that is needed to make the steel begin to move past its elastic limit. Once the area of metal has passed this limit, there is a permanent change in shape, and some degree of work hardening in the area of the bend. The metal will not return to its original position.

Tensile strength refers to the maximum stress per unit of measurement that an area of steel will take before actually breaking or ripping apart.

The unit of measurement for both the yield and tensile stress is kilopascals (kPa) in SI metric or pounds per square inch (psi) in the imperial system. Both the yield and tensile strengths of the high-strength steels are much higher than those of the low-carbon alloy-type steel.

4-11 REPAIRING PANEL DAMAGE

All panels of either mild- or high-strength steel have some degree of resistance to bending. When any panel is struck by an impact force, it will tend to flex and then spring back to its original shape (provided it has not been bent past its elastic limit) and no damage will result to the metal. If, however, the force (yield stress) is strong enough to bend the metal past its elastic limit, ridges and creases will be formed. The metal on each side of the ridge and channel is usually bent out of shape, although it is considered to be undamaged elastic metal. These areas would return to their correct position if it were not for the ridges and channels holding them out of position.

The metal in ridges, creases, channels, or buckles has been forced past its elastic limit and is therefore work hardened. These work hardened areas create additional stiffness in the panel and a holding strain on the undamaged elastic metal, preventing them from returning to their original positions.

When repairing minor damage, the metal resumes its original position when the pressure is released from the ridges and channels by hammer and dolly. Provided the dollying has been done correctly, only the ridges and channels will need metal finishing.

As previously explained, the theory of work hardening and molecular realignment is used extensively by engineers and designers to incorporate added strength into the panels in the form of ridges, flanges, and crowns. A crowned surface may be curved in one, two, or many directions from any given point. High- and reverse-crowned areas are designed into most panels. Ridges are used on front fenders, hoods, doors, and rear quarter panels. Flanges of different shapes are used along the edges of fenders and panels. The strength of any panel depends on the type of metal used in it, the degree of crown in it, the sharpness of its ridges, and the size and design of its flange along the edge. The more pressing needed to shape a panel, the stronger it is, because of the extra molecular realignment and the added work hardening.

When flanges and ridges are bent past their elastic limit, a high degree of strength and work hardening results in these areas. These two areas are so strong that they actually hold much of the damage in the panel. It is impossible to straighten the minor or undamaged areas first. Therefore, when straightening any damaged area, regardless of the amount and type of damage present in the panel, there are certain general straightening rules that must be followed.

Rules for Straightening Sheet Metal

The following areas must be worked in their order as listed. Note that they are listed in order of work hardening strength.

1. The outer flanges or edges
2. Any factory pressed ridges in the panel
3. Any high-crowned areas
4. Reverse-crowned areas
5. Flat areas of the panel (the least strongest area)

A mechanical or hydraulic jack is used to bring the flange out to its correct position. Depending on the amount of damage in the area, the edge of the panel can often simply be jacked or pulled out. In other cases, it will be necessary to bring the edge out slowly while, at the same time, using the hammer and dolly methods to remove some of the ridges and channels in the overall damaged area. At this time it is not necessary to completely remove all the damage buckles in the flange area. The important thing is to get the edge straight without having large waves or "wows" in it.

Depending on the design of the ridge, the shape of the panel, and the extent of the damage, the ridge can sometimes be jacked directly out. At other times it must be brought out slowly with the aid of a jack or spoon as a "pry" while using the hammer

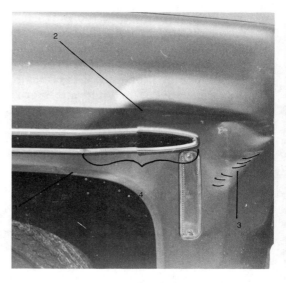

Figure 4-29   Damaged panel containing flanges, pressed ridges high, and reverse and low crown

and dolly methods on the surrounding damage. With some damage areas jacks would be used to bring out both the edge and the pressed ridge at the same time.

The high-crowned areas must be worked on next. Usually these areas are straightened with hammer and dolly. As the crowned areas are being roughly shaped, the straightening action is gradually moved into any reverse-crown areas and from there to the flat areas of the panel. Since these two are the least strong, they bend relatively easily but are not so severely damaged. When all the surrounding stronger damaged areas are removed, larger flat areas will often pop out (Figure 4-29).

Once the damaged area has been brought back to its original position and shape, a combination of the three dollying methods is used to remove any remaining ridges or channels caused by the impact force. As these areas are gradually worked smooth, any surrounding elastic metal still out of shape will return to its original position. There may be some areas of stretched metal, especially at the point of impact or other areas that were badly damaged. Stretched metal will be bulged outward. It is removed by the shrinking process covered in Chapter 9.

4-12 TYPES OF DAMAGE

Force Flow

When a sheet metal panel is struck, the impact force must be absorbed by the metal. The force starts at the point of impact and, if strong enough, continues through the surrounding area until it is expended.

The sheet metal absorbs the damaging impact force by creasing, buckling, crushing, and folding. Special convolutions (creases or folds) and buckling sections are purposely built into both the front and rear structures of the unitized vehicle. When a vehicle is hit these areas fold to absorb the damage force, preventing the force from reaching the passenger compartment.

Crushed or badly folded metal is usually so badly damaged that it is beyond repair. The creased or buckled type of damage takes the form of either ridges or channels of which there are two different kinds: **hinge buckles** and **roll buckles**.

Hinge Buckle

A hinge buckle is the bending point or pivot point where a ridge or channel was formed between relatively undamaged areas of metal (Figure 4-30). The damage created by a hinge buckle is usually of a minor nature. The pivot point has been bent past its elastic limit and work hardened, preventing the

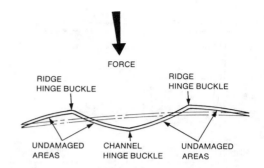

Figure 4-30   Hinge buckle

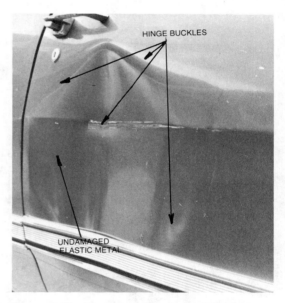

Figure 4-31   Damaged area containing hinge buckles

elastic metal on the side from returning to its original position (Figure 4-31).

Roll Buckle

Roll buckles are usually a more severe type of damage. They occur when the metal on each side of the pivot point is pulled together and forced to roll over on its side

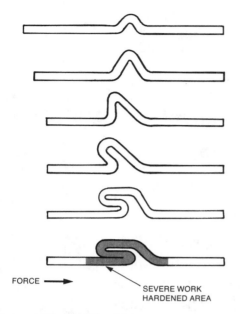

FORCE ⟶

SEVERE WORK
HARDENED AREA

Figure 4-32　Roll buckle

(Figure 4-32). Considerable impact force is required to create this type of buckle. This type of damage is usually found close to the impact area or at the edge of a high-crowned area, when the damage force has moved through the lower crown area into the high crown. These areas are usually badly damaged. A greater degree of work harden-

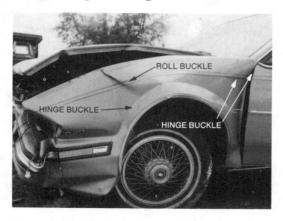

Figure 4-33　Severely damaged area containing roll and hinge buckles

ing is present within the rolled areas, making them harder to remove. (Figure 4-33). Some heat would help in removing this type of severe damage, but it must be used sparingly with high-strength steel. Heavy on-dolly blows can also be used to remove this type of buckle.

Direct Damage

A minor impact force is absorbed by the sheet metal at the point of impact and expended in the immediate area. Slight hinge buckles are formed. This type of damage is **direct damage.** Direct damage can be defined as that damage which is the direct result of the collision force at the point of impact and the immediately surrounding area.

Figure 4-34　Direct damage

However, when a much greater force is exerted against the direct damage area the metal absorbs the force by buckling and folding, first into hinge buckles and then into roll buckles in and around the point of impact. Severe hinge buckles, both convex and concave in shape, will be in the direct damage area. As the metal in the hinge and roll buckles work hardens they become resistant to further bending. The impact force then travels through the panel to the next weaker area and buckling occurs again (Figure 4-34).

Indirect Damage

In many cases, the panel is damaged in several places other than the direct damage area. The complete panel or section might be moved out of alignment before the impact force is expended and a stopping point is reached.

When the impact force travels through the direct damage area surrounding the point of impact and then causes damage to other areas of the same panel or to connecting panels and areas, a secondary type of buckling or damage is caused. This type of damage is **indirect damage** (Figure 4-35). Indirect damage is caused by the direct damage force. It is those areas of damaged metal which have had no actual contact with the impact force. It is not uncommon for a unitized vehicle that has been hit hard in the front to have some indirect damage in the rear of the vehicle. Indirect damage may be hidden in the inner panels, floor pan, frame rails, and hinge pillars. Cracked paint, sound deadener, or surface rust may be cracked or knocked off. These are tell-tale signs that indirect damage is present. Therefore, a complete check of the surrounding damaged section should be made when studying the area to determine the correct repair procedure.

For example, if an impact force occurred against the lower part of the front door and fender at the cowl hinge pillar, the force would be transferred through the door and fender into the hinge pillar. The pillar would be damaged, and the remaining force could push the pillar in, buckling the floor pan. The damage force to the bottom of the cowl, rocker, and floor area could also force the cowl section into a diamond condition. The door and fender damage would be considered direct damage, and the damage to the hinge pillar, floor panel, and cowl diamond would be considered indirect damage. The door and fender could either be repaired or replaced with new parts. The surface damage to the hinge pillar would be repaired. However, if the floor panel and cowl diamond condition were not checked and repaired and if the hinge pillar was not realigned, it would be impossible to obtain the correct fit of the door and fender to the body.

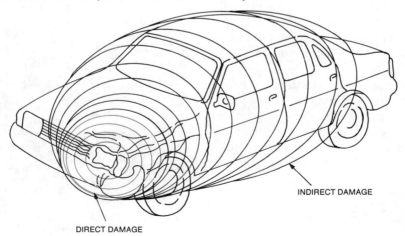

INDIRECT DAMAGE

DIRECT DAMAGE

Figure 4-35   Direct and indirect damage

Repair Procedures

The repair procedure for straightening both direct and indirect damage depends entirely on the areas in which the damage is present and the sequence in which the damage occurred. In some cases, indirect damage must be straightened **before** direct damage to relieve the tension on the other damaged areas. In other cases, the indirect damage may be repaired either at the same time as, or after, the direct damage has been corrected.

For example, if an impact force occurred against a rear corner of a vehicle, the damage immediately surrounding the tail light would be considered direct damage. If the force then continued through the vehicle and buckled the frame rail, trunk floor, and quarter panel in the area of the inner wheelhousing, the damage in these areas would be considered indirect damage. The frame rail would be straightened first to relieve the tension on the quarter panel. Corrective measures would then be applied to the direct damage at the tail light in such a manner that the indirect damage in both the trunk floor and the quarter panel would be corrected either before, or at the same time as, the direct damage.

Bolt-on assembled parts or panels will often shift out of alignment when the direct damage force is exerted on them. For example, a front fender, when hit from the front, could move back into the door, closing the gap and damaging the door; or a force damaging the front of the hood could also force the hood back at the door hinge, closing the gap between the cowl and the hood. In cases such as these, direct damage could be removed first and the indirect damage left until last.

4-13 BODY JACKS

When the corrective force needed to straighten a damaged area is more than the hammer and dolly methods can produce, either mechanical or specially constructed hydraulic jacks are employed to apply the necessary corrective pressure to the edges, pressed ridges, and direct and indirect damage areas.

Jacks are often used in such a way that direct and indirect damage can both be straightened at the same time. The corrective force from the jack can be applied to the damaged areas in gradually increasing amounts. This enables the repairman to relieve the tensions in the damaged areas with the hammer and dolly, and to restore the areas to their original shapes slowly.

The connecting together of the equipment needed to make a single push or pull correction on a damaged frame member is referred to as a **set-up.**

Mechanical Jacks

The mechanical jack works on the principle of friction of the jack head mechanism against a solid steel shaft. The amount of pressure applied to the damaged area is regulated by the amount the jack head lever is moved. The jack head movement is directly proportional to the lever handle movement.

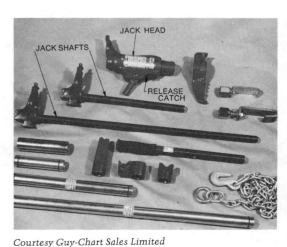

Courtesy Guy-Chart Sales Limited

Figure 4-36   Friction jack and attachments

Friction-type jacks with special attachments designed for body work can be purchased (Figure 4-36). The jack, when combined with the various attachments can be used to push, pull (spread), or clamp (Figure 4-37). A length of hydraulic jack extension tubing can be slid over the end of the shaft against the end of the jack head to extend the reach of the jack for a long push (Figure 4-38). The pressure is released by lifting the handle and pressing down on the release lever.

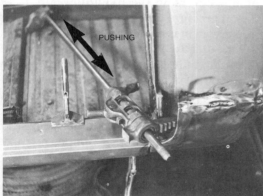
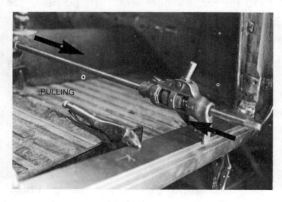

Figure 4-37   Clamping, pushing, and pulling operations

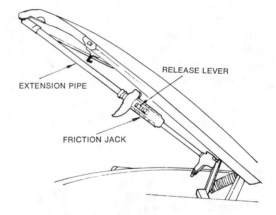

Figure 4-38   Using an extension pipe to obtain a long reach

Never release the jack pressure by hitting the release lever with a hammer, etc. This makes the jack head jump down the shaft. The friction washers in the jack head are damaged and grooves are cut in the shaft and the jack will no longer operate correctly.

The mechanical jack has an advantage over the hydraulic jack in that it is much lighter and easier to use. However, the one big disadvantage of the mechanical jack is that it is not capable of applying as much force against a damaged area as the hydraulic jack.

Hydraulic Jacks

The hydraulic jack consists of four main components: **pump, hose, ram,** and **attachments** (Figure 4-39A, B). It works by liquid being pumped under pressure through the hose into the cylinder, or ram. The pressure of the oil forces out a plunger in the end of the ram. Hydraulic jacks are available with 55, 138, and 275 MPa capacities (4, 10, and 20 tons).

The pumps can be either hand or air operated (a small air-driven motor operates the hydraulic pump). Pumping the handle of the hand-operated pump forces the oil through the hose to the ram. A valve on the side of the pump controls the oil flow. It must be turned in tight for the hand pump to pressurize the oil. To release the pressure

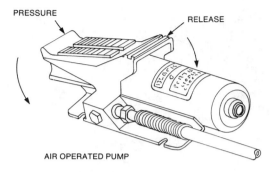

PRESSURE   RELEASE

AIR OPERATED PUMP

Figure 4-39B   Air operated pump

from the ram, the valve need only be turned open approximately one-half to one turn. The air-operated hydraulic pump is operated by a toggle type lever on the top of the pump; tipping it in one direction controls the air supply which drives the hydraulic pump. Reversing the toggle lever releases the oil pressure in the unit. The oil is held in a reservoir in the end of the pump.

Periodically, it is necessary to add oil to the pump unit. Most jack companies specify a special hydraulic-jack oil; the manufacturers' recommendations as to the type and amount of oil to be used should always be followed. When adding oil to the jack, make sure that the valve on the pump is released and that the plunger is fully returned. Otherwise, too much oil could be added, and the plunger would then not completely return into the ram as there would be no place for the oil to go. Both the pump and the ram can be used in any angle or position.

The hose is specially constructed with oil-resistant rubber reinforced with woven steel wire. The woven wire is covered with a layer of fabric and another layer of rubber. The hose must be able to withstand the extreme pressure of the liquid (Figure 4-40).

The length of hose connecting the two units enables the operator to stand back, "out of the line of fire" so to speak, in case the jack should slip or something should break while the jack is being used.

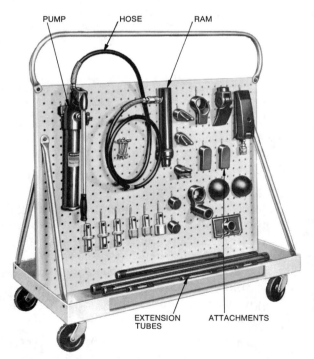

PUMP   HOSE   RAM

EXTENSION   ATTACHMENTS
TUBES

A. Courtesy Blackhawk Mfg. Co.

Figure 4-39A   Hydraulic jack and attachments

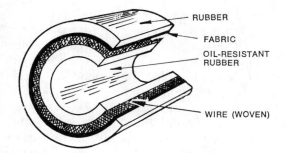

Figure 4-40   Cross-section of a hydraulic-jack hose

Push and Pull Rams

Basically, there are three types of hydraulic jack rams:

- Single-action push ram
- Single-action pull ram
- Double-action push-and-pull ram

In most cases the same pump and hose will work with both the push and pull ram. When changing the pump and hose from one ram to another, make sure that the control valve is open on the pump and that the plunger in the ram has completely returned to its normal position. If the plunger has not returned, the oil will be trapped in the ram and there may not be enough oil left in the pump to operate the second ram.

Note the different places at which the liquid enters the rams (Figure 4-41). In the push ram, the liquid forces out the ram plunger; in the pull ram, the liquid forces the plunger into the ram. When the oil pressure is released, a spring inside the ram pushes the plunger back to its normal position.

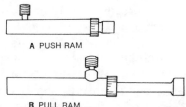

Figure 4-41   Single-action push-and-pull rams

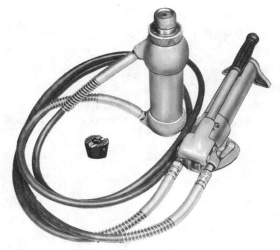

Courtesy The K.C. Shenton Company

Figure 4-42   Double-action push-and-pull jack

A double-action push-and-pull jack has a two-way valve in the pump and a double hose connecting the pump and ram. When the operating valve is turned in and the pump worked, the oil is forced through one hose into the lower end of the ram, and the plunger is forced out. When the valve is turned out and the pump is worked, the oil is forced through the other hose into the top end of the cylinder, and the plunger is pushed back into the cylinder (Figure 4-42).

This type of jack is possibly a little slower to operate because the pressure must be pumped off. On either of the single-action jacks the pressure is released as soon as the valve on the pump is opened.

Shorty Ram. A half-ram, or shorty ram, is also available with most hydraulic-jack sets.

Courtesy Hein-Werner Corporation

Figure 4-43   Shorty ram

It is designed for use in small, confined areas and is used with the single-action pump (Figure 4-43).

Extensions

The ends of the ram and ram plunger are threaded so that a great variety of extensions

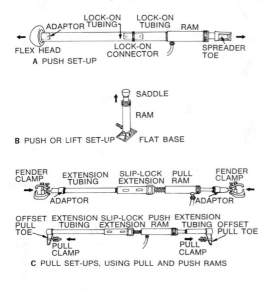

A PUSH SET-UP

B PUSH OR LIFT SET-UP

C PULL SET-UPS, USING PULL AND PUSH RAMS

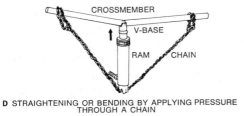

D STRAIGHTENING OR BENDING BY APPLYING PRESSURE THROUGH A CHAIN

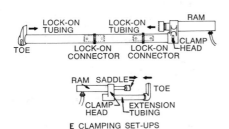

E CLAMPING SET-UPS

Figure 4-44   Typical jack set-ups

and attachments can be added to the ram, permitting the operator to make the necessary "set-up." By using the right combination of extensions and attachments, the jack can be used to push, pull, bend, lift, press, and clamp (Figure 4-44).

The extensions are made of heavy, seamless steel tubing. The threads on the rams, attachments, and extensions are pipe thread. They differ from standard pipe thread in that they are cut deeper and fit more loosely. This enables the operator to tighten the connections by hand.

When ordinary seamed pipe with standard pipe thread is used with the hydraulic jack, the equipment can be damaged and the operator injured.

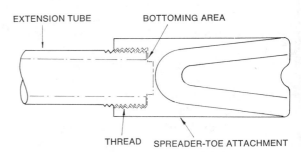

Figure 4-45   End of tubing bottoms on the attachments

When the extension is completely screwed into the attachment, the end of the tubing "bottoms" on the attachment. The ram pressure is then transferred through the tubing directly into the attachment (Figure 4-45). The threads only hold the connections together and do not support the applied pressure. Standard pipe thread is designed to tighten and seal the connection but does not necessarily make a strong joint.

Quick-Change Coupling. Some of the jacks have a type of quick-change coupling for connecting the lengths of tubing extensions

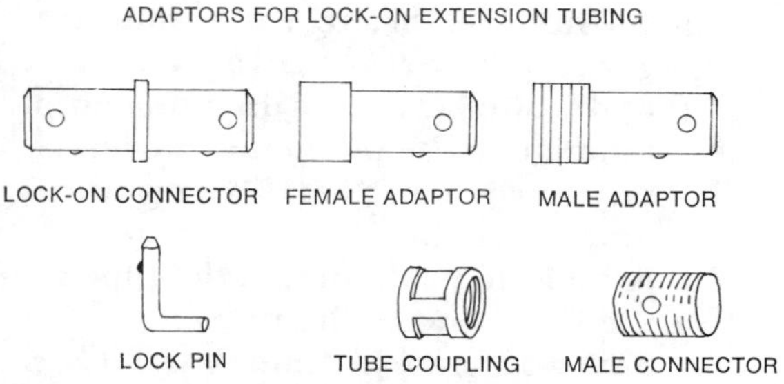

ADAPTORS FOR LOCK-ON EXTENSION TUBING

LOCK-ON CONNECTOR   FEMALE ADAPTOR   MALE ADAPTOR

LOCK PIN   TUBE COUPLING   MALE CONNECTOR

Figure 4-46   Tubing connectors

together. The couplings slip into the tubes and are secured by a lock pin. However, when a long push is needed, it is better to use the threaded couplings (Figure 4-46).

Attachments

The attachments are malleable castings and alloy-steel forgings designed to withstand considerable amounts of pressure without bending or breaking.

Wedgy and Spreader Attachments. The wedgy and spreader attachments work on the scissors principle and are very useful for correcting damaged areas where there is limited working space. The spreader has several attachments which can be screwed into one of the jaws to obtain a longer reach (Figure 4-47).

Adjustable Body Spoon Attachments. The spoon attachments are used as tubing or ram bases. There are several different spoon ends that can be interchanged and used with the same base attachment. Each of the spoons can be adjusted to different positions in the base to fit the contours of the damaged metal. They are locked to the base by a pin. The spoon attachments are especially handy for reaching around an obstacle which is hindering a direct push on the damaged area. They can also be used as dollies when assembled to a length of tubing to provide a long reach (Figure 4-48).

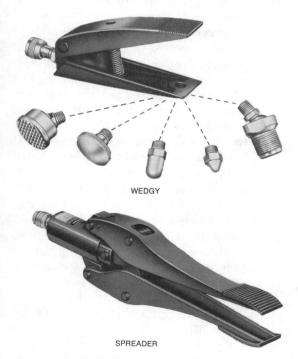

WEDGY

SPREADER

Figure 4-47   Wedgy and spreader attachments   *Courtesy Blackhawk Mfg. Co.*

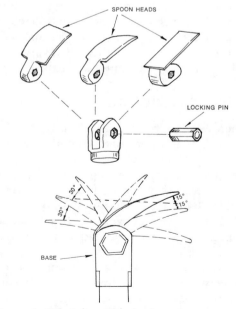

SPOON HEADS

LOCKING PIN

30°
30°
15°
15°

BASE

Figure 4-48   Adjustable body spoons

Courtesy Blackhawk Mfg. Co.

Figure 4-49 Rubber bumper or flex heads

Rubber Bumper Attachments. These are also known as **flex heads.** They take the shape of the area on which they are being used and distribute the force over the complete area. The rubber ends are used as tubing or ram-end bases. They prevent the areas subjected to the jack force from being marked (Figure 4-49).

It is impossible to illustrate and explain the many different combinations that can be produced with the attachments. From the various examples given in this chapter, a basic understanding of the jack and its attachments should be gained. The individual body repairer can then produce the set-up which is best suited to the repair work. Many other jack set-ups are illustrated in Chapter 13.

Safety Precautions

When using a hydraulic jack, one must remember that it produces equal forces in both directions. Therefore, make sure that the anchored area is strong enough to withstand the pressure needed to straighten the damaged area. It is often necessary to reinforce the anchored area with a block or length of angle iron to spread the force over a larger area.

Certain safety precautions must be observed when using the hydraulic jack to prevent the operator from being injured and the equipment from being damaged.

1. Do not use brake fluid, alcohol, glycerine, or anything else but hydraulic-jack fluid in the pump. Damage to the pump may occur. In an emergency, SAE 10W engine oil may be used.

2. For a long push, install the pipe on the fixed end of the ram.

3. Never drag the jack along the floor. Pick it up and carry it.

4. Do not overextend the ram, particularly if it is under load. A pressure of 55 MPa (4 ton) would damage the internal working parts and might even force the plunger out of the ram. If you should suddenly feel back pressure on the handle when pumping with the ram extended to its limit, stop at once.

5. Tighten the attachments or extensions together until they "bottom" to prevent damage from occurring to the threads.

6. Protect the threads on all parts, but particularly on the ram plunger. Always keep the cap on the plunger when it is not in use. Throwing the extensions or attachments carelessly into a box after using them is hard on the threads. If they should accidently become burred or nicked, use a small file or thread restorer to clean and restore them.

7. Avoid off-centre loads as much as possible. If it is necessary to work in an off-centre position, pump carefully. Stop as soon as possible, and try to adjust the jack for a more direct push. Off-centre loads are hard on the ram plunger seals (Figure 4-50).

8. Keep the ram away from the heat when you are welding or heating metal. Place the tubing end of the

jack near the area to be heated. Excessive heat will damage the ram's internal parts and eventually cause the jack to fail.

9. Handle the hose with care if you expect it to give long service. Do not apply pressure if the hose is kinked or has sharp bends. Watch for obstructions that could cause damage to the hose or couplings as the ram is extended. Avoid dropping a heavy object on the hose as this may kink the wire strands which give the hose strength. Once these wires are damaged, further use of the hose under pressure will eventually cause a break. If you must use a welding torch near the hose, do so with caution, particularly if the hose is under load.

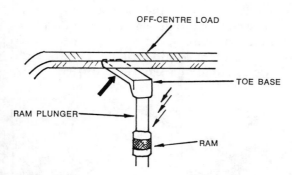

Figure 4-50   Off-centre loads

4-14 TYPES OF IMPACT FORCES

All body damage is caused by a type of impact force. **Pressure**, or **pushing force** is one type; **tension**, or **pulling force** is another. A push force is one that exerts a pressure **against** the metal, while a pull force creates tension **in** the metal (Figure 4-51).

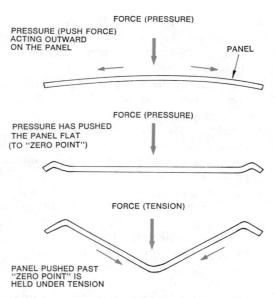

Figure 4-51   Pressure and tension

Considering the effect of pressure and tension forces on the different high, low combination and reverse crown areas will help in developing the best repair procedure.

Facts That Determine the Type of Damage

It should be noted that all of the repair procedures described in this chapter are only of a general nature. Because no two damaged areas are exactly the same and because so many different circumstances may be involved with each damaged area, it is impossible to describe all repair procedures. Some of the factors that determine the type and amount of damage and corresponding repair procedures are:

• The type of body construction involved; whether the force was exerted against a flat, crowned, combination-crowned, or reverse-crowned panel.

• The type of metal used in the panel.

• The metal's yield strength.

- The tensile strength of the metal.
- The shape of the impact area, that is, the amount of stamping that was necessary to shape the panel.
- The direction from which the force hit the area — a head-on direct force or a side-swiping pulling impact.
- Whether the area of metal is forced through pressure or tension forces.
- The speed of the impact force on the panel.
- The size and rigidity of the impact object. For example, an automobile striking a post is usually not damaged as severely as an automobile hitting a tree. The post will often give or break, whereas the tree will not move.
- The shape of the impact object. When a large truck with a large front bumper strikes an automobile, the force is absorbed over a large area of the automobile. Depending on the amount of force exerted, a great deal of both direct and indirect damage results. However, if a small, solid object, such as a tree, contacted the area in the same manner, a great deal of indirect damage would result, pulling the inner construction out of alignment. The direct damage caused in this case would be much less.

All of these factors must be considered before the correct repair procedure can be developed for straightening any damaged area.

Crowns

As previously explained in this chapter, the amount of resistance to bending in an area depends to a large extent on the degree of crown in that area. Most panels have areas of both low and high crowns. The high-crowned area is usually at right angles to the flat, or low-crowned, area. When a panel or area of metal has a high crown crossing a low

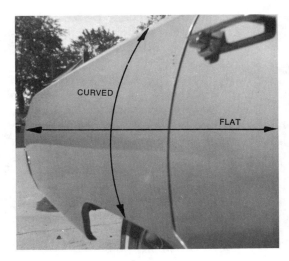

Figure 4-52   Combination-crowned panel

crown at right angles, it is said to have a **combination crown** (Figure 4-52).

Very few automobile panels have true crowns. That is, they are not curved, or crowned, the same amount from all directions. Some areas, although not true crowns, are close to it. These areas are called **double high-crowned areas** (Figure 4-53).

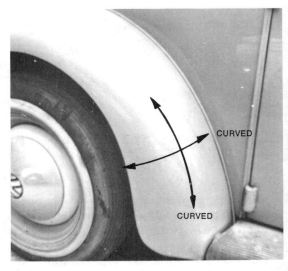

Figure 4-53   Double high-crowned area

Results of a Pushing Force Exerted on a Double High-Crowned Panel

When a force of sufficient pressure is exerted directly against the top of a double high-crowned sheet-metal surface, a pressure is created in the elastic metal surrounding the point of impact. Because of the height of the crown, the pressure at the point of impact forces the surrounding elastic metal up and back to allow the point of impact area to move in. As the crowned area moves in, hinge buckles around the point of impact are created. As the force continues on through the metal, this hinge buckle is

Figure 4-54   Damaged double-crowned area

forced sideways through the high crown in an outward direction from the point of impact. When the work-hardened hinge buckle becomes stronger than the surrounding metal, and if the impact force is not yet expended, pressure acts against the elastic metal around the outside of the hinge buckle. This pressure forces more metal up and out and another area in. A new hinge buckle which rolls outward is then started. This process repeats until the force is expended or the buckles have moved completely through the high-crowned area (Figure 4-54).

The further the direct damage area moves in, the higher the pressure in the surrounding metal is increased, until a **through-centre**, or **zero**, **point** is reached. After that, any movement of the direct damage area will result in tension, or a pull, being exerted upon the surrounding elastic metal. A sharp ridge or crown will be left between the edge of the direct damage area and the surrounding elastic area.

Repair Procedure. To straighten a double high-crowned area, it is necessary to bring the metal back in the reverse order to that in which the damage occurred.

Because the surrounding undamaged metal exerts pressure against the damaged area, the metal in the dent must be rolled back to its original shape, starting at the outside and working around the dent toward the centre or lowest area of crown. The point of impact is usually the last part or area to be completely straightened, but this is not true in every case. If the point of impact were close to an edge, it would be roughly straightened first, along with the edge.

Use the hammer to tap off the ridges, starting at the ends of the hinge buckle and working toward the sharpest bends. Hold the dolly under the channel closest to the ridge being hammered down. Hold the dolly under the slightest degree of bend in the channel and work toward the deepest area.

The hammer forces the ridges down and the pressure on the dolly forces the channels up. Once some of the pressure on the ridges and channels has been released, the dolly is used as a driving tool to force up the damage channels. There is no rule stating when, or for how long, to dolly. If the metal will not lift when the dolly is used as a driving tool, the tension on the ridges and channels has not been removed sufficiently, and the dollying procedure should be repeated.

This entire process is repeated, working around the outside of the dent and toward the impact area, until the complete area is "rough bumped" back to its original shape. A combination of the three dollying methods is then used to smooth and level the area before beginning the metal-finishing operations. The on-dolly method is used to thin and stretch severe roll buckles which might be present in the area. The light, on-dolly method is used to smooth and level all the ridges and buckles in the area.

Results of a Force Exerted on a Low-Crowned or Flat Panel

When a force is exerted against a flat or slightly crowned panel, very little pressure is needed for the panel to reach the zero or through-centre point. Most of the force is of the tension type, so that the complete panel is often "popped" in. The low-crowned area is pulled flat or distorted. Hinge buckles or ridges are left around the outside of the direct damage (Figure 4-55).

A pushing or pressure force directed at a relatively flat panel creates little or no indirect damage. However, when the panel goes past the zero point and goes into tension considerably more indirect damage is caused by the pulling force.

Figure 4-55   Damaged low-crowned area. Note that the door gap has increased because the edge of the door panel has been pulled.

Very little pressure is needed to create tension forces on a low-crowned panel, whereas considerable movement is needed to create tension forces on a high-crowned panel. A high-crowned damaged panel is likely to be under **pressure forces** and contain more hidden or indirect damage, whereas a low-crowned panel is likely to be under **tension forces.**

Repair Procedure. Because low-crowned areas are usually under tension, the sides or surrounding supporting parts will often be pulled in toward the point of impact. The body jack is used to push or pull these supporting parts back to their original positions, thus removing the strain from the rest of the damaged flat panel. When the strain is released from the panel, it will often "pop out" on its own. The repairer may apply pressure behind the panel with a jack, a spoon, or an arm or foot to pop out the panel. The hammer and dolly (or spoon, if the dolly cannot be used) are then used to straighten both concave and convex buckles.

> On a flat panel care should be taken to avoid stretching the metal. A slight stretch will cause much more trouble in repairing a flat panel than it will a high-crowned panel.

Results of a Force Exerted on a Combination-Crowned Panel

When a force is exerted directly against the two areas of a combination-crowned panel, the panel folds or buckles inward. A very slight ridge or hinge buckle is left at the edge of the damage in the low-crowned area. A roll buckle is often created at the edge of the high-crowned area because the hinge buckles, meeting resistance from the high crown, move sideways into the area (Figure 4-56).

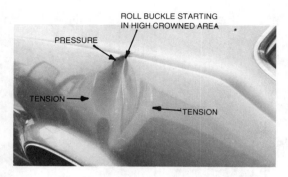

Figure 4-56   Force on combination-crowned panel

The extra strength of the high-crowned area resists pressure, so that the damage, following the line of least resistance, shifts into the low-crowned area.

Both tension and pressure forces are created in the metal surrounding the damaged areas. The tension forces will be in line with the low crown; the pressure forces will be in line with the high crown. A minimal amount of the impact force will usually be transferred to the adjacent construction.

Repair Procedure. Damage to a combination-crowned panel is usually removed by using either a push or a pull jack to relieve the tension in the lower area. Once this tension has been relieved, the hammer and dolly are used to relieve the pressure forces present in buckles along the high-crowned area. In some cases, another jack is used to push out the high-crowned metal. When the damage forces have been sufficiently removed in the high- and low-crowned areas, the rest of the damaged area will often "pop out," leaving very little damage in the elastic metal.

Buckles in the crowned areas should be rolled back in reverse order to that in which they were formed. The metal should be straightened, beginning at the highest crown and working toward the lowest crown. Any edges and pressed ridges should be straight-

ened and aligned in conjunction with the removal of the pressure and tension forces.

When the complete panel has been straightened back to its correct contour, a combination of the three dolly methods is used to prepare the damaged areas for metal finishing.

> If the point of impact in the low-crowned area is brought back to its normal position before the high-crown damage is removed, the metal that shifted from the high-crowned area to the low-crowned area during impact will not return to its proper position. As a result, the low area will appear high or stretched, while the high crown will remain too low.

Results of a Force Exerted Against the End of a Single-Crowned or Combination-Crowned Panel

When either a pushing or a pulling force strikes the end of a single-crowned panel or a combination-crowned panel, a great degree of indirect damage is usually created in areas divorced from the point of impact. The

Figure 4-57   Pushing force striking a panel from the end

crowned panel often has a strong enough resistance to bending that some of the damage will travel through the panel to the lower-crowned areas. More of the adjacent construction is also liable to be bent out of shape (Figure 4-57).

Repair Procedure. This type of damage is repaired by jacking out the damage in reverse order to that in which the damage occurred. Either a push or a pull set-up is made directly to or from the point of impact. Other jacks also may be used to help straighten any edges and pressed ridges in the panel. These extra jacks are used at the same time as the push or pull jack is applied to the direct damage, point of impact area.

When pressure is exerted on the direct damage, it will usually be found that the indirect damage will automatically straighten first, or that both areas will straighten together. While the jack pressure is exerted on the various areas, a heavy bumping hammer is used to tap along all seams, weld corners, and reinforced areas. This relieves the strain so that when the jacks are released the area, or even the complete panel, will not "spring back." All the damaged areas are then shaped and dollied smooth before the metal-finishing process is started.

Results of a Force Exerted at a Right Angle to a Single-Crowned Panel

Whenever a single-crowned panel is damaged at a right angle to the length of the crown, the metal is easily pushed in. Single-crowned metal has little resistance to this type of bending. The damage is localized with little of the impact transferring to the surrounding construction to create indirect damage. Part of the damage will be under tension, with the metal closest to the higher

Figure 4-58   Right-angle damage to a single-crowned panel

crowned areas under pressure (Figure 4-58).

Repair Procedure. To straighten this type of damage, the dolly is held at the end of the channel closest to the high-crowned area, then pushed tightly against the metal. The ridges are tapped off starting at their ends where the least amount of bend is. When some of the strain has been removed from the high-crowned area, the dolly is used to drive up the channel. This procedure is repeated, working from the ends of the channel toward the centre or deepest part, until the area can be popped out to its original position. The three dollying methods are then used to prepare the area for the metal-finishing.

Results of a Force Exerted Along the Length of a Single-Crowned Panel

When a minor impact force is exerted along the length of the flat area of the crown the damage is usually in the form of a crease. The metal is easily transferred from a pressure to a tension state, on each side of the crease (Figure 4-59). However, should the impact force be severe, a greater area of the panel is

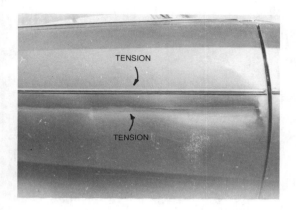

Figure 4-59   Crease type damage

likely to be pushed in with indirect damage transferred to the adjacent construction.

Repair Procedure. If the damage is a crease, it can easily be "bumped" back by using the dolly as a driving tool. Start at the least damaged area and drive up a portion of the crease. Use the off-dolly and light on-dolly method to roughly level the area. Continue this procedure, gradually working toward the deepest end. Once the complete area has been rough bumped, use light on-dolly blows to smooth and level the area.

More severely damaged areas would need hydraulic jacks to first straighten and align any indirect damage, then to help straighten any edges, flanges, pressed ridges, crowned areas, etc., (in that order) in the panel. The hammer and dolly would be used in conjunction with the jack to remove the strain of the ridges and channels in the damaged areas.

The effect of the three preceding types of damage against a single-crowned panel can be demonstrated with an ordinary metal container such as a pail or soft drink can. It will withstand much more force from the ends than it will when hit on the side. It can also be easily creased along the length of the crown.

Results of a Force Exerted on a Reverse-Crowned Area

When an impact force acts upon a reverse crown, tension forces are immediately set up. A sharp, concave buckle is formed along the centre or lowest part of the reverse crown. The metal on the sides of the reverse crown is pulled closer together.

Repair Procedure. To straighten a reverse-crowned area, the hammer is often used on the inside of the panel and the dolly on the outside, if this is at all possible. When this procedure cannot work, the dolly is used to tap out the sharp crease running along the length of the lowest crown. When a dolly cannot be used, a spoon or pry is used to pry out the crease. It is then dollied smooth.

Stretched Sheet Metal

The average sheet metal panel, after being formed in a press, has a fairly high degree of yield and tensile strength. Depending on the type and amount of force of the damaging impact, the metal will withstand a great deal of crushing and buckling before it stretches any great amount. When the sheet metal does stretch, it is usually caused by a gouge-type damaging impact (Figure 4-60).

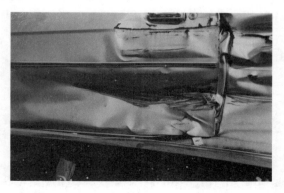

Figure 4-60   Stretched sheet metal

A **gouge** is usually caused by a solid, sharp object. The metal at the impact point gives, or stretches, before the surrounding metal can fold, or buckle, out of shape. Once the metal starts to stretch, there is a molecular rearrangement, and therefore work hardening, created in the area. The metal becomes stronger and more resistant to further bending. If the force remains constant or increases, the metal might continue to stretch until it rips. If the force weakens, the metal will resist further stretching in that area and buckles will be created surrounding the stretched area of metal. The point at which the sheet metal starts to stretch is known as the **yield point.**

Some stretched metal is usually found in the area of the point of impact and along the ridges and channels. Any area of sheet metal in the direct damage area that has not been bent past its elastic limit usually does not contain stretched metal, although it may appear to be stretched or **high.**

A shift of the metal from the point of impact into surrounding elastic area is possible. Unless the repair procedure is carried out in the correct order, it is almost impossible to move this shifted area of metal back to its proper position. It must then be considered stretched metal. Stretched metal can be brought back to its original shape by **shrinking.** The shrinking process is covered in Chapter 9.

Repairing a Crease in a Panel

A standard blade screwdriver is excellent to tap out a crease in a panel, provided the crease is accessible from the inside. The screwdriver blade is held directly on the crease while the screwdriver is tapped with a hammer. The corner of a dolly block can also be used to tap out the crease but is somewhat harder to control.

When the crease is not readily accessible from the inside, a spoon or a pry bar can be

Figure 4-61   Prying out a crease through a hole in the door frame

used to pry out the crease. The pry bar is best. The crease is worked out from the shallowest end to the deepest. After the crease has been completely lifted, it may be necessary to use light on-dolly blows to smooth and level the area. Any high spots are shrunk and the area is then metal finished or filled (Figure 4-61).

When driving or prying to lift a crease, keep the pry points close together, directly along the centre of the crease. Be extremely careful to pry only a small area at a time, so that the whole crease will gradually be lifted. Do not try to lift a large area at one time. When too much force is exerted in one spot in the panel, a knot or pimple is raised above the surrounding metal.

REVIEW QUESTIONS

1. Explain the terms "elasticity" and "elastic limit" as they refer to automotive sheet metal.
2. Explain, with diagrams, the physical changes that take place when sheet metal is bent.

3. When metal is bent in its cold state, the area of the bend becomes work hardened. Why?

4. a) Explain how the molecule movement is different when the panel is stamped compared to a bend made by hand or because of an accident.

   b) What determines the amount of work hardening in a panel?

5. Define the terms "bumping," "metal finishing," and "filling."

6. Why is it important to straighten damaged areas as much as possible before "filling" them over?

7. What three variables govern the force exerted by the hammer on the metal?

8. When dollying why is it usually not necessary to lift the hammer for the next hammer blow?

9. Why should a light, flat-faced dinging hammer be used for most metal-straightening operations?

10. Explain the principles of the hammer and dolly straightening action.

11. What variables determine the lifting action of the dolly against the metal?

12. a) Explain the results obtained by:
       (i) heavy, hammer on-dolly blows;
       (ii) hammer off-dolly blows;
       (iii) light, hammer on-dolly blows.

   b) What type of dolly should be used with each method?

13. What prevents a dent or damaged area from springing back to its original position?

14. a) Where are the ridges and channels usually found in a damaged area?

   b) What type of metal is usually found between the ridges and channels?

15. Why is the point of contact in a damaged area usually the most severely damaged?

16. Explain the correct procedure for removing the underseal, or sound deadener, from the underside of a panel.

17. Why should the underseal be removed before beginning the dollying operations?

18. Draw a diagram of a minor dent. List the identifiable areas. Indicate in sequence where the dolly should be placed and the hammer blows directed to remove the dent.

19. a) What three methods are used to detect high and low spots in the metal?

   b) How should the hand be held and moved on the metal when checking for high and low spots?

20. Why is it possible to hold the file at an angle to the direction of travel and still obtain the correct cut?

21. Explain how the body file is held and pushed when filing: (i) a flat panel; (ii) a crowned panel.

22. What is the purpose of cross and X filing a panel?

23. Why should the first and final file scratch patterns be made lengthwise along the length of the panel?

24. What type of impressions are raised by: (i) a blunt pick; (ii) a sharp pick?

25. What type of pick should a beginner use to raise the low spots? Why?

26. Why should solder or body fillers not be levelled by the grinder?

27. Why should an area of metal not be continually ground?

28. List three safety rules that should be followed while using the grinder.

29. How far should the back side of the disc be off the metal?

30. Why should too much pressure not be applied to the grinder while grinding?

31. a) Explain the two methods in which the disc grinder is used. Draw diagrams to support your answers.

   b) For what purpose is each method used?

32. Why is a disc cut in square, hexagon, or octagon shapes sometimes used to grind welds or rough areas?

33. Why are the front and rear of the vehi-

cle purposely designed to fold and crush when they are involved in an accident?

34. How thick is 20 gauge steel in thousandths of an inch and in millimetres?

35. A stamped panel has more "resistance to bending" than sheet metal in its cold-rolled form. Explain why.

36. Explain the difference between low-carbon steel, high-strength steel, and high-strength low-alloy steel.

37. List an advantage and a disadvantage of using high-strength steel.

38. How must the high-strength steel be welded? Why?

39. Why is a crowned panel stronger than a flat panel?

40. What are three factors that govern the strength of any panel?

41. Why must any flanges and ridges in a panel always be straightened first?

42. List the correct order in which the areas of a panel should be straightened.

43. a) List and explain the two types of buckles that are found in sheet metal damage.
    b) Which type is the hardest to repair? Why?

44. a) Describe direct and indirect damage conditions.
    b) When both types of damage are present, which type should be repaired first? Why?

45. List an advantage and a disadvantage of using a mechanical jack in place of a hydraulic jack.

46. Explain how the pressure is released on a mechanical jack.

47. List the four main components of the hydraulic jack and explain the purpose of each.

48. Why must the ram plunger be fully returned before oil is added to the pump?

49. List the three types of hydraulic-jack rams and explain where the oil enters each one.

50. Why are the extension tubes designed to bottom against the attachments when they are connected together?

51. Why should the extensions be installed on the fixed end of the ram for a long push?

52. Why should the ram plunger never be over-extended?

53. Explain what is meant by a "combination-crowned panel."

54. a) Explain the movement of the metal when a "pressure force" is exerted directly against a high-crowned panel.
    b) At what point does this same force start to exert a "tension force" on the surrounding elastic metal?

55. Explain what effect pressure or tension will have on a high-crowned panel when it travels in a direction parallel to the high crown. Why?

56. Are the forces in a low-crowned panel more of the pressure or tension type? Why?

57. What types of forces and buckles will be present in the high- and low-crowned areas of a damaged combination-crowned panel? Why?

58. Explain the straightening procedures for: (i) a high-crowned area; (ii) a low-crowned area; (iii) a combination-crowned area.

59. Why, when prying out a crease, should only a small area be pried at a time?

60. A crease should be worked out from the shallowest to the deepest end. Why?

5 BODY FILLERS

5-1   Resins
5-2   Fillers
5-3   Catalysts
5-4   Surface Preparation
5-5   Application
5-6   Finishing Procedures
5-7   Application Over Previous Coats
5-8   Body Filler Problems: Causes and Remedies

Most body fillers consist of mixtures of resins, fillers, and colour additives. Small amounts of a catalyst are added to the mixture to make it cure or harden.

5-1 RESINS

The **resins** are of the polyester type and are made through a chemical reaction of organic acids and glycols. Varying the types and amounts of both the acids and glycols used determines the characteristics of the resins, especially their degree of hardness, flexibility, adhesion, tensile strength, shear and pull strength, baking temperature, and gel time.

Body fillers differ from solders, especially in their method of attachment to the metal. Solders alloy to the metal surface, to become part of it. Plastics simply bond or adhere to the metal surface. The resin used in the body fillers must therefore be able to bond securely to the metal, quickly gel or **cure** (from liquid to solid) to a certain hardness, yet remain soft enough to be worked and flexible enough to give with any slight metal movement; i.e., flexing, expanding, or contracting without cracking, chipping, or separating from the metal.

5-2 FILLERS

Materials such as talc or finely ground aluminum particles are added to the resin to give it body or "filler." The filler and resin must be throughly mixed by the manufacturer until the resin has completely surrounded each fine particle of talc.

Talc is a mineral which is mined, crushed, pulverized, and screened to various mesh sizes and grades. Two common minerals used for talc are silica and magnesium oxide. Four different grades of talc are used, with the finer grade making the best quality body filler. It is more easily mixed into the resin, remains suspended in the liquid resin longer, and is not as prone to settling as the coarser, heavier grades of talc. However, all types of body fillers tend to "settle" in time. Always stir the contents of a new container before using. Store the unopened containers upside down. The solids settle to the top of the can and are then much easier to remix into the resins.

Body fillers containing finer grade talcs tend to spread smoother, sand easier, and feather out better, especially along the outer edge of the fillers.

If the filler is put to use before the resins and talc are properly mixed, the top part of the contents of the container will be overly thin and runny. It will be difficult to apply, shape, or level and will do a poor job of filling. The bottom part of the contents will be overly thick, making it hard to mix with the hardener. It will spread badly, cure unevenly, and bond poorly to the metal. When the filler does not cure evenly, the softer areas tend to file or sand off quicker than the surrounding harder areas, producing a wavy, uneven surface.

5-3 CATALYST

The **catalyst** is also often referred to as the activator or hardener. Catalyst materials are added in small amounts to resin filler mixtures to create a chemical reaction that produces heat to harden, or "cure" the resin. The mixture is quickly changed from a thick liquid to a hard fusible solid. The percentage of hardener added to the filler determines the length of time of the curing process. Without the use of the catalyst, the plastic

Figure 5-1   Liquid and cream hardeners

filler would take many days to complete the change from liquid to solid. There are two basic types of catalyst materials used: liquid and cream hardeners (Figure 5-1).

Liquid hardener is usually a ketone peroxide. It has a high percentage of active oxygen which creates a faster reaction time, making the plastic filler gel in three to five minutes.

Cream hardener is usually benzoyl peroxide. It has less active oxygen and therefore has a slightly slower gel time of from five to ten minutes. The liquid hardener is usually used with the red type fillers; the cream hardeners are used with the white fillers.

Both types of hardeners are poisonous. Use them with caution. ALWAYS wear safety glasses, especially when working with liquid hardener.

Since there are many different body filler manufacturers, it is strongly advised that their recommendations as to the amount of hardener to be used with a given amount of filler be strictly adhered to.

The fact that these fillers can be applied in a putty state at room temperature and that they will in a short time harden to a solid without the use of any external heat make their application a relatively simple process. However, there are certain rules that should be followed in their use if favourable results are to be obtained.

1. Use up to 25% less hardener in temperatures over 22°C to decrease the curing temperature, because plastic will cure much faster in warm temperatures.
2. Do not apply body fillers over either heated or hot metal surfaces. The additional heat from the metal "speed cures" the filler, especially the material that is actually in contact with the metal. The speed cure results in an uneven cure and a poor bond.
3. During moist or wet weather, the bare metal will sweat. Let the metal warm to room temperature or apply heat to the area to be filled, and then allow the metal to cool to room temperature before applying plastic filler.
4. Never use fillers over moist or cold surfaces. These are the two main enemies of body fillers. When the filler is applied over a moist or cold surface, the heat generated as the filler cures expands the moisture, causing slight blisters or separations of the filler from the metal. When the filler cools, the moisture condenses in the blister. This moisture causes the metal to rust. Through time the rust will creep along the surface of the metal between it and the plastic filler, and the blister will begin to swell and show in the paint surface. Eventually the filler will crack and separate from the metal.

5-4 SURFACE PREPARATION

It is most important that the damaged area be brought back as close as possible to its original contour before any body filler is applied. If the area is not correctly "bumped," there will probably be extreme high, low,

soft, or oil can spots in the damaged area. The low areas take more filler than necessary to fill and the high spots keep coming through the filler, creating an uneven surface. Soft spots or oil can areas are areas in the damaged metal that tend to collapse or pop in as soon as any pressure is applied over them, such as that from normal filing or sanding.

It is almost impossible to obtain a smooth plastic "fill" over an area if any of these conditions are present in the metal. Because of the metal surface flexing, the area may appear smooth but in fact will be wavy.

Each time the file or file board passes over the soft area, it pops in and very little filler is removed, while the rest of the surrounding area is sanded smooth. The complete area may look smooth. However, the soft area will feel high and wavy. The soft area can be tightened by picking or prying it from underneath with many light lifts. Use a very sharp pick hammer, the corner of a cold chisel, or a scratch awl. Do not hit the metal hard to raise a large point as this could crack the filler. Many sharp, light picks or prys are best. If this is not sufficient to tighten the soft spot, the filler must be removed from that area and a small shrink placed in the centre of the area. If the soft spot will "pick tight" it should be sanded over without using any pressure on the board file.

When the damaged area has been bumped back to its original shape, the beginner may wish to check the smoothness by filling the area with the body file. The scratch pattern will indicate any low, high, or soft spots which can be corrected. Body filler should never be applied to a smooth surface that is not clean of all paint, dirt, rust, grease, and welding flux.

Grind all surfaces, including any welded sections, with a 16- or 24-grit disc to clean the bare metal. The disc scratches provide an added "tooth," or grip, to which the plastic will bond. The entire damaged area must be ground out to and including part of the surrounding undamaged metal.

> Never apply fillers over rusted areas, or over metal with small perforations (rusted-through pin holes). The rust will continue to creep along the metal under the filler. In time, it will crack, blister, or fall out.

Mixing Preparation

Stir the filler in the container from the bottom up, to mix it thoroughly. Use a putty knife or other flat-bladed instrument to remove only enough filler to do the job. Place the filler on a smooth non-porous surface, such as a piece of glass, plastic, or metal (Figure 5-2). Use another putty knife or applicator to scratch off any filler left on the putty knife. Add it to the filler on the mixing board (Figure 5-3). If the filler is left on the knife, and the same knife is used to mix and/or apply the filler, some of it will not be mixed with hardener. It will not cure properly when it is applied to the metal. Do not leave the filler in a ball or gob on the mixing

Figure 5-3   Scraping filler off the putty knife

Figure 5-4   Flattening the filler

board. Level it out somewhat before adding the hardener (Figure 5-4). Add the hardener by spreading it out over the flattened surface of the blob of filler. The hardener should be added to the filler in a mixture ratio according to the manufacturer's recommendations. A typical liquid hardener mixture is approximately 5 to 10 mL (8 to 10 drops) of hardener to an amount of filler equal to the size of a golf ball.

A suggestion for adding cream hardener is to first flatten out the filler into a rather flat blob, then apply the cream hardener in a large W over the filler. Make the W shape the

Figure 5-2   Mix filler on a smooth non-porous surface

full size of the blob (Figure 5-5A). For cooler temperatures use a full W shape. In hotter temperatures shorten the centre of the W (Figure 5-5B). Using this method, the amount of hardener added is easier to meter thus controlling the hardening time, and the two materals can be quickly yet thoroughly mixed.

Use a plastic applicator or a flexible putty knife to mix the filler and hardener together. Do not stir or flop the mixture. This action will trap air bubbles in the mixture and cause pinholes to appear in the material after it has been applied. The best method of mixing is wiping or spreading the mixture across

Figure 5-6   Use a wiping/spreading action to mix the filler and hardener together

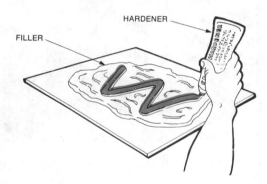

FILLER

HARDENER

Figure 5-5A   Apply the hardener in a full W shape for cooler temperatures

the smooth surface, then scooping up the residue and repeating the action several times until the hardener and filler are thoroughly mixed (Figure 5-6).

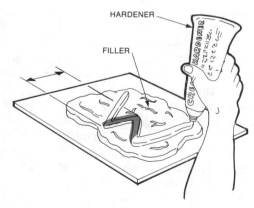

HARDENER

FILLER

Figure 5-5B   Use a small centre section for warmer temperatures

Do not use excessive amounts of hardener. Poor adhesion, separation, blistering, and slow curing problems can occur. Never return any leftover activated filler to the container.

Never remove the filler from the container with a putty knife or other instrument that has activated uncured material on it. Whenever uncured activated filler comes in contact with the filler in the container, it is turned into a hard, lumpy mess.

5-5 APPLICATION

Always straighten and level the damaged area as much as possible before applying the plastic filler.

Apply a thin coat of the activated filler over the prepared metal as a bonding coat. Keep the fingers close to the bottom of the applicator (Figure 5-7). Apply pressure and use a good firm stroke. It is most important that this first coat be applied with a suitable pressure, to force the filler into all the small imperfections in the metal, thus eliminating any trapped air pockets or poorly bonded areas. Succeeding coats are then applied directly over the bonding coat to build up the damaged area to the correct contour.

Use long strokes, starting from one side of the top or bottom, and pull the filler across the complete area to the opposite side. Hold the applicator firmly, pressing each suc-

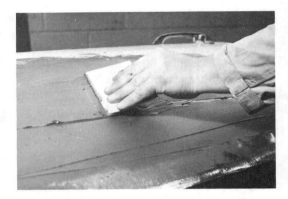

Figure 5-8   Applicator positions

Figure 5-7   Use the fingers to apply pressure on the applicator

ceeding coat into the last. Holding the applicator in a near right angle position to the surface of the metal tends to deposit less filler than when it is held on a close angle to the metal (Figure 5-8).

The angle of the applicator is changed as it is pulled across the damaged area, according to the amount of filler needed to be deposited in any one area. Pick up any unused material left at the end of the stroke and start again. Depending on the shape of the area being filled, it is often better to cross-coat the area by coating the area at a right angle to the direction of travel of the last coat. Make a special effort to feather-edge the outer edge of the filler to the metal. Quickly apply the filler and rough shape it to the area. Using the applicator, continue to shape and level the filler until it starts to cure. It can even still be lightly worked, i.e., fine graded, after the filler has started to cure. However, once it starts to cure, use only light pressure on the applicator. Using too heavy a pressure may tend to tear or roughen the surface of the filler.

A general recommendation is to not apply plastic fillers in thicknesses greater than 12–15 mm per application. Provided the correct amount of hardener has been added to the plastic filler, it will quickly cure ready for smoothing.

Do not place leftover activated filler in waste containers, especially near oily rags, paper, etc., until the mixture has completely hardened and cooled. The heat generated by the curing process could contribute to spontaneous combustion.

It is most important to keep the plastic filler tools, i.e., the mixing board, putty, knives, applicators, and squeegie, smooth and clean of any plastic residue. Clean the tools immediately after finishing with them. The filler is much easier to scrape off while it is still in a rubbery, semi-cured state. Do not clean the tools by grinding them, as the grinder scratches would allow the next mix of the filler to grip in the scratches of the tool, and it would therefore be more difficult to clean.

5-6 FINISHING PROCEDURES

The method used to finish (smooth and level the plastic filler) varies according to personal preference (Figure 5-9).

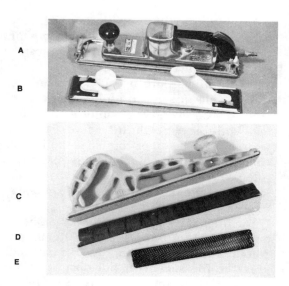

Figure 5-9   Body filler filing/sanding and levelling tools: (A) air sander, (B) clip-on file board, (C) file board, (D) hose, (E) file

The fillers can be filed with a Surform file while slightly soft and then sanded using coarse sandpaper, by hand with a board file, or by machine. They can also be left to completely harden and then machine sanded with coarse sandpaper. There are certain advantages to each method. For the beginner or on areas where additional coats of filler are going to be added, the filing process is strongly recommended. The file provides a scratch pattern to indicate the high and low spots. Most importantly it cuts down the high uneven areas to provide a level surface for the next coat. Filing the filler does not create the dust which occurs when the filler is applied, left to completely harden, and then either hand or machine sanded.

The one problem with filing plastic fillers is that the fillers are best filed at a certain stage of the curing process. When they are filed while they are still too soft the cuttings ball together and plug the file teeth. Allowing the fillers to fully cure makes them very hard to file. It is therefore important both for time consumed and ease of filing, to catch the filler at the right time of cure.

Plastic fillers cure by quickly changing from the plastic stage to a solid. The surface tends to skin over, yet remain soft and porous, while the rest of the filler cures from the bottom out. The outer surface is the last to completely harden. The filler is ready for filing when the surface can be lightly cut or scratched with the corner of the file or one's fingernail.

The filler at the bottom of the scratch will be hard and will appear to be lighter in colour. The topcoating may tend to ball and plug the file somewhat but once it is removed, the remaining filler is easily filed.

The standard body file is not well suited for filing body fillers. The fillers very quickly dull the cutting edge of the teeth and the filing residue tends to plug the U-shaped groove between each tooth. The Surform cheese-grater type half-round file (described in Chapter 3) is much better suited for shaping the fillers. The tooth design of the two files is very different. The body file, which has rows of continuous curved teeth, can be used from a variety of different angles. The Surform file has many small separate teeth set in rows at a 70° angle across the blade. The Surform file is usually used without a handle. The cut is made on the pull stroke. It can sometimes be used on the push stroke but usually the teeth tend to catch in the plastic, causing the file to vibrate or flutter as it is pushed over the filler. The best cutting results are obtained when the file is held so that the rows of teeth are as close to a right angle to the direction of travel as possi-

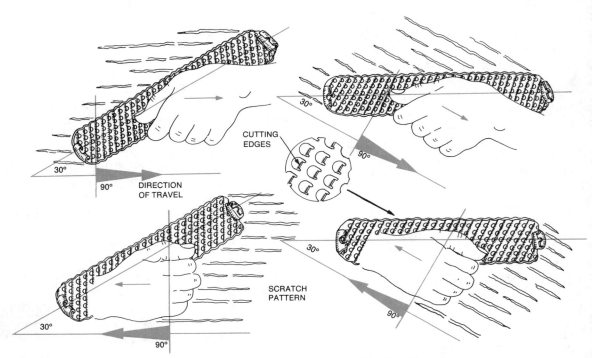

Figure 5-10   Hold the file with the teeth at a 90° angle to the direction of travel

Figure 5-11   Rough-filed filler

Figure 5-12   Machine finishing the surface

ble. The file should be held on a 30° angle from the horizontal surface and pulled straight using as long a stroke as possible. The file can also be held straight and pulled on a 30° angle. Although the angle remains the same, the blade must be turned around when the direction of travel is reversed. Note that in all the examples, the direction of the file movement is at a 90° angle to the rows of cutting teeth (Figure 5-10). The farther off 90° the cut direction is, the less cutting will occur. These lesser angles are sometimes used when very little material needs to be removed.

When the filler is soft, use little pressure on the file. Soft filler can be easily ripped away from the metal. When the filler is hard, it is necessary to apply more pressure to the file.

Once the filler has been rough-filed, (Figure 5-11) the area is either recoated, if necessary, or file-board sanded either by hand or machine (Figure 5-12). Usually a #40 paper is used with the board file to finish smoothing and levelling the area. A coarse, heavy #36 paper is sometimes used with the machine. A #80 paper can be used last on the file board to remove any deep scratches in the surface before priming.

The board file can be used in any direction or angle. However, the best results are obtained when the board file is held and used at angles similar to those used with the body files for metal finishing (described in Chapter 4). A short length of radiator hose or a cardboard tube makes an ideal sanding board for reverse-crowned areas (Figure 5-13).

Continue to file and shape the filler until metal areas start to file through. Do not continue to file over any metal areas. Try to use the file or sanding board on a different angle to miss the high spots and further level any sections of filler not smoothed out.

Figure 5-13   A sanding block constructed from rubber hose

Any low spots in the filler or metal high spots showing through the filler indicate uneven conditions which must be corrected by adding more fill. Once high spots start to come through, there is little advantage in filing that area any more.

When more fill has to be added, blow and/or wipe all dust and filings off the complete area before recoating. When more filler is added over filler dust, adhesion between coats is prevented. If filed shavings get into the filler, they are dragged through the soft filler by the applicator and create deep grooves that are hard to remove.

Another coat of filler should not be applied over the previous coat unless its surface has been filed or sanded to roughen it up. Usually the outer surface cures to a smooth, glossy film which should be removed so the next coat can obtain a proper bond.

5-7 APPLICATION OVER PREVIOUS COATS

Clean the area or plastic filings and dust. Feel the complete area, carefully checking the overall contour. Note especially any excessively high or low spots.

High spots can be tapped down. If they are large, use the flat face of the hammer. Smaller spots are often more easily brought down by using the pick end of the hammer. For this operation the sharper the pick is, the better. Low spots can be picked or pried up, although care should be used, as the plastic might be fractured. Again, better control can be gained by using a sharper pick and many light blows rather than a blunt pick and a few

heavy blows. Excessively high spots in the metal must be shrunk down as explained in Chapter 9.

If it is necessary to place a heat shrink on a high spot, grind the heat marks off before applying any plastic over the shrink area.

Once the area has been checked, first apply the filler to any noticeable low spots. Then, using the same procedure as previously explained, apply a coat of filler to the complete area. Use long strokes, moving from one side to the other whenever possible. Apply pressure to the applicator and pull it across the level areas. Do not leave a thick edge of filler around the outer edge of the filled area. Feather-edge it out so that it tapers gradually to the metal (Figure 5-14). Continue to work the filler until it is as smooth as possible. As soon as the outer surface becomes rubbery, start to file the area lightly. Use very little pressure at first, as the file will sometimes tend to tear the filler away from the metal, especially if it has not cured enough or if it is only a thin coat. Continue to file the area only until metal begins to appear. Metal spots indicate that either the metal is still too high or that the complete area still needs more filler. No benefit can be gained by continuing to file or

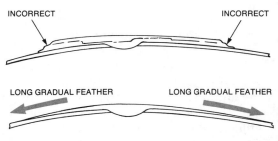

Figure 5-14   Feather out the edges when applying the filler

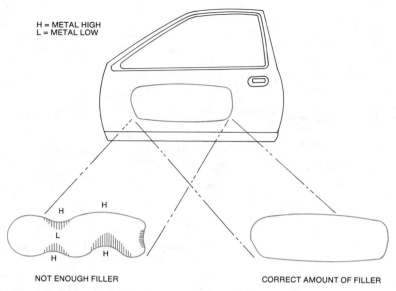

H = METAL HIGH
L = METAL LOW

NOT ENOUGH FILLER

CORRECT AMOUNT OF FILLER

Figure 5-15   Scalloped or wavy edge indicates too little filler

sand that particular area once the metal starts to cut through. If no high spots appear, file the area until there are no low spots and all the edges are relatively well feathered. Finish sanding smooth the surface with the file board and #40 sandpaper.

Should another light coat be necessary to fill any slight imperfections, it is applied over the complete area again, left to fully cure, then sanded smooth with the file board and #40 paper. The file board and #80 paper are used to "finish off" the complete area.

The beginner sometimes has difficulty determining whether there is enough filler on the area. It is no use to waste time and sandpaper if there is still not enough filler over the area. In the description of metal finishing in Chapter 4 it was explained that the levelness and smoothness of the surface can be told by sight, by feel, or by using the body file to provide a scratch pattern. Small, low spots in the fillers are easy to see when the filler is either Surform or board filed. However, a gradual waviness — slight high and low areas — over a large area is much

harder to detect while the area is being sanded with the board file. The coarse sand scratches in the filler make it somewhat harder to get the "feel" of the area of the fillers compared to getting the feel of metal finished areas. Keep the complete hand flat on the surface and slowly move it over the surface. Feel the surface from all different directions. Looking at the filled area can also indicate if it has been filled enough. A telltale sign of either the complete area (or a section of an area) being too low and/or wavy is that the outer edge of the filler is **scalloped.** If the area has been filled enough then the edges of the filler will be relatively straight.

When a flange around the wheel openings or a pressed ridge in a panel has to be filled, the straightness of the edges can be checked by sanding with the board file up to a pencil line scribed along the ridge. The board file should be held parallel with the line and moved in straight back-and-forth strokes (Figure 5-15). Sand the filler on both sides of the line. Gradually work the file board

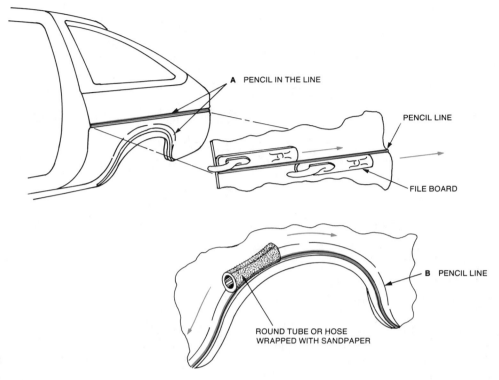

Figure 5-16   Sand to the scribed pencil line

closer to the line until the sanded edge of the filler just meets the scribed line (Figure 5-16).

> Do not use ink type markers on plastics. If any is left on or in the filler it can bleed through into the final coat of paint.

5-8 BODY FILLER PROBLEMS: CAUSES AND REMEDIES

Blisters are usually caused by soft spots in the filler. They are a result of not thoroughly mixing the hardener with the plastic. Mix smaller batches and mix more thoroughly.

Pin holes can be caused by using too much hardener or by entrapped air. When air pockets are left between the metal and filler or between coats of filler, the heat generated through the curing process can expand the air and cause a blister or a pin hole. Applying pressure to the applicator forces out entrapped air from the filler as it is being applied.

Blisters can also be caused by small moisture or water pockets. After the filler cures, it cools. The moisture in the entrapped air condenses to create a small water pocket which will in time blister the filler.

Blisters and cracks may appear whenever plastic filler is applied over rusted or porous areas of metal. The rust and/or moisture tends to creep along the metal under the filler. Eventually the filler blisters, cracks, and separates as the rust destroys the bond between the filler and the metal.

> Never apply body filler if there are perforated holes in the metal, regardless of how small they may be.

Blisters can also be caused by filling over areas of metal not properly cleaned, i.e., along welds, over weld flux, burned paint and black spots, and rusted areas. The filler will not stick to these areas. It only bridges across them. Eventually blisters may occur.

Make sure the metal surface is ground clean and rough. Use a #24 disc. The surface must be free of oil, grease, acids, etc.

Priming

Be sure the filler is fully cured and cold before applying primer. If the filler is soft and warm, moisture or solvents from the primer could be absorbed. Do not apply the first coat of primer in a full wet coat because entrapped primer solvents could cause the plastic to soften and blister.

Some filler manufacturers recommend that the fillers be washed with acrylic thinner before they are primed. This material will bring out any blind blisters and trapped air bubbles which can be repaired quite easily before the area is primed or painted.

Staining

Under certain conditions **bleeding** or **staining** of the paint topcoats can occur in areas over body fillers. This staining effect tends to occur more often with basecoat/clearcoat paint systems.

There are two main reasons for topcoat staining. One is the use of too much hard-

ener in the filler. The benzoyl peroxide used in cream hardener is a bleaching agent. When excessive amounts of hardener are used, the unused material remains in the filler. Under certain conditions it will travel or "migrate" through the paint undercoats and topcoats to bleach the paint pigments. Blues, greens, and some metallic colours tend to stain worse than others. Staining can also occur because during the curing process, certain chemicals in the resins must react with the benzoyl peroxide in the cream hardener to make the resin cure. This reaction creates new chemical substances, specks or particles, that tend to be very sensitive to light. When exposed to light, they can turn different shades of brown. The thinner in the paints can actually pull these chemical specks from the filler through the undercoats and into the topcoats. If they reach the clear topcoat, the light quickly turns them to a yellow or brown colour creating a stain in the paint film.

Aluminum-based body fillers are somewhat more successful in preventing bleed-through. Some manufacturers also recommend applying a special final thin coat of polyester glazing material over the body filler before the area is primed to prevent bleed-through.

REVIEW QUESTIONS

1. Briefly explain how body fillers attach to the metal.
2. List the two main materials body fillers are made from and explain the purposes of each.
3. Why is it important to thoroughly stir the filler in a newly opened container?
4. For what purpose is the hardener, or activator, added to the filler?
5. What determines the length of the curing, or hardening, process?

6. a) List the two types of hardeners.
   b) Which type of hardener is used with the white fillers?
   c) Which type of hardener has the faster reaction time? Why?

7. List the two main enemies of body fillers.

8. List the problems that might occur should the filler be applied over areas not properly bumped to their correct contour.

9. To what type of metal surface should the body fillers be applied?

10. Why should body fillers never be applied directly over rusted metal?

11. Explain the procedure for adding and mixing the hardener and filler.

12. Why should the "glob" of filler on the mixing board first be flattened or levelled off somewhat before the hardener is added?

13. Why is it important to not use excessive amounts of hardener?

14. Why is it important not to contaminate the filler in the container with any hardener?

15. a) The first coat of body filler is applied as a thin "bonding" coat. Why?
    b) Why should each coat be applied with pressure and a good firm stroke?

16. How should the applicator be held in relation to the metal surface when (i) depositing the filler, (ii) levelling the filler?

17. Should the filler be worked with the applicator after it has started to cure, it must be done lightly. Why?

18. Why should the left-over activated filler not be immediately placed in the waste container?

19. a) When is the best time to file body fillers?
    b) What method can be used to check to see if the filler is ready for filing?

20. a) Explain the two methods of holding and using the Surform file.
    b) On what part of the stroke does the file do the cutting?

21. What number sandpaper is generally used to board file the filler?

22. What procedure must be followed when the metal starts to show through the filler?

23. Before adding more filler, the dust and filings must be cleaned off the area. Why?

24. A new coat of filler should not be applied over a previous coat unless its surface has been filed or sanded. Why?

25. Explain briefly the procedures that can be used to remove metal high spots that cut through the filler.

26. Briefly explain the causes of the metal coming through the filler.

27. Explain two methods of checking the filler for uneven or low areas.

28. Make a chart to list and explain three causes of blisters and one preventive remedy for each of the three causes.

29. List two causes of staining from the filler into the paint.

6 PLASTICS AND FIBREGLASS

6-1   Types of Plastics
6-2   Identification of Plastics
6-3   Repairing Plastics
6-4   Plastic Welding
6-5   Fibreglass Repairs
6-6   Panel Replacement Procedures

Automotives parts, panels, and complete bodies are made from plastics. There are approximately 31 000 different types of plastics used in industry, about 15 of which are used for automotive purposes. Of those 15, five or six types are the most commonly used.

Plastics are made from resins. **Resins** are synthetic materials, chemically produced by combining two or more different compounds using various types of chemical or mechanical processes. By varying the type and ratio of the basic compounds and by adding small amounts of other materials, changes can be made to the characteristics of the resins, thus making the plastics either as strong as steel, for example, for an automobile spring leaf, or as soft and flexible as rubber, for example, the front and rear bumper covers (facias).

6-1 TYPES OF PLASTICS

There are two different categories of plastics: **thermosetting** and **thermoplastic**.

Thermoplastic Plastics

These plastics will soften and melt when heat is applied. They can either be rigid or soft and flexible. Either type may also have some kind of reinforcing to add tear strength to the panel.

Rigid thermoplastics are commonly used to make fender inner splash aprons, fan shrouds, and some bumper covers and grilles. Soft thermoplastics are used to make bumper covers and filler panels. Since both types are remeltable, they can be repaired by plastic welding methods.

Thermosetting Plastics

With these plastics, once the part is formed and the resin has cured its shape cannot be changed by heating, nor can the plastic be remelted. A thermosetting resin cures through a chemical reaction between the resin and a catalyst. The catalyst, when added to the resin, produces a chemical reaction that generates heat to raise the temperatures of a resin enough to cure and harden it into a tough, infusible solid. For example, body fillers are made from polyester resins, which are thermosetting materials.

Many automotive thermosetting plastics contain additional reinforcing fibres, such as, glass cloth, matting, or flakes. Thermosetting plastics can be made in either rigid or soft form. The rigid reinforced plastics are tough and strong. They are used to make major parts such as grille opening panels and fenders, as well as complete bodies. The soft thermosetting plastics are also used to make bumper covers and facia filler panels. Thermosetting materials are not remeltable and therefore usually cannot be welded. The normal repair method is bonding with structural adhesives. (However, certain types of urethane thermoset materials can be welded, using special plastic rods.)

6-2 IDENTIFICATION OF PLASTICS

Since there are 15 types of plastics, the major problem is identifying them. Most thermosetting materials can be bonded, but not welded. Both rigid and soft thermoplastic materials can be welded, but some of the soft facia plastics are better repaired with structural adhesives so that the repaired area remains flexible. In order to identify the plastics, the manufacturers are branding the rear side of the panel with an internationally used code of letters. Some of the plastics can also be identified by other means, such as, its feel, flexibility, or colour, and by burn and smoke tests. Examine Table 6-1, which lists the 15 different types of plastics, including their codes, their characteristics, and their methods of repair.

6-3 REPAIRING PLASTICS

Thermoplastic material can be repaired by either welding or bonding. Thermoset plastics cannot be remelted and therefore must be repaired by bonding with structural adhesives. Fibreglass panels can be joined and repaired by using the fibreglass repair methods discussed later in the chapter.

Adhesives and Glues

The **epoxy structural type adhesives** are the most reliable for bonding plastics, especially the soft types, because most remain somewhat pliable and will "give" and flex with the plastic part after they have cured.

These structural adhesives are epoxy two-part materials. Usually two parts are mixed equally for maximum adhesion and strength. Not all epoxies are the same. Some remain flexible after they have cured, others do not. Some work better when they are used in a tight-fitting type of crack. Others are designed for filling in V-shaped areas. Some others can be used as a filler as well as a bonding agent. Always read and follow the directions given for each type of epoxy material used.

Glues such as **cyanoacrylate** (superglue) can be used to bond some types of plastics. These types of glues dry by absorbing very small amounts of moisture. When too much glue is applied to the edges, there is insufficient moisture for the glue to dry correctly. Do not flood the edges; use only a very thin covering.

Some thermoplastic materials that cannot be welded because of the location of the break can be bonded by melting or softening the edges of the crack with a solvent, then holding them tightly together until the solvent has evaporated and the edges have bonded. Acetone, for example, will melt some types of plastics. Use a knife or razor blade to scrape some particles of the plastic from an outer edge of the part into a very small amount of the solvent. As the solvent melts the particles, the mixture will thicken into a paste which can be applied to the broken edges. The paste mixture will melt into the edges. When they have softened, the edges can be brought together to form a successful bond.

ABS and PVC solvents are readily available from plumbing and electrical suppliers. They are used to melt and join together plumbing and electrical pipes.

> No adhesive will work correctly if the surfaces to be bonded are not clean. First wash the area with soap and water, then sand, scrape, and wash the edges to be bonded with cleaning solvent. Always read the directions on the adhesives container.

Mix the materials according to the directions. Do not add extra hardener. The bond could be destroyed. Don't try to force the material to dry with additional heat if the directions do not recommend using heat. Usually adhesives are designed to be used at or near room temperature. Force-drying the materials can cause the surfaces to skin over, preventing the base materials from curing evenly. Allow sufficient time for the material to dry (up to 24 h). Often the longer the curing time, the better the bond.

Repairing Flexible Plastic Parts

Flexible parts can be constructed of either thermoset polyurethane (PUR) materials or thermoplastic polyurethane (TPUR) materials. Both types can be welded, but the more common repair method is by bonding with structural adhesives, as in the following examples.

> In each example, play a soft neutral flame over the area to be bonded before applying the structural adhesive. The flame tends to sweat the surface providing a better bond for the adhesive materials. Keep the torch moving. Do not char or burn the repair area.

Small Clean Tears. Add the adhesive mixture directly to the edges of the tear. Devise some method of holding the two edges tightly together in alignment while the adhesive cures. Aluminum tape, a small piece of wood, and clamps can be used. When the adhesive has cured, use the following steps to reinforce and finish the repair.

1. Clean the complete panel outer surface, first with soap and water, then with wax and grease remover solvent. On the back side clean only the immediate area to be repaired.
2. Machine sand (back sand) the paint surface from the surrounding area.
3. Grind a V-shaped taper along the original tear (along both sides if possible). If any area did not bond from the first coat, grind this area deeper.
4. Mix the adhesive material and fill the V plus the area slightly out from the V.
5. Allow the adhesive to fully cure and then finish-sand the area smooth.

Larger Rips and Tears (Figure 6-1). For a large, clean tear or rough, jagged tear use the following steps:

DIFFERENT TYPES OF PLASTICS: CODE, CHARACTERISTICS, REPAIR

Code	Name	Common Uses	Types		Identifying Characteristics	Repair Procedures
			Thermo-set	Thermo-plastic		
ABS	Acrylonitrile Butadiene Styrene	flexible or hard body panels		*	• rigid • burns with sooty, black smoke	• welding • structural adhesive • cyanoacrylate adhesive (superglue) • fibreglass repair
ABS/PVC	ABS/vinyl	crash pads		*		• welding
EPDM	Ethylene Propylene Diene-Monomer	bumper impact strips, some bumpers	*			• structural adhesive • welding
PA	Nylon	exterior finish trim panels, mechanical parts	*			• fibreglass repair • welding • cyanoacrylate adhesive (superglue)
PC	Polycarbonate Lexan	grills, instrument panel parts, lenses		*		• welding • fibreglass repair • cyanoacrylate adhesive (superglue) • structural adhesive
PE	Polyethylene	valance panels, interior parts		*	• flexible • feels like wax and burns with a smell like burning wax • drips when burning	• welding
PP	Polypropylene	interior kick panels, hard plastic trim, fender aprons, splash shields, fan shrouds,		*	• bendable • burns with no smoke	• welding

Code	Name	Applications			Characteristics	Repair
PPO	Noryl	some heater-evaporator cases, chrome grilles, head-lamp doors, bezels, ornaments	*			• fibreglass repair • welding
PS	Polystyrene			*		• welding
PUR	Polyurethane	bumper covers, padding for crash pads and seats	*			• structural adhesive • welding
TPUR	Thermoplastic Polyurethane	soft filler panels, bumper face bars, gravel deflectors, soft bezels		*	• flexible • light yellow • burns with a yellow-orange flame	• welding • structural adhesive
PVC	Polyvinyl Chloride	bumper filler crash pads, upholstery and interior trim		*	• flexible • chars and gives off grey smoke	• welding • cyanoacrylate adhesive (superglue) • vinyl adhesive
SAN	Styrene Acrylonitrile	instrument panel gauge lenses		*		• welding
TPR	Thermoplastic rubber	valance panels, filler panels		*		• welding • structural adhesive
UP	Polyester	fibreglass panels, grille openings, auto body fillers	*			• fibreglass repair

Table 6-1 Different types of plastics: code, characteristics, repair

1. Clean the area on both sides in the same way as for a small clean tear.
2. Grind each edge of the tear to a deep taper.
3. Apply a foil type backing tape to the underside to hold the two edges in alignment.
4. Carefully read the structural adhesive directions and mix the adhesive accordingly.
5. Apply a thin coat of adhesive to the bottom of the V against the foil tape. It may be necessary to allow this first coat to cure before applying the next coat.
6. Apply another coat to fill the V. Bring it up higher than the surrounding panel surface and out beyond the V edges.
7. Allow plenty of time for the material to cure and use standard sanding methods to level and smooth the repair area.

If there are any low spots it may be necessary to add more adhesives. Small pin holes can be filled with special soft plastic primers. It may be necessary to support the area from behind with a small piece of wood while the repair is being sanded smooth.

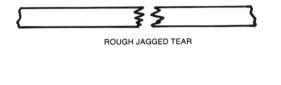

ROUGH JAGGED TEAR

PUNCHED HOLE

GRIND TO A DEEP TAPER

TAPER BACK EDGES

APPLY REINFORCING TAPE AND ADHESIVE

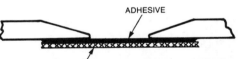

ADHESIVE

BOND A BACKING TO THE UNDERSIDE WITH ADHESIVE

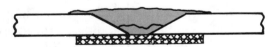

FILL V WITH ADHESIVE

APPLY FIRST COAT OF ADHESIVE

SAND ADHESIVE SMOOTH

Figure 6-1   Repairing a rough jagged tear

ADD SUFFICIENT ADHESIVE TO FILL LOW AREA

Figure 6-2   Repairing a hole in soft plastic

Punched Holes in Soft Plastic (Figure 6-2). Use the following steps to repair punched holes in soft plastic.

1. Clean both sides, back sand the paint, and taper the material back from the edges of the hole.
2. Use a foil back-up tape, a single layer of fibreglass cloth, or a piece of the same material from a discarded panel. The foil is self-sticking; the other materials must be bonded to the underside of the panel.
3. Apply a thin coat of structural adhesive to the hole, packing it into the edges and against the backing. When this has cured, fill the remaining low area. Bring the adhesive out past the tape and pile it up past the surrounding surface.
4. Sand the surface smooth when the adhesive has fully cured.

6-4 PLASTIC WELDING

Thermoplastic and some thermoset materials (both hard and soft), can be welded.

Plastic Welders

There are at present two different plastic welders: the **hot air** type and the **airless** type (Figure 6-3A, B). They are similar in design. The airless type melts the plastic with a heated tip. The procedure is similar to soldering with an electric soldering iron. The end of the tip is actually dragged along the surface, melting the rod and base material together. A temperature control dial controls the heat needed for the various types of materials.

The hot air type welder contains an electrical element which heats air or gas passing through the gun. **Compressed air** or **inert gas** is used as the hot air source. Some hot air welders have a small, enclosed, electrically-

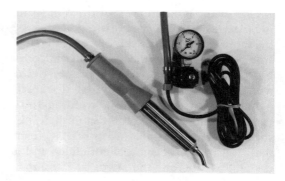

Figure 6-3A   Plastic welding unit

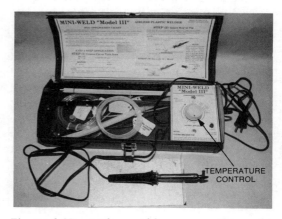

Figure 6-3B   Airless welder

variable speed fan that pulls in air and forces it through the heater element. Others obtain their air from a compressed air line or gas cylinder. A small regulator is used to regulate the pressure, usually from 14–20 kPa (2–3 psi). Lowering the pressure increases the hot air temperature. Compressed air contains oxygen, and also could contain other contaminants such as small amounts of oil and water. With some plastic materials, the oxygen in the compressed air and the other contaminants can affect the quality of the weld. Nitrogen or other inert bottled gases are then used, as they will have no effect on the weld. Polypropylene and polyethylene will usually weld better with nitrogen.

One of the most important rules in welding plastics is that the **welding rod** must be the same material as the piece being welded. If thin strips 3 mm wide can be cut off from a hidden edge of one of the pieces being welded or from another similar discarded panel, they make excellent welding rods. First wash the area and then sand the outer surface before the strips are cut. This cleans the area of any surface contaminants and is easier done before the strips are cut than after.

Commercial welding rods can be purchased to match the weldable plastics. Unfortunately all manufacturers do not use a standard colour code to identify the rods. They are identified only by their packaged labels. The plastic materials to be welded can be identified by the code letters branded into the back side of the panel. If the panel is not branded, various tests can be used to identify the type of plastic. A simple method for identifying weldable materials and what type of rod to use is to clean a small area on the back side of the material and then heat it.

If the material starts to soften and melt, it is weldable. To identify the correct rod, try to melt each type into the base. Only the correct type will melt into and bond to the base material. The Burn Test Chart in Table 6-2 lists the common burn tests that can be used on the materials to be welded (and the rods if their identity is unsure). To conduct the burn test apply a small flame to a hidden area of the material.

Joint Preparation

Most repairs will be either butt or lap joints (for example, when a reinforcement is added to a part).

Butt Joints. These are cleaned back from the crack by either sanding, grinding, or using a small rotary wire brush in an electric drill. The crack itself is tapered to a V-shape with a knife, a small grinder, or grinding burrs in an electric drill.

Lap Joints. The surface of the lower piece and the edges of the upper layer must be thoroughly cleaned by sanding or grinding.

BURN TEST CHART

Type of Plastic	Identifying Features
Polyethylene (PE)	• no smoke • blue flame • candle wax odour
Polypropylene (PP)	• no smoke • orange flame • acid odour
Acrylonitrile Butadiene (ABS)	• black and sooty smoke hangs in the air • sweet odour
Polyvinyl chloride (PVC)	• self-extinguishing • will not flame
Thermoplastic Polyurethane (TPUR)	• black smoke • sputtering effect

Table 6-2   Burn Test Chart

When grinding plastics, it is important **not** to use a machine that turns with a high speed. The heat that is created tends to melt and glaze the surface of the plastic materials, which prevents good weld adhesion.

Welding Tips

Both the hot air and airless welders use a variety of tips. Figure 6-4 shows three common types.

The **flat base tip** is used with airless welders. The tip is skated over the surface of the base material. The rod is fed through a small hole in the front of the tip. The shoe part of the tip melts the rod and base materials together and smooths the surface as the weld is made.

The **tacking tip** can be used with either the airless or the hot air welder. It is used to provide a small tack to the two pieces to hold the edges in alignment. The end piece on the tip is dragged along the bottom of the V-joint. Both sides of the joint are lightly melted and seamed together. As many tacks as necessary to hold the pieces in alignment are applied along the joint (Figure 6-5A). No rod is used to make the tacks because poor adhesion would occur at these areas when

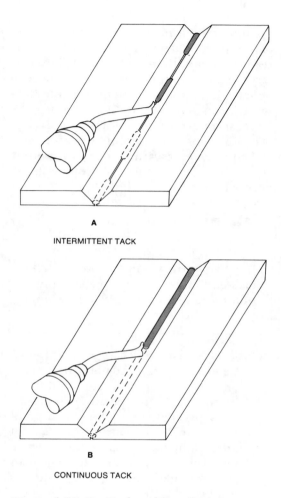

A

INTERMITTENT TACK

B

CONTINUOUS TACK

Figure 6-5A, B   Tack welding the joint

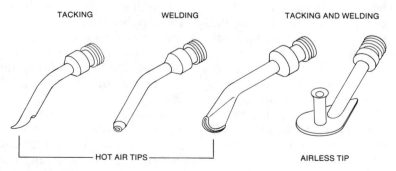

Figure 6-4   Typical plastic welding tips

the final weld is made, as the extra material of the tack would not melt at the same rate as the seam area without tacks. Once the necessary number of tack welds have been made to hold the joint in correct alignment, the tacking tip can actually be dragged along the entire seam to create a continuous seal (Figure 6-5B). After the joint is sufficiently tacked in its correct alignment, the **round tip** is used to make the next weld with the hot air welder.

Welding Procedures

Hot air plastic welding is done "backhanded," that is, in the opposite direction to normal oxy-acetylene welding (covered in Chapter 7).

Procedure to Weld With an Airless Unit.

1. Match the correct rod to the base material.
2. Set the welder temperature control to the suggested setting for that type of rod. Allow sufficient time for the unit to reach operating temperature. Some units have an indicator light that comes on when the operating temperature is reached.
3. Hold the welder with the shoe part of the tip flat on the base material.
4. Feed the rod down through the hole in the front of the tip and slowly skate the tip over the rod and from side-to-side along the V-joint.

When thicker materials are being welded, the back end of the shoe can be used to actually "tamp" the melted welding rod into the bottom of the V groove to insure better melt into the sides of the V. Weld approximately 25–30 mm and then tamp the weld while the material is still soft.

Procedure to Weld With a Hot Air Welder.
The hot air welders can be used with tips, using similar procedures to those for the airless welder, or they can be used without a tip, using procedures similar to oxy-acetylene welding.

Cut the end of the rod at a 60° angle. A tapered end on the rod is more easily heated and melted to start the weld. Hold the torch on a 45–60° angle to the work. Keep the torch tip 6–10 mm from the weld zone. Play the hot air on both sides of the weld area at the start of the weld joint. Hold the rod on a 90° angle to the work, close to and directly over the weld start area. The heat from the torch will start to sweat the sides of the V, and the rising heat will also heat and soften the end of the rod. When the surfaces of the V and the rod appear to sweat, press the end of the rod straight down into the V area.

For plastics to weld, they do not need to melt. Only their outer surfaces need to become tacky for a correct bond.

Move the torch in a slight side-to-side and vertical-weaving motion, directing the heat toward the sides and base of V-shaped area and bottom of the rod. Continue to hold the rod on a 90° angle and push it downward with a firm even pressure.

As the weld is made, the rod softens. The slight downward pressure forces the end of the rod into a continuous loop shape in the V-joint (Figure 6-6).

Continue to weave the torch over the weld area and rod at the bottom of the loop. Play most of the heat on the base material — the rod, being smaller than the base material, needs very little direct heat. Also, as heat naturally rises, it automatically heats the rod. Slowly move the torch backwards as the rod rolls into the sweating V-joint.

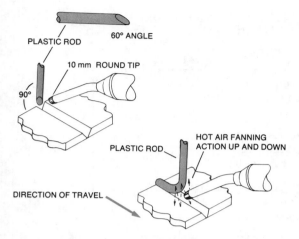

PLASTIC ROD

60° ANGLE

10 mm ROUND TIP

90°

PLASTIC ROD

HOT AIR FANNING
ACTION UP AND DOWN

DIRECTION OF TRAVEL

Figure 6-6   Welding the V joint

> If the rod is overheated it becomes rubbery, making it hard to apply an even downward pressure. When the base material is overheated it will char or melt, possibly causing a poor bond.

At the end of the weld direct a quick application of heat directly on the rod and base material, and then remove the heat. Hold the rod steady, maintaining the same downward pressure on the rod until it has cooled. Either cut or twist the rod off at the end of the weld. If insufficient heat has been used, the rod will be in its original form. It can be pulled away easily from the weld joint. A good weld will have small **flow lines** or **waves** on either side of the bead.

Lap Welding

Basically the same procedures are used for lap weld joints, except that two-thirds of the heat is directed to the base material with the remaining heat directed at the edge of the top layer of material and the rod.

Common Plastic Welding Problems

Table 6-3 indicates some common problems and their causes.

6-5 FIBREGLASS REPAIRS

Glass-reinforced, plastic body parts are commonly referred to as **fibreglass** parts. They are constructed of layers of glass mats which are soaked with a thermosetting polyester resin. This polyester resin is the same resin that is used in plastic fillers. The glass mats are made from fine filaments mechanically drawn from a stream of molten glass. The mats are available in a number of filament sizes, patterns, and weaves. Some of the different forms are continuous-strand mats, fabrics, and chopped-strand mats (Figure 6-7).

A **thermosetting resin** cures through a chemical reaction with the use of outside heat or pressure, although a heat lamp can be used to shorten the curing time. The synthetic resins are mixed with a **catalyst** (hardening agent) and then saturated into the glass matting. The catalyst, when added to the resin, produces a chemical reaction that generates heat to raise the temperature of a resin enough to cure and harden it into a tough, infusible solid. When the liquid resin mix cures, or hardens, it binds together the filaments of the glass to create a strong, shock-resistant panel. The glass fibres provide the strength of the panel, while the resin merely acts as a bond to hold the filaments in place.

Fibreglass-reinforced plastic is both rust- and corrosion-proof. It does not rot or deteriorate in any way. Collision damage to a section or panel is usually confined to the point of impact. Fibreglass-reinforced plastic does not take a permanent bend or buckle after

COMMON PLASTIC WELDING PROBLEMS
AND THEIR CAUSES

Problem	Causes
Poor Penetration	• V too narrow • rod too large • speed too fast
Porous Weld	• porousness in the rod • rod too large • stretching the rod
Scorching	• temperature too high • welding too slow • uneven heat
Stress Cracking	• improper welding temperature • chemical attack • rod and base material are not of the same composition • oxidation of the weld
Poor Fusion	• wrong speed • faulty joint preparation • cold weld • rod too large

Table 6-3   Common plastic welding problems and their causes

impact. It either deflects the impact force and then springs back to its original shape or, on severe impact, breaks at the point of contact and surrounding areas until the damage force has been absorbed.

Repair Methods

Fibreglass repair kits are available which can be used to repair both cracks and holes. Complete panels and sections can be purchased from the original body supplier to facilitate large damage repairs. Smaller repair panels can be hand formed from the materials in the repair kits and then installed and reinforced into the damaged area.

In general, all repairs to fibreglass parts consist of:

1. Removing the damaged material.
2. Filling the damaged areas with resin and glass (both fibrous and milled).
3. Allowing the activated resin to cure (harden), and then finishing and smoothing down the repaired area.

Steel Reinforcement. Fibreglass-reinforced plastic panels will not bend or set permanently from collision damage as will steel parts. Therefore, there is never any straightening work needed on the panels themselves. However, steel struts and braces are often used to reinforce the fibreglass body shell. These steel reinforcements will bend when the body has been subjected to collision damage and will hold the fibreglass panels out of alignment. The braces must be

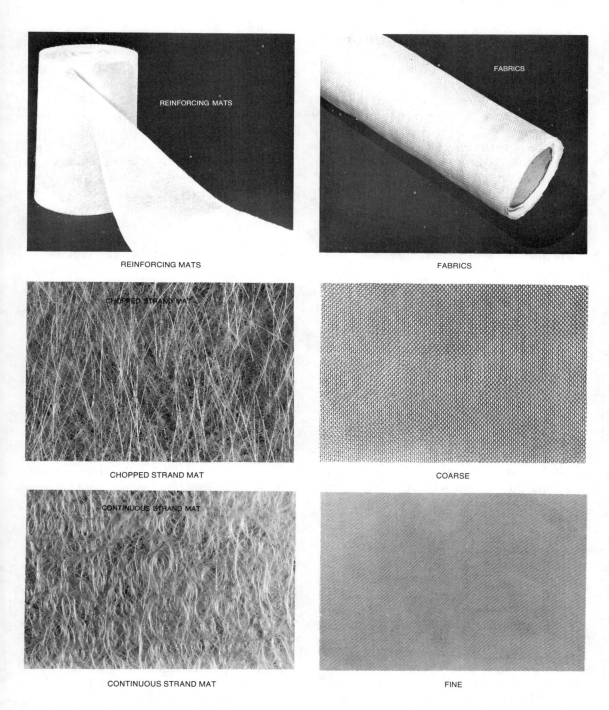

REINFORCING MATS

FABRICS

CHOPPED STRAND MAT

COARSE

CONTINUOUS STRAND MAT

FINE

Figure 6-7   Types of fibreglass material

Courtesy Owens-Corning Fibreglass Corporation

checked and straightened first, to relieve any tension present in the fibreglass panels, before any actual fibreglass repairs can be made.

Straightening the steel parts while they are still in the body must be done with care. When hydraulic jacks (or similar equipment which operates by exerting force) are used, remember that the part used to brace the stationary end of the jack must be able to withstand pressures greater than those needed at the opposite end for straightening the damaged parts. Whenever a jack must be used directly against any fibreglass part, make sure the area is well reinforced with either a wooden block or a steel plate. Otherwise, since the fibreglass will not yield, a crack or break-through could result.

Fibreglass Repair Procedures. Apply the fibreglass mat from the inside if possible. Grind, sandblast, or sand the under surface to remove any dirt or foreign substances. The clean area should be large enough to allow the mat to overlap the crack by 25 mm or 50 mm. Any number of mat layers can be applied both before and after the curing is completed. However, when a hole is repaired it is advisable to allow the first layer to harden, so that it forms a solid base, before building up the area with additional mats.

Welding techniques also apply to fibreglass repairs.

1. Staggering the joints in multiple-layer repairs will increase the durability and strength of the repair.
2. Grinding a bevel or valley and then filling it with repair material will always produce a bond stronger than a butt joint.

Precautions

Making repairs to fibreglass-reinforced plastic bodies is a relatively simple matter providing a few precautions are observed during the repair procedures.

Working with fibreglass must be a clean operation. The repair must be a clean and free from grease, water, and paint, or a satisfactory bond is impossible. Since the repair of fibreglass produces dust (powdered glass and cured resin), it is recommended that efforts also be made to keep the work area clean. Although the dust is not toxic, it can irritate the skin. Those sensitive to the dust should wear protective clothing and a respirator.

Be careful to remove any resin, resin mix, and hardener from skin, clothing, and tools before the curing (hardening) progresses. Wash with lacquer thinner or acetone and then with soap and water. This is important, since failure to remove the wet, resinous compound may cause dermatitis (skin blotches and irritation).

Collect all tools, materials, and replacement parts in advance. When the resin and hardener are mixed and ready to cure, there is no time to hunt for tools. Study the repair and think through the steps. The time spent in planning is important. Any repair work on fibreglass panels will usually fall into one of four categories:

- holes
- gouges, cracks, and fractures
- delaminates and hair-line cracks
- replacement of either regular or hand-formed panels

Preparing the Resin Mix

As the resin suppliers' recommendations will vary somewhat as to the amount of hardener to be added to a given amount of resin, it is always advisable to read the mixing directions on the resin container and to follow them as closely as possible.

Always mix the resin and hardener in a clean, dry, wax-free container. The more hardener that is added to the resin, the shorter its "pot life" will be. (A faster chemical reaction will occur and the set-up time will be reduced accordingly.)

Never return any unused, activated-resin mix to the stock can. Also, do not throw unused material into waste containers especially near oily rags, papers, etc., because the heat generated during the chemical reaction could cause a fire hazard.

Repairing Small Holes (Punctures)

1. Grind away all loose glass fibres and any grazed or fractured material. Bevel the solid edges of the holes to a long, thin taper (about 30°) on the outer surface. Make sure that the paint has been completely removed from the area surrounding the holes and that the surface has been roughened. The resin will not adhere to paint or to smooth surfaces. Sandblasting the areas creates an excellent surface to which the resins may adhere.

2. Use a clean container (i.e., a glass jar, tin can, etc.). Mix a quantity of clear resin and hardener together according to the instructions on the package. Use a paint brush or flat stick to apply a coat of activated resin to both inner and outer surfaces surrounding the hole to a width of 40 mm to 65 mm from the edge of the hole. Saturate two layers of glass cloth with the activated-resin mix. Apply them to the inside, or back, surface of the hole (Figure 6-8).

   The resin-saturated, glass-cloth patches are most easily prepared by first laying them on a sheet of cellophane. Wood or glass can also be used. Pour the activated resin over the cloth and work it in with a paint brush

or stick. Keep the resin-soaked, glass cloth on the cellophane and place the patches over the hole. Keeping the cellophane over the patches, press them tightly against the roughened inner surfaces surrounding the hole to remove any air pockets. The cellophane prevents the resin from sticking to the hands.

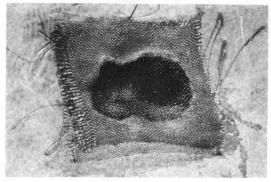

Courtesy White Trucks Division, White Motor Corporation

Figure 6-8 Two layers of fibreglass cloth in place on the inner face of a door panel

3. Similarly, saturate a single layer of glass cloth and apply it to the outside surface, making certain that this layer of glass cloth is in contact with the inner layers across the entire opening. Allow the patches time to cure. Add as many layers of glass as necessary to bring the patch area up close to the level of the surrounding area (Figure 6-9). An infra-red lamp, situated no closer than 300 mm, can be used to decrease the curing time needed.

4. Fill the area with ordinary plastic fillers or specially designed filler for use over fibreglass. The cured resin-soaked patches should be lightly ground to level the area and roughen the surface to provide a better bond for the fillers. Apply the filler with a squeegie or applicator. Build the area up sufficiently

Figure 6-9   Fibreglass cloth and activated resin on the outer face of a door panel

to allow it to be filed and sanded smooth. Don't apply the fillers over the surrounding paint. If the surface has a gel coat finish (resins and coloured pigment mixture) make sure it is lightly ground or roughened.

5.   File and sand the fillers using regular procedures (Figure 6-10).

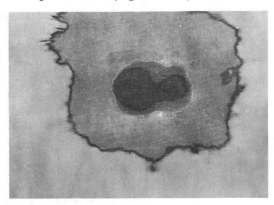

Figure 6-10   Outer face of door panel sanded smooth and ready for priming

When holes occur in panels in areas where the underside is inaccessible, the following

procedure can be used to repair the damage:

1.   Place a sheet of cellophane over the hole, and tape it to the surrounding panel.

2.   Mix a quantity of resin and catalyst. Saturate a layer of fibreglass cloth, cut larger than the hole, with the resin mix.

3.   Lay the saturated fibreglass mat over the cellophane and allow it to cure.

4.   Remove the cured patch, and fix a loop of wire through two holes in the centre of the patch.

5.   Cut the fractured fibreglass out from around the hole in a rectangular shape smaller than the hand-formed, cured patch.

6.   Clean and roughen the inner surfaces surrounding the hole, and clean and taper the outer surfaces of the panel around the hole.

7.   Trim the newly formed patch so that it will pass through the hole in the panel, yet still cover the hole.

8.   Apply resin mix or special bonding filler around the edge of the rough surface of the cured patch, and insert the prepared patch through the hole, keeping hold of the wire loop (Figure 6-11).

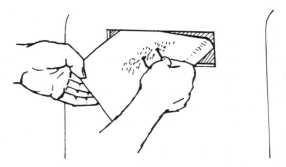

Figure 6-11   Installing a patch onto the back of an area that is inaccessible from the underside

9. Insert a convenient lever through the loop, and apply pressure to pull the patch into contact with the underside of the body panel. Allow the patch to cure (Figure 6-12).

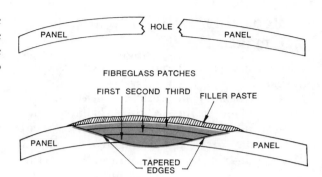

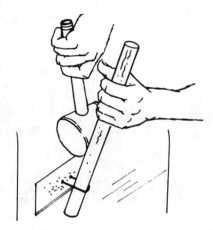

Figure 6-12   Using a lever to pull the patch into contact with the reverse side of the panel

10. Remove the wire loop and add saturated fibreglass patches to the outer surfaces. Make sure the top patches are pressed tightly against the inner patch. When these patches have cured, fill the surface in the usual manner with the filler material.

11. When the filler is cured sufficiently for working, file and sand the area using the regular procedure.

Holes in inaccessible areas on the underside of the panel can be repaired by adding the saturated fibreglass patches to the top surface only. Extend each patch out further than the last one. When the patches have cured, grind the area level and add the filler to smooth and fill any porous area. Allow the filler to cure and file the area smooth. The greater the taper of the material around the hole, the better the repair will be (Figure 6-13).

Figure 6-13   Repairing a hole in a panel that is inaccessible from the underside

Repairing Scratches and Gouges

In many instances, a scratched panel will require only a paint refinishing job. Figure 6-14 shows a panel which has been scratched through into the plastic.

The scratched area should be feather-edged down to the plastic and then cleaned and primed following normal procedures. However, if any part of the scratch is actually gouged into the plastic, a coat of body filler can be applied over the gouge and allowed to cure. When the curing process is complete, the area should be ground and filed smooth. If the filler was not added and the gouge was filed out, that area of the panel would be weakened considerably.

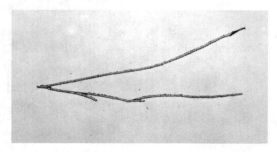

Courtesy Chevrolet Motor Division, General Motors Corporation

Figure 6-14   Typical scratched panel

Repairing Split, Torn, or Cracked Parts

Figure 6-15 illustrates a typical cracked panel.

1. Cut along the break line with a hacksaw blade to remove the broken or fractured portion of the panel. Grind away any loose and damaged material on both the inner and outer surfaces of the break.
2. Bevel the edges of the break at approximately a 30° angle. Use C-clamps to align the panel portions. Leave approximately a 3 mm gap between the panels to allow for panel alignment (Figure 6-16).
3. Cut two or three pieces of glass cloth so that 40 mm to 50 mm extend beyond the break. The extent of the damage area will determine whether two or three layers of glass cloth will be required.

4. Mix a quantity of clean resin and hardener, and saturate both the glass cloth

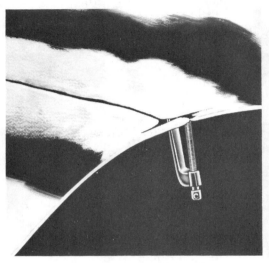

Courtesy Chevrolet Motor Division, General Motors Corporation

Figure 6-16   Cracked panel preparation

Courtesy Chevrolet Motor Division, General Motors Corporation

Figure 6-15   Typical cracked panel

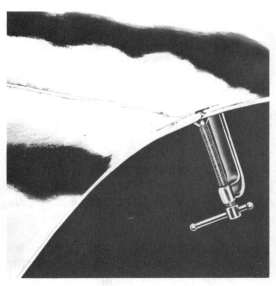

Courtesy Chevrolet Motor Division, General Motors Corporation

Figure 6-17   Use of back-up laminates

and the repair area with this activated resin mix.

5. Apply the saturated glass cloth to the back of the broken area and press it firmly into the bevelled crack and panel surfaces (Figure 6-17). Use a piece of cellophane over the glass for hand protection.

6. Once the glass strips have cured on the underside, add additional strips to the outer surfaces. When adding strips to either surfaces of the panels, pack them tightly into the crack and the panel surfaces. Allow the strips to cure.

7. When the area has cured, rough grind the patch. Fill the areas with filler and level and smooth the area using normal procedures.

When cracks occur along seams or junctions of two panels, they can usually be repaired simply by bevelling the edges along the crack and filling the area with a glass-powdered resin mix or ordinary fillers.

Repairing Delaminates and Hair-Line Cracks

Delaminates and hair-line cracks are often found in both direct and indirect damage area. They can sometimes be found easily by placing a light behind the damaged panels. Small cracks and delaminates often will grow larger if they are left unattended. Any small imperfections should be ground out and filled with a glass-powdered resin mix or plastic fillers. (A delaminate is fibreglass that has been damaged in such a way as to separate the layers.)

Always take time to trace the damage forces. Check the body panels closely for broken bonds and cracks before, during, and after making the repairs. The time spent will pay off.

6-6 PANEL REPLACEMENT PROCEDURES

Either a complete panel can be installed or a section large enough to replace the damaged area may be cut from a replacement panel. In either case, the new panel or section of panel must always be properly fitted, and any adjoining parts must also fit properly. Replacement panels can be either butt or lap joined to the surrounding areas.

Butt Joining a Complete Replacement Panel

1. Cut out the damaged panel with a hacksaw blade. Thoroughly remove all dirt and paint from both sides of the surrounding panel or panels for a distance of 50 mm to 80 mm from the joining line.

2. Bevel all joining edges at approximately a 30° angle across the entire thickness of the plastic, so that a single V butt joint will be formed when the two pieces are joined (Figure 6-18). If the replacement panel does not fit the break closely, reshape it.

3. Cut two back-up pieces of woven fibreglass cloth to run the entire length of the joint. Shorter lengths of cloth may be lapped over the entire length of the joint. Cut the patches wide enough

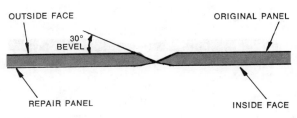

Figure 6-18   Correct bevelling at repair area

for them to lap the junction line on either side by 50 mm or 80 mm.

4. Align the replacement panel and clamp it in place to form a closed, V butt joint at the panel junction. When the panel cannot be clamped, suitable bolts and large, flat washers or straps and sheet metal screws can be used to hold it in place temporarily (Figure 6-19A, B).

5. Saturate the strips of fibreglass mat with the activated resin by dipping or brushing.

6. Place the resin-saturated strips of fibreglass along both sides of the V joint. Press them well into the joints and both panels. If necessary, hold them tightly to the panels with cellophane or paper until the mixture has a putty-like consistency.

A USE OF STRAPS IN PANEL REPLACEMENT

A. Courtesy Chevrolet Motor Division, General Motors Corporation

Figure 6-19A   Use of a strap in panel replacement

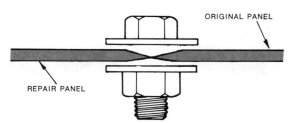

B TEMPORARY BOLT, NUT, AND WASHER INSTALLATION

Figure 6-19B   Temporary bolt, mat, and washer installation

7. Continue to add strips of resin-soaked fibreglass until the V joint is filled. Each strip should be slightly wider than the last.

8. Lightly grind the area to level and roughen it and use the normal procedure to fill the area for normal finishing operations.

Lap Joining a Partial Replacement Panel (Figure 6-20)

1. Cut along a predetermined line with a backsaw blade mounted in a wooden handle or grip or sabre saw. When the line of cut crosses reinforcing members or undamaged panels, take care not to cut into this material (Figure 6-21).

2. Cut or grind away all remnants of broken members.

3. Bevel the solid edge of the panel to be repaired rather flatly (about 30°) on the outer surface. Be certain to remove the paint from the vicinity of the repair area, because the resin mix will not adhere otherwise.

Courtesy White Trucks Division, White Motor Corporation

Figure 6-20   Damaged section

Courtesy White Trucks Division,
White Motor Corporation

Figure 6-21   Damaged portion removed

Courtesy White Trucks Division,
White Motor Corporation

Figure 6-22   Repair panel held temporarily by C-clamp and self-tapping screws

4. Using the broken part which was cut away as a pattern, lay out a replacement panel, making it about 12 mm larger along every edge at which a bevelling lap will occur.

5. Grind a **reverse**, or **mating**, bevel (flat lap) along the inner edges of the repair piece where it overlaps the bevels made in Step 3.

6. Fit the repair panel closely by filing, sanding, or grinding any high spots along the mating bevels.

7. Roughen all the surfaces to be joined, in order to obtain a tight bond with the fresh resin mix. (This includes all underside areas which will be patched with fibreglass cloth.)

8. With the fitted repair piece held temporarily in place with C-clamps, drill a series of small holes along the lap joints for self-tapping screws or rivets. The fasteners should be no further than three inches apart.

9. Remove the fitted repair piece and paint all the bevelled edges and lap surfaces with activated resin. Then quickly add a specially prepared bonding filler or a thick paste of chopped glass and activated resin. Painting the

lap edge with activated resin first helps to increase the bond between the panels and filler.

10. Install the repair section, holding it in place with the C-clamps and screws or rivets, and draw all the joints down evenly (Figure 6-22). As the repair panel is brought down tightly, some of the resinous repair material will

Courtesy White Trucks Division,
White Motor Corporation

Figure 6-23   Repair joints filled and sanded smooth

squeeze out from between the joints. It should be wiped away before it hardens.

11. Saturate pieces of glass cloth with fresh, activated-resin mix and apply them to the reverse side at all accessible points along the joint line.

12. When the resin mix has cured, remove the fasteners. Fill the holes and the seam with the chopped glass powdered resin mix. After allowing sufficient curing time, grind or file the areas smooth and prepare them for painting (Figure 6-23).

REVIEW QUESTIONS

1. How can plastics be made to be as strong as steel or soft and pliable?

2. Explain the difference in the two categories of plastics.

3. Where are soft plastics usually used? Why?

4. Briefly explain the three methods used to make plastics.

5. How are some thermoset plastics reinforced?

6. List two methods of checking for the type of plastic.

7. List one plastic that will burn, yet produce no smoke.

8. What two methods can be used to repair plastics?

9. What are epoxy adhesives?

10. What types of glue can be used to glue some types of plastic?

11. Explain the procedure to use a solvent to melt the edges and make a bond.

12. Explain in point form the procedure to repair with epoxy a tear in a soft plastic part.

13. With a large tear it is sometimes necessary to use some type of backing behind the tear. Explain why.

14. Why is it recommended to preheat the area with a flame before applying the epoxy adhesive?

15. Briefly explain: (i) how a hot air welder operates, (ii) how an airless welder operates.

16. What advantage is there in using a strip cut from a hidden edge of the panel being repaired as the welding rod?

17. Why should a rod not be used to tack weld the joint?

18. Why should the end of the rod be cut on a 60° angle before starting the weld?

19. How should the rod be held in relation to the work?

20. Using point form, list the steps to make a weld with a hot air unit.

21. Why should the plasic not be overheated?

22. When is the speed tip usually used?

23. What is the purpose of: (i) the resin mix; (ii) the glass fibres?

24. Why is fibreglass-body collision damage usually confined to the area immediately surrounding the point of impact?

25. What type of container should be used to mix the resin and hardener? Why?

26. a) How should any unused, activated-resin mix be treated?
    b) Why should it not be returned into the container of the unactivated resin?

27. Why are fibreglass panels often prevented from returning to their original shapes and positions after receiving a collision impact force?

28. What precautions must be taken whenever a hydraulic jack is used to straighten and align fibreglass parts that are reinforced with steel?

29. Why must repairers be concerned with cleanliness, both of themselves and of the work area, while working with fibreglass materials?

30. For repairing a hole, the edges surrounding the hole should be ground to a long, thin taper. Why?

31. Why must all traces of paint be removed from the area to be repaired?

32. Why is it important that no air pockets be left between the fibreglass layers?

33. When filling a hole, each additional layer of fibreglass should be increased in size. Why?

34. A slight gouge in a fibreglass panel should be filled rather than filed out. Why?

35. Explain the procedure for repairing a split, torn, or cracked panel.

36. What method can be used to check a panel for small hair-line cracks or delaminates?

37. How should hair-line cracks be repaired?

38. In replacing a new panel, it is important that the panel first be fitted to the surrounding panels. Explain why this step is so important.

39. What two types of joints can be used to fasten a replacement panel to a vehicle?

40. Explain two methods of holding the replacement panel in position temporarily while it is being bonded to the other panels.

41. In your own words list the steps, in the correct order, for replacing a new panel. Consider either joint design.

7
OXY-ACETYLENE PROCESSES

7-1   Safety
7-2   Oxy-Acetylene Equipment
7-3   The Oxy-Acetylene Flame
7-4   Welding Positions and Joints
7-5   Fusion Welding
7-6   Welding Sheet Metal
7-7   Oxy-Acetylene Cutting
7-8   Braze Welding

The next two chapters of this book deal with different welding processes and techniques. Welding, a very necessary part of auto body repair, is undergoing change like many other areas of the trade. The **oxy-acetylene process,** which has been commonly used for welding and cutting sheet metal panels, is now gradually being replaced with **spot welding, gas metal arc welding** (GMAW), and **plasma arc cutting** (PAC). (Electrical welding and cutting are covered in detail in Chapter 6.)

The new types of high-strength metals being used in many areas of the vehicle cannot be welded with the oxyfuel process. High-strength metals must be welded quickly with a very small heat zone. The oxy-acetylene process is rather slow in bringing this metal up to its melting point. A prolonged temperature rise overheats too large

an area and the "high strength" is lost. The strength of the special steel in the heated area reverts to that of mild steel. However, not all of the body is made of high-strength metal. The ordinary mild steel panels can still be oxy-acetylene welded or braze welded.

7-1 SAFETY

Safe work habits are very important when using welding equipment, since the work involves a very hot, open flame or an electrical current producing damaging arc rays.

Welding is often done on vehicles close to tanks containing gasoline, propane, or natural gas fuel. Each of these fuels is dangerous by itself and is even more dangerous when exposed to open flames, sparks, and hot welding rods. Certain paint products, especially thinners and reducers, are flammable. Empty solvent cans are explosive. Carelessly leaving them in the work area can add to already hazardous conditions. Be very careful when welding in the shop and on the vehicle, and be aware of the locations of fire extinguishers.

Check for leaky gas tanks, a missing filler cap or a broken fuel line before welding or cutting around the vehicle. Always wear goggles when you are oxy-acetylene welding or cutting to protect your eyes from the heat, light, and sparks.

Propane and Natural Gas

Shut off the main tank valves on propane and natural gas powered vehicles while the vehicle is in an enclosed area. Propane is heavier than air. Any gas leaking from a broken line or a damaged tank would settle on the floor in the lowest area, such as around the floor drain. A very small spark could set off a tremendous explosion.

Propane vehicle tanks are equipped with safety release valves that open to relieve excessive pressure build-up in the tanks. If a vehicle is overfilled during cold weather, brought into a warm shop, and subjected to additional heat from welding equipment or paint drying lights the pressure in the tank could increase sufficiently to open the safety release valve and allow some of the propane gas to escape. Natural gas fuel is not quite so dangerous as propane since it is lighter than air; it tends to dissipate into the air.

Welding Galvanized Metals

Many lower body panels that are subject to corrosion are given a thin coating of zinc by the manufacturer to prevent rusting. These panels can be welded in the same manner as uncoated sheet steel (galvanized high-strength steels, like plain high-strength steels, should not be oxy-acetylene welded). The only difference in welding is that the zinc coating will burn off, forming white fumes of zinc oxide. The operator may become ill if these fumes are inhaled. Welding for any length of time on galvanized metals should, therefore, be done in well-ventilated areas whenever possible.

Drinking milk just before or after welding, or even after the operator becomes sick, is beneficial in combatting the sickness.

Using Welding Equipment Around the Automobile

1. Be very careful not to cut into a fuel line or the tank when welding or cutting on the vehicle.
2. Never weld or cut near a gas filler pipe without first removing the filler cap and plugging the filler pipe with a wet rag. Then replace the cap and fold a wet rag over and around the cap and the end of the filler pipe.
3. Do not cut or weld around areas covered with grease or oil. Oil combined with oxygen under pressure could result in an explosion or flash fire.
4. Use a friction lighter to light the torch. Do not use a match or lighter, as the hand may be burned.

5. Do not weld over closed cans. Remove empty cans from the vicinity of the welding operation. Explosions have occurred from fumes which accumulate in any empty cans. Always replace the caps on all containers of flammable material.
6. Never weld or heat on a concrete floor because the concrete may explode.
7. Be very careful when welding around upholstery materials and plastics. Either remove them or make sure they are protected with a wet cloth.
8. Never weld or cut near glass without first covering the glass with a wet rag. The hot sparks will leave pit marks in the glass.

7-2 OXY-ACETYLENE EQUIPMENT

Oxy-acetylene equipment is used to braze, to steel weld, to cut metal, to apply solder, to shrink stretched metal, and to heat metal for bending.

Oxygen Cylinders

The oxygen cylinder is made much stronger than the acetylene cylinder to safely hold the relatively high gas pressure. The cylinder walls are about 8 mm thick and do not have any welded seams, unlike the acetylene cylinder. The **cylinder valve** at the top of the cylinder is designed to operate at high pressure and has a two-way sealing action. It seals the pressurized oxygen in the cylinder when the valve is closed, and it seals around the valve stem to prevent leakage when the valve is opened. To ensure proper sealing, the main valve should be opened fully when the welding unit is being used.

On the back of the oxygen cylinder valve, there is a **safety nut** containing a special metal disc. The disc will burst and release the oxygen if the pressure becomes excessive, for example, if the cylinder were exposed to fire. A **safety cap** that screws onto the neck of the cylinder protects the cylinder valve from damage during shipping and handling. This cap should always be placed on the valve when the cylinder is not in use (Figure 7-1).

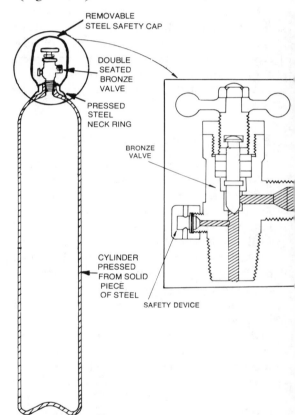

Figure 7-1 Oxygen cylinder construction and cross-section of a double-seated oxygen valve

Acetylene Cylinders

Acetylene cylinders have much thinner walls. They are also shorter and wider than oxygen cylinders. Their seams are welded.

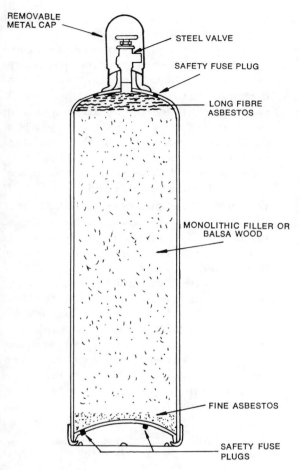

Figure 7-2 Acetylene cylinder construction

When acetylene is compressed to a pressure exceeding 100 kPa it becomes very unstable and explosive. To obtain a pressure in excess of 100 kPa (15 psi) the cylinder is filled with a porous material having absorbing properties, such as asbestos or charcoal. This sponge-like material is saturated with **acetone,** a liquid chemical capable of dissolving and absorbing many times its own volume of acetylene. Acetylene stored in this manner is perfectly safe (Figure 7-2). The **acetylene cylinder valve** should only be opened 1.5 turns so that, if any trouble oc-

curs, the acetylene can be shut off quickly. For shipping and handling, the valve is protected by a safety cap. Safety fuse plugs are provided in the top and bottom of each cylinder. They melt out and release the acetylene pressure in the cylinder whenever the temperature reaches 105°C (220°F). Therefore, there is no danger of the acetylene pressure becoming so great that the cylinder may explode.

Precautions for the Proper Use and Care of Acetylene and Oxygen Cylinders

1. Store and use cylinders in vertical position only. If the acetylene cylinder is used while on its side the acetone will transfer into the regulator, plugging it.
2. Never use a cylinder that is leaking acetylene. If acetylene leaks around the valve spindle when the valve is open, close the valve and tighten the packing nut. If this does not stop the leak, move the tank to the open air, away from fire hazards. Tag it, and notify the supplier.
3. Always secure the tanks to the wall or cart with a strong fastener which allows quick detachment of the cylinders.

Regulators

Regulators are used to control the rate of gas flow. In the auto repair trade they are used to regulate the compressed air flow, as well as the flow of the gases used in welding and cutting.

Regulators are attached to the main valve outlets of oxy-acetylene tanks by threaded fittings. Acetylene connections always have left-hand threads, while oxygen cylinders al-

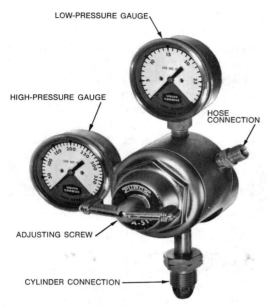

LOW-PRESSURE GAUGE

HIGH-PRESSURE GAUGE

HOSE CONNECTION

ADJUSTING SCREW

CYLINDER CONNECTION

Courtesy Union Carbide Canada Limited

Figure 7-3 Acetylene regulator

ways have right-hand threads. This prevents them from being interchanged.

The regulator reduces the high cylinder pressure to a lower working pressure at the torch or blowpipe. Regulators also keep the working pressures of the gases at the blowpipe from fluctuating so that the flame will be steady and uniform.

Each regulator is equipped with an adjusting screw for setting the pressure to the required amount (Figure 7-3). Two basic types of regulators are used: a **single-stage regulator** and a **two-stage regulator.** Regulators may vary in design but the basic operating principles are the same.

A single-stage regulator reduces the pressure from the cylinder directly to the working pressure at the blowpipe in one step. The two-stage regulator reduces the pressure from the cylinder to the blowpipe in two steps. The first stage reduces the pressure from the cylinder to the intermediate pressure. The second stage reduces the pressure

from the intermediate pressure to the working pressure at the blowpipe.

Both types of regulators operate by means of **rubber diaphragms** and **pressure chambers.** A single-stage regulator has one diaphragm and one pressure chamber. A two-stage regulator has two diaphragms and two pressure chambers. A diaphragm is a flexible rubber disc which is held around its circumference between two metal housings, creating a sealed chamber on one side of the disc which can be pressurized.

Operating Principles of Single-Stage Regulators. When the adjusting screw is turned inward (clockwise), it compresses a spring against the rubber diaphragm, forcing it to flex or bow in the centre. The diaphragm in turn forces the valve seat away from the high-pressure nozzle, allowing gas from the cylinder to fill the chamber. When enough gas enters the chamber it forces the diaphragm back and compresses the spring, and the valve closes so that no more gas can enter from the cylinder. As the gas is used, the pressure in the chamber drops and the process is repeated (Figure 7-4).

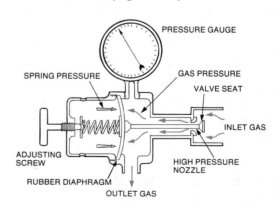

PRESSURE GAUGE

SPRING PRESSURE

GAS PRESSURE

VALVE SEAT

INLET GAS

ADJUSTING SCREW

HIGH PRESSURE NOZZLE

RUBBER DIAPHRAGM

OUTLET GAS

Figure 7-4 Cross-section of single-stage regulator

Operating Principles of Two-Stage Regulators. In this system, the tension spring against the high-pressure diaphragm is set to

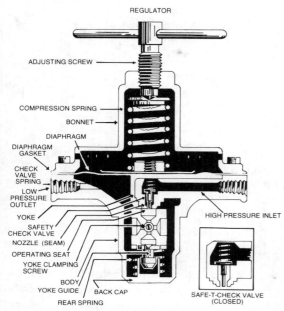

ADJUSTING SCREW

COMPRESSION SPRING

BONNET

DIAPHRAGM

DIAPHRAGM GASKET

CHECK VALVE SPRING

LOW PRESSURE OUTLET

YOKE

SAFETY CHECK VALVE

NOZZLE (SEAM)

OPERATING SEAT

YOKE CLAMPING SCREW

BODY

YOKE GUIDE

BACK CAP

REAR SPRING

REGULATOR

HIGH PRESSURE INLET

SAFE-T-CHECK VALVE (CLOSED)

Courtesy of Modern Engineering Co., Inc., St. Louis, MO

Figure 7-5   Cross-section of two-stage regulator

operate at a certain pressure. The gas from the cylinder will enter the high-pressure chamber until the pressure becomes greater than the spring pressure. The high-pressure valve then closes so that no more gas can enter from the cylinder. When the adjusting screw is turned in, another valve is opened, and the gas from the high-pressure chamber enters the low-pressure chamber. When the pressure in the second chamber is sufficient to compress the adjusting spring, the low-pressure valve closes. As the gas is used, the procedure is repeated (Figure 7-5).

Regulator Valve Gauges

Regulators usually come with two gauges. One shows the gas pressure at the blowpipe while the other shows the pressure and volume of gas left in the cylinder.

The **pressure gauge** consists of a semi-flattened bent tube (a Bourdon tube) as shown in Figure 7-6. The tube tends to straighten out as pressurized gas is forced

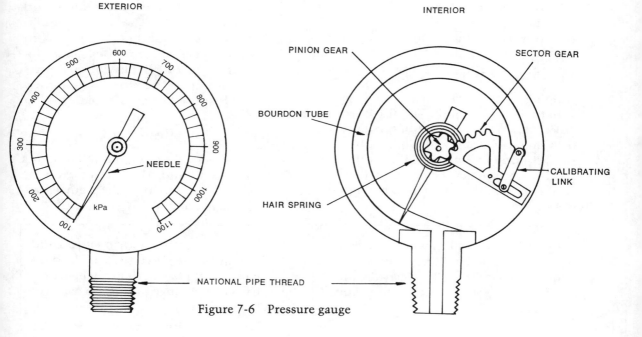

EXTERIOR

INTERIOR

NEEDLE

kPa

PINION GEAR

SECTOR GEAR

BOURDON TUBE

HAIR SPRING

CALIBRATING LINK

NATIONAL PIPE THREAD

Figure 7-6   Pressure gauge

into it. A pointer, which is connected to the closed end of the tube by the gauge mechanism, moves around the face of a calibrated dial as the tube is straightened.

Hoses

The purpose of the hose is to carry gas from the regulator to the blowpipe. The acetylene hose is always red, and the oxygen hose is either green or black. The acetylene hose connections have left-hand threads and the oxygen hose connections have right-hand threads.

Blowpipe or Torch

The purpose of the blowpipe, or torch, is to direct the flame. Each blowpipe has two valves: one for the acetylene and one for the oxygen. A **mixer,** connected to the end of the blowpipe handle, combines the acetylene and oxygen gases (Figure 7-7). The amount of gas allowed into the mixer depends on:
(a) How much pressure is flowing from the regulator;
(b) How far the torch valves are opened.

Welding Tips

Welding tips of various sizes are supplied with each welding unit. The size of the tip orifice determines the size of the flame and the amount of heat it will produce. Welding tips are sized by numbers: the smaller the number, the smaller the tip. A number 1, 2, or 3 tip is generally used for welding sheet metal.

Care should be taken when cleaning a tip orifice. It should never be reamed or filed, but should be cleaned with a tip cleaner specially designed for that purpose.

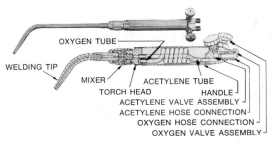

Courtesy Union Carbide Canada Limited

Figure 7-7   Blowpipe or torch

Precautions to take when Assembling Welding Equipment

1. The cylinder valves should be "cracked open" and then quickly closed before the regulators are connected to the valves. This cleans any foreign material out of the main valve openings.
2. When connections are tested for leaks, soapy water should be used.
3. Under no circumstances should oil ever be used on the oxygen equipment. Oil combined with oxygen under pressure could cause a violent explosion. Greasy or oily mitts should never be worn when units are installed or connected.

Turning on Welding Units

1. Make sure the regulator adjusting screws are turned out completely, so that no pressure is on the regulator adjusting springs.

If the cylinder valves are opened with the adjusting screws turned in, the sudden surge of gas entering the regulator chamber and gauge tube could damage the units.

2. Slowly open the cylinder valves: oxygen all the way, acetylene from one to one-and-a-half turns.

3. With the oxygen torch valve open one-quarter turn, adjust the oxygen pressure to the required amount by turning the oxygen-regulator adjusting screw clockwise. Then close the torch valve.

> Be careful not to allow excess gas to escape into the room.

4. Repeat the same procedure for the acetylene.

The regulator pressure should be at least 7 kPa (1 psi) higher than that of the welding tip. The torch valves should be open while the pressures are being adjusted, to compensate for possible faulty gauge readings.

7-3 THE OXY-ACETYLENE FLAME

Any oxy-acetylene welding torch can produce three basic types of flame. The kind produced depends on the ratio of oxygen to acetylene burning at the blowpipe tip. The mixture is controlled by the valves on the blowpipe handle.

Lighting the Welding Torch: The Three Flames

1. Open the acetylene torch valve approximately one-quarter turn. The acetylene torch valve is on the left-hand side of the handle.

2. Using a specially designed flint lighter, ignite the acetylene gas. If the acetylene torch valve has not been opened sufficiently, a black, carbon soot will be produced by the burning acetylene. If it has been opened too far, there will be a gap between the end of the tip and the start of the flame. This gap is called **blowoff.** The torch valve should be adjusted to keep the burning acetylene between **smoke** and **blowoff.**

3. The type of flame produced depends on the amount of oxygen added to the burning acetylene gas. Slowly open the oxygen torch valve. As the oxygen is added to the burning acetylene, a noticeable change in the shape and colour of the flame is seen.

Carburizing Flame. When there is more acetylene gas than oxygen in the mixture, the flame is known as a **carburizing flame.** A carburizing flame consists of three parts: inner cone, feather, and envelope (Figure 7-8A).

The acetylene feather is expressed as being so many times the length of the inner cone, both being measured from the end of the tip. If the excess acetylene feather is twice as long as the cone, it is called a 2X carburizing flame. If the feather is three times as long as the cone it is called a 3X carburizing flame.

Because the carburizing flame has an excess of acetylene, it deposits carbon in the weld. A weak, brittle weld results. The weld puddle has a thick scale over it and tends to boil.

A slight carburizing flame is used to weld certain non-ferrous metals, such as white metal. It is also used in body soldering.

Neutral Flame. As more oxygen is added to the mixture, the feather gradually disappears into the cone. When the feather has just completely disappeared into the cone, a **neutral flame** is produced. This is known as a **balanced flame** because it contains equal parts of acetylene and oxygen (Figure 7-8B).

The neutral flame is used to weld steel. It produces a clean, molten puddle with no sparking.

Oxidizing Flame. This type of flame is produced when additional oxygen is added to

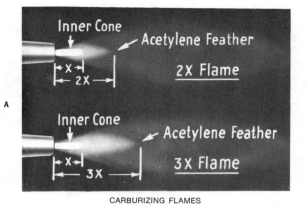

CARBURIZING FLAMES

Courtesy Union Carbide Canada Limited

Figure 7-8   The three flames

the neutral flame mixture, so that more oxygen is being consumed than acetylene. An **oxidizing flame** has two parts, as has the neutral flame, but the cone is pointed and the envelope is short and bushy (Figure 7-8C). The flame makes a hissing noise.

The oxidizing flame adds excess oxygen to the weld joint. The metal is oxidized, weakening the weld. The weld puddle has a tendency to foam and spark during welding.

Backfire and Flashback

A **backfire** is caused when the flame momentarily pops back into the torch tip. The flame may either reappear or be blown out. The molten metal is usually blown out of the puddle in a spray.

A **flashback** occurs when the flame pops back into the tip and continues burning in the blowpipe. A shrill, hissing sound is produced and black soot, or smoke, is emitted from the end of the tip. A flashback may cause serious damage to the torch and regulators. When a flashback occurs, close the oxygen torch valve first to put out the fire, and then close the acetylene torch valve to clear out any soot that may have accumulated in the passages. Check the equipment before relighting the torch.

Causes of Backfire and Flashback

- A dirty or partially clogged tip orifice
- An overheated torch or tip
- A torch tip touching the metal
- A kinked or pinched hose
- An oversized or distorted tip orifice or a loose tip
- Worn mixer seats
- Insufficient regulator pressure for the size of the tip being used
- Insufficient torch-tip pressure for the size of the tip orifice

Although the regulator pressure may be correct, there may not be sufficient pressure or flow of gas through the tip orifice to prevent the flame from popping back into the tip. This is why it is important to adjust the acetylene torch valve so that an acetylene flame between smoke and blowoff is produced, before adjusting the oxygen torch valve. This assures the operator that a sufficient flow of gas will be emitted through the tip orifice.

The regulator pressures are adjusted with the torch valves open to allow for any fluctuation that might occur in the gauge readings.

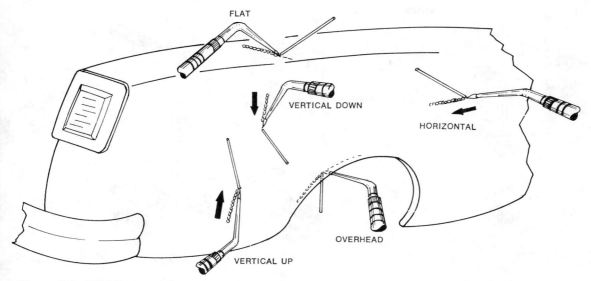

Figure 7-9   Welding positions

7-4 WELDING POSITIONS AND JOINTS

Positions

There are four main welding positions: **flat, vertical, overhead,** and **horizontal.** The flat and horizontal positions are considered the easiest positions in which to weld, while the overhead and vertical positions are considered the hardest. Most automotive welding is done in the vertical and horizontal positions (Figure 7-9).

The vertical weld can be made by welding from the bottom up or from the top down. These methods are called **vertical up** and **vertical down.** The vertical down method is usually used in the auto repair trade, because it involves less heat build-up and therefore less metal warpage. It also provides a flatter, smoother weld.

Welding Joints

The most common weld joints used are as follows (Figure 7-10):

Corner Joint. When two pieces of metal are joined at right angles, and when the two edges of metal being melted together appear on the outside of the joint, a corner joint is formed. Often, a welding rod is not needed to weld a corner joint.

Edge Joint. The edges of the two pieces of metal are even. The weld is run along them, which melts the two edges together. Usually filler rod is not needed for this joint.

Butt Joint. In this type of joint the plate edges are butted together, leaving a gap between the two edges at least as wide as the thickness of the welding rod. If the weld is made correctly, the two plate surfaces will be level with each other.

Lap Joint. In this joint, one piece of metal is lapped over the other. The edge of one piece of metal is welded to the top face of the other piece.

Tee Joint. A tee joint is formed when one piece of metal is placed perpendicular, or at right angles, to the other.

The weld used with the tee and lap joints is called the **fillet weld.** It actually fills in the

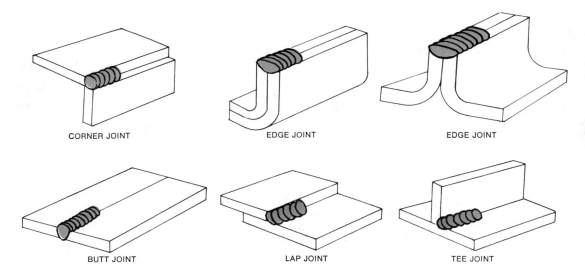

CORNER JOINT   EDGE JOINT   EDGE JOINT

BUTT JOINT   LAP JOINT   TEE JOINT

Figure 7-10   Weld joint designs

right-angle corner, which provides a very strong weld.

A lap joint is commonly used when repairing rusted areas. The vehicle's manufacturer would have used the lap joint and spot welds to join the two or more layers of metal together. The repairer would use the lap joint and plug weld procedure as a substitute for the original factory spot welds when replacing the panel.

Plug Weld. These are made by drilling holes through one of the layers of metal and then plugging the holes with weld filler metal. The excess weld is then ground smooth. This type of joint and weld prevents warpage, eliminates the need to fill the area, and duplicates the original factory joint and weld. Braze welding has been used in the past to make plug welds. However, GMAW (MIG) is now used almost exclusively.

Tack Welds. These are short, small welds placed at intervals along the joining areas of the metals. Since they are small, they can be made quickly, which in turn means that little heat actually goes into the panel. They are used to hold two pieces of metal tightly together in correct alignment. Once they have been made, the joint can be either welded completely or welded at "weld and miss" intervals.

7-5 FUSION WELDING

In **fusion welding,** two or more pieces of metal are melted together to form one solid mass. A welding rod may be used as an added filler. In some cases a welding rod is not necessary, but for most welding operations it is required to fill the crack or gap as well as to strengthen the weld.

Running Beads Without a Welding Rod

This procedure is easy to master because only one hand has to be moved at a time. By practising running beads without a welding rod, a beginner can learn to judge the speed

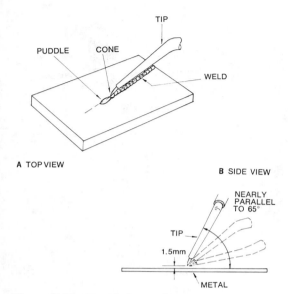

A TOP VIEW

B SIDE VIEW

Figure 7-11   Torch tip angles

at which the torch should be moved, and to observe the characteristics of the puddle as it moves along the joint. The **puddle** is the area of metal which has been melted by the welding torch.

The point of the cone has to be held very close to the metal (approximately 1 to 2 mm). The end of the torch tip is held in line with the seam to be welded. The tip can be held at an angle anywhere from almost flat with the metal to 65° above it. The angle

chosen depends on the thickness of the metal being welded and the amount of heat needed (Figure 7-11).

Torch Movement. The torch tip must be moved ahead in the direction in which the cone is pointing. The torch tip is moved in one of the following ways (Figure 7-12):

• In a small, circular motion advancing 1 to 2 mm with each new circle.
• In a back-and-forth, half-circle motion, advancing 1 to 2 mm each time.
• Steadily along the seam, as fast as the puddle forms and complete fusion takes place.

Procedure

1. Obtain a neutral flame.
2. Hold the cone of the flame 1 to 2 mm from the metal.
3. The end of the tip should be directly in line with the direction of travel and tipped back at a 45° to 65° angle to the metal.
4. Hold the torch steady and watch the metal directly under the point of the cone. That area will become a dull red colour, then light red, and, finally, white. At this point the metal will begin to melt and a puddle will be formed.

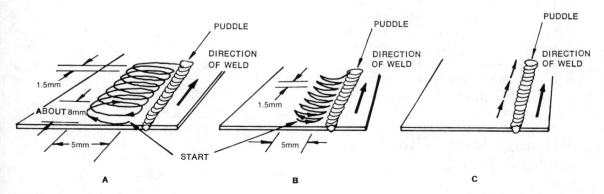

Figure 7-12   Torch movement

5. When the puddle is about 5 mm to 6 mm wide, slowly move the torch ahead in a circular motion. Each circle should advance approximately 2 mm.

> Watch the puddle, not the torch.

If the puddle is carried across the metal plate at the proper speed, it will leave a slight trough, with smooth, even ripples along the surface of the bead. The ripples are caused by the movement of the torch. The **penetration**, the distance the puddle has melted through the metal, should be completely through to the underside of the metal (Figure 7-13).

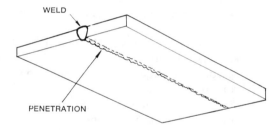

Figure 7-13   Penetration to underside of metal

> If the torch movement is too slow, the puddle will become too large and will be molten through to the bottom of the metal. The puddle will then drop away, leaving a hole in the metal. If the torch movement is too fast, the puddle will be very small, may even dry up and will not leave a ripple in the metal.

Running Beads With a Welding Rod

The welding rod is held at a 45° angle to the metal, in line with the weld seam. It can be

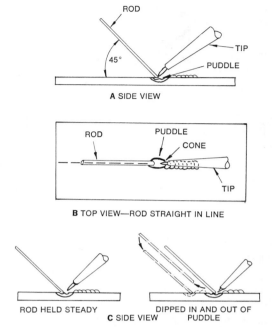

Figure 7-14   Welding rod control

held in the puddle, or it can be dipped in and out of the puddle. The method used depends on the type of joint being welded and the amount of filler rod to be added (Figure 7-14).

In plate welding the weld should normally be built up higher than the face of the metal being joined. This extra reinforcement is

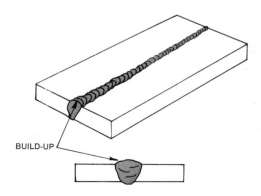

Figure 7-15   Build-up

known as **build-up** (Figure 7-15). However, for welding sheet metal, a smooth, flat weld with no build-up is preferred. This makes the weld area easier to file smooth or fill over.

Procedure

The same torch procedure is used as with welding without a rod, but the rod, which is held in the free hand, is added to the puddle.

1. Using a neutral flame, hold the cone 1–2 mm from the metal. Keep the end of the torch tip in line with the direction of travel and at a 45° to 65° angle to the metal. Obtain a puddle and then add the welding rod to it.

2. The welding rod should be held at a 45° angle to the metal, ahead of the torch, and in line with the bead to be made. The torch is moved in small circles and advanced 1–2 mm with each circle. The height of the bead will depend on the amount of rod added to the puddle. The rod can be either dipped in and out of the puddle or held in it at all times.

It is important to remember that the torch melts the puddle, and the puddle in turn melts the welding rod. If the torch move-ment is too slow, the weld will be wide and hollow. If the torch movement is too fast, the weld will be stringy and not melted into the plate (Figure 7-16).

Fusion Welding Two Pieces

The procedure is the same as for running beads. The cone is held 1–2 mm from the edges until they start to melt. Provided the edges are close together, they will melt at the same time, forming a puddle. The puddle is then moved along the seam by the torch flame. A welding rod is usually not needed unless the metal separates.

Welding a Butt Joint in Flat Position.

1. Light and adjust the torch to a neutral flame.

2. Line up the edges of the two plates leaving a gap between them at least the thickness of the welding rod. This gap allows the metal to expand.

3. Tack the plates at each end, or at regular intervals, to keep them in position.

4. Hold the tip at a 45° angle, in line with the seam, and with the cone 1–2 mm from the metal. The point of the cone should be played on the edges of both plates until they begin to melt.

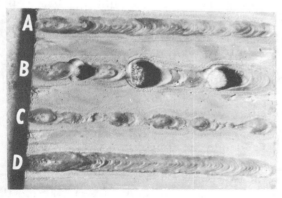

Courtesy Union Carbide

Figure 7-16   Torch speed control

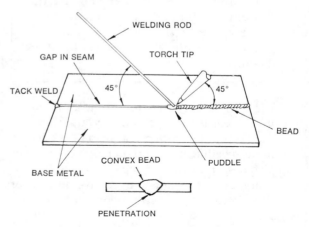

Figure 7-17   Welding a butt joint in flat position

5. Add the welding rod to the seam to form a puddle across the gap and into the edges of the plates. The welding rod is held straight with the line of travel and pointed into the weld at a 45° angle to the metal. The pressure from the flame will push the puddle along the seam. Continue adding the welding rod as necessary (Figure 7-17).

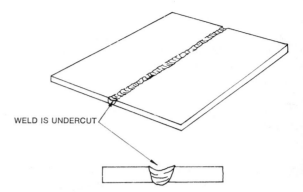

WELD IS UNDERCUT

Figure 7-18   Undercut weld

The speed at which the torch is moved depends on the characteristics of the puddle. Always watch the puddle as the welding process is performed. If the torch is moved ahead too quickly, the puddle will dry up and the welding rod will not be fused into the edges of the plate. If the torch is moved too slowly, the puddle will become excessively large and sink through the metal, leaving a trough, or undercut, effect. When the top of the weld is lower than the surface of the metal, the weld is said to be **undercut** (Figure 7-18).

If too much welding rod is added, the weld will build up too high and there will be little penetration. If not enough welding rod is added to the puddle, the weld will be noticeably undercut and the edges of the plate will not melt together. Holes along the weld will result.

Welding a Flat Lap Joint. In a lap joint, more heat is required on the larger area of the bottom piece of metal than is needed to melt the edge of the top piece. The top sheet also has a tendency to separate from the bottom metal, resulting in excessive melting of the top edge. It is therefore necessary to tack weld the two plates together at intervals. This ensures that the two metals will be held tightly together.

Use a neutral flame and apply the same torch rules as for the other operations. Heat the lower plate, holding the point of the cone from 3 to 5 mm away from the edge of the top plate. This directs most of the heat to the bottom plate. When the bottom plate begins to melt, or sweat, on the surface, move the point of the cone in closer to the top plate. Proceed to melt a puddle along the edge of the top plate, and into the bottom sheet. Add the welding rod when necessary.

The welding rod should be kept in the puddle and against the edge of the top plate. The point of the cone should be directed at the bottom plate and kept approximately the thickness of the welding rod from the edge of the top plate. The tip should be held at a 60° angle to the bottom plate, as shown in Figure 7-19.

More welding rod is needed to complete this type of weld because the corner area has to be filled with welding rod to obtain maximum strength. This type of weld is called a **fillet weld.**

Welding a Tee Joint. The tee joint is welded in the same manner as the lap joint, but the heat is distributed evenly between the two plates (Figure 7-20).

Always keep the cone close to the metal (1.5 mm to 3 mm). If a hole burns through the metal, do not move the cone away from

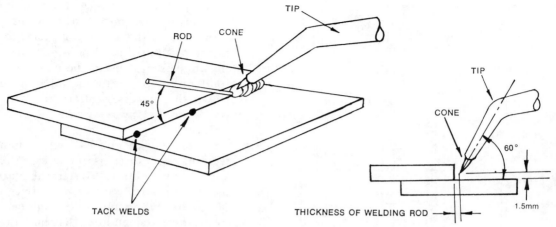

Figure 7-19   Flat lap joint — fillet weld

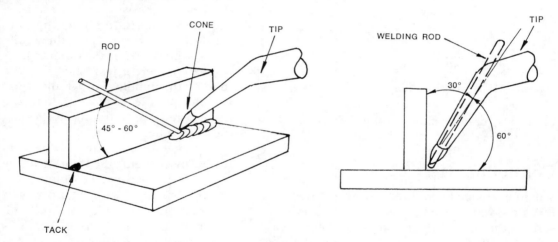

Figure 7-20   Tee joint — fillet weld

the metal. Instead, advance the puddle faster.

7-6 WELDING SHEET METAL

Vertical Position. Sheet metal is always welded "vertical down," to obtain a flatter, smoother weld with good penetration. The torch and welding-rod techniques are the same as for flat position welding (Figure 7-21).

Horizontal Position. The torch and welding-rod angles are the same as those used for welding in the flat position. The only difference is that the torch tip should be held at a slight downward angle to the weld joint instead of directly in line with the weld. This directs the flame more against the lower

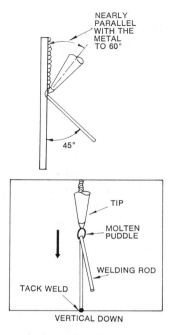

Figure 7-21   Vertical welding

plate. The upper plate will melt faster because of the rising heat.

Controlling Heat

When sheet metal is welded, the heat builds up in the weld zone very quickly and then spreads throughout the metal. If this heat is not controlled, it will warp or buckle the panel. A heavier metal is capable of absorbing more heat without distorting. It is necessary to vary the torch techniques slightly according to the type of metal being worked on. When welding metals which are more than 5 mm thick, it is often necessary to preheat the area to be welded before actually running the weld. Preheating is accomplished by playing the flame over the area to be welded to raise the temperature of the metal.

1. Sheet metal is never preheated. The point of the cone should be brought down quickly to within 1–2 mm of the surface of the metal, the puddle formed, and the weld completed as quickly as possible. When more heat than necessary is used, the panel will tend to warp. Welding done more slowly than necessary often causes the puddle to melt away, producing blow holes.

2. Another way to control heat when welding sheet metal is to decrease the angle of the torch tip. To start the puddle, hold the tip at an angle between 60° to 80°. When there is enough heat to produce the puddle, decrease the angle of the torch tip to 45° or 50°. As the heat in the weld zone increases, keep decreasing the torch-tip angle until, if necessary, the tip is almost flat with the metal. When the torch angle is decreased, there is less flame pressure to force the puddle through the metal and the puddle is moved along the metal faster, concentrating less heat on the weld zone.

3. Excess puddle heat can also be controlled by changing the location of the end of the flame cone, the welding rod, or both. In normal welding procedure, the cone melts the puddle and the puddle melts the filler rod. The cone is kept at the back and the rod added at the front of the puddle. Should the puddle become too hot and start to sink away, the cone can be momentarily moved to the front of the puddle so the flame is directed toward the end of the welding rod. The heat is absorbed into the welding rod, the extra filler rod melts into the undercut puddle, and less heat is absorbed into the metal.

4. Usually, for welding sheet metal, the welding rod is dipped in and out of the puddle. However, should the puddle become too hot, the rod should be held

in the puddle for a moment to transfer the heat from the puddle into the rod. In doing this the undercut area is filled and the correct puddle temperature is maintained. To transfer more heat from the puddle to the rod, move the rod into the middle of the puddle or directly under the cone.

Always keep 1–2 mm between the point of the cone and the metal. Do not move the flame away from the metal as a means of controlling the heat over an even larger area of metal.

When it is necessary to weld two pieces of metal of different thicknesses, direct the point of the cone toward the heavier metal.

7-7 OXY-ACETYLENE CUTTING

An oxy-acetylene cutting attachment is a necessity around the auto body shop. It is used to cut apart mangled sheet-metal assemblies; to cut off rusty bolts, welds, and rivets in the frame; and to remove panel sections that are to be replaced.

High-strength steels can be cut with the oxy-acetylene equipment as long as the cut is made 75 to 100 mm away from the final join location. The final cut at the joint must be made with a saw or cut-off disc equip-

Courtesy Union Carbide Canada Limited

Figure 7-22   Oxy-acetylene cutting attachment

PURE OXYGEN ORIFICE
PREHEAT ORIFICES

Courtesy Union Carbide Canada Limited

Figure 7-23   Cutting attachment tip

ment so the high strength of the steel is not lost. The cutting attachment is designed to connect to the end of the torch handle (Figure 7-22).

Each tip has four preheat orifices that heat the metal to the required temperature. They surround a centre orifice which supplies the cutting oxygen stream. When the lever is pressed, a stream of pure oxygen is emitted from the central orifice on the cutting attachment (Figure 7-23). The oxygen torch valve should be completely opened to allow the full flow of oxygen from the regulator into the cutting attachment.

The four preheat flames are controlled and adjusted by the acetylene torch valve and the oxygen control valve on the cutting attachment. The preheat flames should be adjusted to neutral with the oxygen lever pressed down.

The acetylene regulator pressure is usually adjusted to between 20 and 40 kPa (3 to 6 psi). The oxygen pressure will vary, depending on the thickness of the metal to be cut. For cutting sheet metal, 140 kPa (20 psi) is usually sufficient.

Cutting Plate

1. Set the regulator adjusting screws to the desired pressures.
2. Fully turn open the oxygen torch valve.
3. Light the acetylene, and adjust the acetylene valve so the flame is between smoke and blowoff.
4. Slowly open the cutting attachment oxygen valve, and adjust the preheat

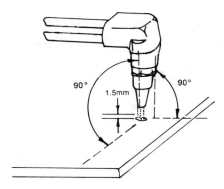

Figure 7-24 Starting the cut

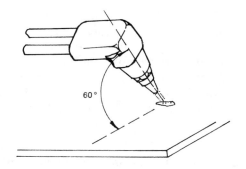

Figure 7-25 Making the cut

cones to a neutral flame, pressing the oxygen lever.

5. Hold the cutting attachment tip at a 90° angle to the metal, with the end of the preheat cone 1–2 mm away from the metal (Figure 7-24).

6. Start at the edge to heat the metal.

7. When the metal turns red, press the oxygen lever and lower the head of the attachment to a 60° angle. The tip should be held straight with the line of travel (Figure 7-25).

8. Move the attachment as fast as the torch cuts completely through the metal.

If the cutting action stops, the oxygen lever should be released and the metal at the end of the cut should be re-heated.

Cutting Sheet Metal

Because of the thinness of sheet metal, lower pressure and different torch angles are used.

1. Adjust the preheat flames to neutral.

2. Hold the attachment at a 90° angle to the metal to start the cut.

3. When the cut is started, lower the attachment to 10° or 20°, and point the

tip slightly toward the section of metal to be discarded (Figure 7-26).

The pressure from the oxygen orifice blows all the slag toward the metal to be discarded, leaving a clean cut along the other piece of metal. Because the oxygen is directed along the cutting line instead of through it, the cut is made much faster than it would be in heavier metal.

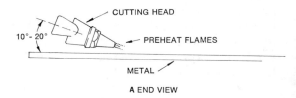

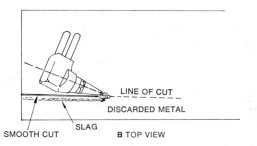

Figure 7-26 Cutting sheet metal

Cutting the Heads Off Bolts or Rivets

1. Adjust the torch to a neutral flame.
2. Hold the torch almost flat on the metal, with the preheat cones 3 mm from the head.
3. When the head becomes hot, press the oxygen lever and move the attachment as fast as cutting takes place.

If the attachment is not held almost flat on the metal, the heat from the preheat flames will be absorbed by the metal around the bolt or rivet. When the oxygen lever is pressed, this metal will be oxidized and blown away.

7-8 BRAZE WELDING

Braze welding is the process used to join two or more metal pieces together by flowing a low-melting, non-ferrous filler material over the surfaces to be welded. This creates a solid alloy between the two metals.

The advantage of braze welding is that dissimilar metals can be joined. Also, the metals to be welded need not be heated to the molten state. The surfaces are simply heated to a cherry red and a brass filler rod (approximately 40% zinc and 60% copper) is melted onto the metal. Because less heat is needed to complete the weld, there will be less distortion of the sheet metal panels than there would be if the oxy-acetylene fusion welding process were used.

Braze welding is **not** the same thing as brazing or bronze welding. In **brazing**, a flux is applied between two pieces of metal and a thin film of metal filler is run into the joint. (Silver soldering is an example of a brazing process.) **Bronze welding** is used for fusion welding bronze castings with non-ferrous bronze rod.

Braze welding, including braze welded plug welds, must not be used on high-strength steels. The length of time needed to make the weld and the high temperatures required, will remove the high strength of the metal throughout the welded area. These heated areas will return to mild steel strength.

Braze welding is often used by the manufacturer on mild steel outer panels to seal small spot-welded lap joints or seams that may leak, or those that are hard to grind smooth after MIG welding. The brazing rod flows easily enabling a smooth thin coat to be deposited to seal the seam. Original factory seams in the rear quarter trunk opening gutter or the seams in the windshield opening fence have been braze welded by the manufacturer if the metal used is not high-strength steel.

The Braze Welding Process

Fluxes. In order to provide a strong bond between the melted rod and the metal, the surfaces to be welded must be cleaned of all oxides and impurities with flux. A **flux** is a chemical compound used to prevent oxidation and other unwanted chemical reactions between the molten welding rod and the metals being joined.

The flux dissolves, coats and/or floats off any oxides or dirt present on the metal. It also helps protect the molten puddle from oxygen in the air during the welding process. There is a thin coating of flux on the welding rod. It melts off the rod readily since it melts at a lower temperature than the metal. Flux also helps the melted rod flow freely.

The Alloying Process. When heat from a torch is applied to a flux-coated rod, some of the flux melts off. The flux chemically cleans the metal. By then the torch has melted the end of the rod itself. The rod flows over the area cleaned by the flux. The flux and heat help to set up a chemical reaction between the metal surface and the zinc/copper mixture in the rod. An alloying process takes place when the fluxed surface of the metal melts or sweats to fuse with the zinc/copper alloy. The surface of the metal actually melts to form a new metal/zinc/copper alloy at a temperature far below the normal melting point of steel.

Heating the Metal. A slight oxidizing flame is used to braze weld. The excess oxygen creates a thin, oxide film over the melted rod, preventing the zinc in the rod from fuming or burning out. This oxide film also helps to protect the cooling weld from the oxygen in the air. The tip size, torch movement, and rod procedures for braze welding are much the same as those used for fusion welding.

The temperature of the metal is controlled by lowering the torch-tip angle. The cone is held 1–3 mm from the metal. If the cone is not held close to the metal, too large an area of metal will be heated and the flux and the rod will spread over this area, creating a poor weld. The panel will also be subjected to extra heat which could warp the metal.

Fusing the Metal. When a small spot in the metal has been heated to a dull, cherry red, the rod is touched to the metal at the point of the cone. The flux melts off the rod and cleans the metal. Then the end of the rod melts and flows onto the metal. As the torch is moved ahead, more flux and rod are melted onto the metal, providing a solid alloyed fusion between the two metals.

The rod may be dipped or scratched along the joint, or held on the seam and moved just

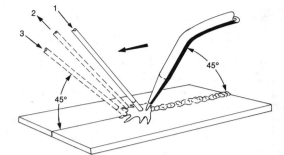

A   DIPPING THE ROD (UP AND DOWN)

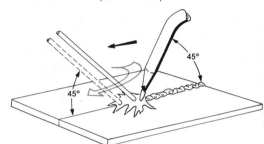

B   SCRATCHING THE ROD

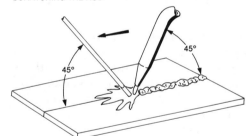

C   HOLDING THE ROD JUST AHEAD OF THE CONE

Figure 7-27   Three methods of adding the rod

ahead of the cone point (Figure 7-27). The method used depends on the amount of rod to be deposited on the joint. The scraping method is often used in sheet metal welding, especially if the metal is slightly rusty. As the rod is scraped ahead of the cone, some of the flux is melted onto the metal. It tends to clean and prepare the metal for welding, slightly ahead of the flame. The rod flows more easily, the welding speed is increased, and a smoother, neater weld is produced. There is less build-up and rod waste with this method of welding, and the increased speed results in less panel warpage.

If the torch is moved too slowly along the joint, the metal will overheat and fume the zinc out of the rod. When the zinc fumes or burns, it makes a cracking noise and produces a thick, white smoke. If the torch is moved too quickly along the joint, the metal will not reach its proper temperature and poor flow will occur.

> For braze welding heavier castings and metals, preheating is recommended. However, when working with sheet metal, the cone should be brought close to the work quickly. As soon as the metal is red, the filler rod should be added and the weld completed as quickly as possible. This prevents more heat than is absolutely necessary from entering the metal.

Limitations to Braze Welding

Because there is no penetration in a joint that has been braze welded, the braze welding process is limited somewhat in automotive sheet-metal welding. There are certain types of joint designs and areas where this type of weld will have very little strength. Braze welding should never be used on butt joints or around fender edges. Braze welds have very little strength in butt-joined areas that are subject to stress, strain, and vibration. All butt joints and any edges should always be fusion welded to ensure complete penetration of the weld through the metal.

No strength is lost in a fusion weld when it is ground or filed flush. Most of the strength of a braze-welded joint is lost if it has to be ground or filed, because the rod filler has only penetrated the metal surface a slight amount. Also, any area that must be hammered to shape or shrunk after welding should be fusion welded.

> Once an area has been braze welded, it is impossible to fusion weld over it unless the weld plus the alloyed metal has been completely ground off. Even then a poor weld will result.

Braze Welding Positions

Vertical Position. The same vertical down method used for fusion welding should be practised when braze welding sheet metal. The cone is kept very close to the metal, and the torch tip is held almost parallel to the metal. The rod is touched to the metal at the point of the cone. It then may be either scraped along the joint or lifted back from the flame. When the melted filler rod has been smoothed along the seam, the rod is again touched to the metal at the point of the cone.

The melted rod sometimes has a tendency to ball up and run along the joint ahead of the flame. If this happens, the torch is moving too slowly and the metal is overheating. Keeping the torch tip parallel and the cone close to the metal helps to control the heat. Moving the flame completely away from the metal for a second will allow the melted rod to solidify and the metal to cool off. The ball of rod is then remelted and moved down the joint.

If the vertical up method is used, it is very hard to make a smooth, even weld that has no build-up.

Horizontal Position. Braze welding in the horizontal position is done in the same manner as in the flat position. It is sometimes advisable to hold the torch tip at a slight upward angle to the weld joint instead of directly in line with it. The force of the flame tends to prevent the puddle from sagging.

Braze Welded Plug Welds

The GMAW welding process has replaced braze welding operations. However, should brazed plug welds be used, the holes should be at least 6 mm in diameter. The two layers of metal must be clamped tightly together. The bottom layer of metal is heated, through the hole, to a cherry red. The hole is then filled with filler rod, bonding the bottom layer of metal to the edge of the hole in the top layer of metal. The holes are filled flush with weld and ground smooth.

It is necessary to bring the cone very close to the bottom layer of metal to ensure that the metal will be heated sufficiently to obtain a proper bond between the two pieces of metal.

REVIEW QUESTIONS

1. Why must the operator wear goggles when using the oxy-acetylene equipment?
2. Explain why the oxy-acetylene process is not suitable for welding high-strength metals.
3. Why is the wall of the oxygen cylinder thicker than that of the acetylene cylinder?
4. The oxygen cylinder valve has a two-way sealing action. Why?
5. Why should acetylene, in its free state, never be compressed or used at pressures above 100 kPa (15 psi)?
6. What is the purpose of the acetone in the acetylene cylinder?
7. How far should the acetylene cylinder main valve be opened? Why?
8. What safety methods are used with both the oxygen and acetylene cylinders to release the gas should the pressure become excessive?
9. a) What is the purpose of the regulators?
   b) How is the regulator adjusted to regulate the pressure from the tank to the tip?
10. a) What two types of welding regulators are there?
    b) Explain how they differ.
11. a) What is the purpose of the two gauges used with each regulator?
    b) Explain the operating principle of the regulator pressure gauge.
12. a) Why are the two hoses used to carry the gases of different colours?
    b) Which colour of hose is used to convey each gas?
13. What two types of threads are used to connect the oxygen and acetylene equipment? Why?
14. What precautions should be exercised when cleaning the welding tips?
15. List the steps for turning on welding equipment, in the correct sequence.
16. Why should the torch valves be opened slightly while adjusting the regulator pressure?
17. Draw diagrams of the three welding flames and label the parts.
18. Explain what is meant by the terms "smoke" and "blowoff," when referring to the amount of acetylene gas being burned.
19. List two different adjustments that can be made to change a neutral flame to a carburizing flame.
20. What effects will a carburizing flame have on the weld? Why?
21. What effects does the oxidizing flame have on a molten puddle?
22. Why should the acetylene torch valve be shut off first when the welding flame is shut off?

23. Explain the difference between backfire and flashback.

24. List the causes of backfire and flashback.

25. Vertical welding of sheet metal is always done "vertical down." Why?

26. a) List the four different welding positions.
    b) Which two are the hardest positions in which to weld?

27. Draw diagrams of the five standard welding joints.

28. Explain the difference between tack welding and plug welding.

29. How far should the point of the cone be from the metal?

30. Why is the torch tip not held at a constant angle in relation to the metal?

31. In what direction should the torch be moved?

32. a) List the different methods that can be used to add the welding rod to the puddle.
    b) What two conditions govern the method that should be used?

33. Define the terms "penetration" and "build-up."

34. How much penetration should a sheet metal weld have?

35. Describe the procedure for running beads using a welding rod.

36. Why is it important to watch the puddle when welding rather than the torch flame itself?

37. What type of weld would be produced if: (i) the torch speed were too slow, (ii) the torch speed were too fast, (iii) too much welding rod were added?

38. Define "undercut."

39. Why is more heat required to form the puddle on the bottom plate of a lap joint?

40. How is it possible to prevent the edge of the top plate in a lap joint from burning away before the lower plate is heated?

41. Where should the point of the cone and the end of the welding rod be directed when welding a lap joint?

42. Why should sheet metal never be preheated before it is welded?

43. List the techniques of controlling heat when welding sheet metal.

44. Where should the point of the cone be directed when welding two pieces of metal of different thicknesses?

45. Explain the principles of oxy-acetylene cutting.

46. At what angle should the head of the cutting attachment be held to cut sheet metal: (i) when starting the cut, (ii) while making the cut?

47. When cutting sheet metal, why is the cutting attachment pointed slightly toward the section of metal to be discarded?

48. While cutting rivets or bolt heads, the cutting attachment head is held almost flat on the surrounding metal. Why?

49. List the one main advantage of braze welding sheet metal.

50. What is the composition of a braze welding rod?

51. What is flux, and why is it used with braze welding rods?

52. What type of welding flame should be used to braze weld sheet metal? Why?

53. Why is it important that the cone be held close to the metal when braze welding?

54. a) In what three ways can the braze welding rod be added to the weld?
    b) Which method is often used with rusty metal? Why?

55. List the areas where the braze welding process should not be used, and explain why.

8

ELECTRIC WELDING

8-1   Types of Electric Welding
8-2   Safety
8-3   Electric Welding Principles
8-4   Shielded Metal Arc Welding (SMAW)
8-5   Gas Metal Arc Welding (GMAW)
8-6   GMAW Techniques
8-7   Spot Welding
8-8   Plasma Arc Cutting (PAC)

8-1 TYPES OF ELECTRIC WELDING

Electric or arc welding and cutting processes are those in which an electrical current is used to produce a small, intense heat between the end of the welding rod and the face of the metals to be welded. The welding rod (filler rod) metal is deposited into the molten puddle. There are several different arc welding processes. Two common processes are **shielded metal arc welding (SMAW)** and **gas metal arc welding (GMAW).** Plasma arc cutting (PAC) is a related electrical cutting process.

SMAW makes use of a flux-coated rod which is changed frequently as it is used up. As the flux coating on the rod burns it produces an inert gas which **shields** the molten pool from the oxygen in the air. The weld is covered with a flux coating which must be

chipped off. This welding process has been commonly referred to as arc welding. SMAW is seldom used to weld sheet metal panels. The intense heat from the arc tends to burn through the thin metal faster than the filler metal from the rod can be transferred across the arc and deposited on the metal. Its use is limited to trucks, conventional vehicle frames, trailer hitch attachments, and other heavy brackets.

GMAW refers to wire feed welders. It is also called MIG welding and has a continuous wire for the rod. The molten pool is protected by a gaseous shield, as in SMAW. In GMAW the shield is produced from various types of gas supplied in welding tanks or cylinders. The weld produced has no coating. GMAW is capable of handling very thin metals, as well as any heavy metals.

There are many similarities between SMAW and GMAW. Both produce a very small, intense heat zone as the weld is being made. Both arcs are protected by a gas shield while the weld is being made. The weld is made quickly. Very little heat is transferred into the surrounding weld zone. This results in little warpage and distortion.

8-2 SAFETY

Make sure that all flammable materials have been removed from the work area when electric welding or plasma cutting. This includes paint solvents, as well as empty solvent cans. Be aware of the location of the shop's fire extinguisher. Check for leaky gas tanks, a missing filler cap or a broken fuel line before beginning work. Precautions for welding on propane or natural gas powered vehicles are discussed in Chapter 7.

Check the electrical plugs and receptacles. Do not use plugs if they or their connections are damaged, i.e., broken, loose, or with frayed wires. Remember that the equipment is electrically "hot." Make sure the machine and work area are insulated from dampness to prevent electric shock.

Always wear an approved welding helmet (Figure 8-1) and protective clothing when electric welding or plasma cutting. The arc is intense and bright, and contains ultra-violet and infra-red rays which are very damaging to the eyes and skin. Never attempt to strike the arc or to look directly at the arc flash unless your face and eyes are protected by an arc welding helmet. Direct exposure to flash will result in a very painful, but not permanent, burning of the eyes.

The helmet shield lens should be at least a Shade 10. The higher the glass shade number, the darker the glass. Oxy-acetylene goggles are only Shade 5. They should not be used for anything but oxy-acetylene welding. The shade of lens being used can also depend on the amperage and welding process. A lighter shade could be used for a brief low amperage tacking operation. At least a Shade 10 or darker must be used for high amperage continuous welding operations.

If the eyes are exposed to the rays of the arc, application of a few drops of 5% argyrol every four or five hours is helpful. A soaked tea bag held on the eyes will also bring relief. Aspirin will relieve pain and headache and permit rest, which is very helpful in promoting recovery.

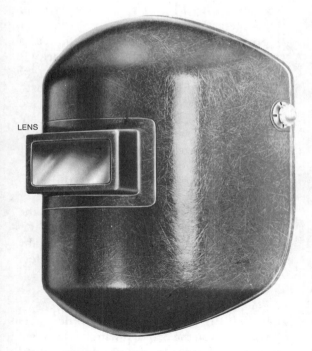

LENS

Courtesy The Fibre-Metal Products Company

Figure 8-1 Electric welding helmet

Using Electric Welding and Cutting Equipment Around the Automobile

1. When welding around a gas filler pipe, first remove the filler cap, plug the pipe with a wet rag, replace the cap, and fold a wet rag over and around the cap and the end of the pipe.

2. Place a wood scrap between the tank and body section when welding with the wire-feed (GMAW) welder. Should a burn-through on the panel occur, the machine will continue to push the wire through the burn hole. The wire could touch the tank, causing a further arc or burn-through and possible explosion.

3. Before attempting to electric weld on any vehicle equipped with an alternator, disconnect the battery ground cable. An electrical current will follow the path of least resistance. It can cause damage to the battery or alternator.

4. When welding around upholstery materials, plastics, or glass, make sure they are protected with a wet cloth.

8-3 ELECTRIC WELDING PRINCIPLES

An electric welding machine produces a strong electric current that jumps the gap between the end of the welding rod and the metal being welded. This electric current produces an arc of such intense **heat** that the end of the rod and the surface of the metal are melted. The **force** of the arc directs the molten metal from the end of the rod across

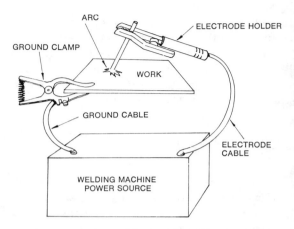

Figure 8-2 The welding circuit (SMAW)

the gap into the puddle where the metals are fused together. Moving the electrode along the small gap between the metals at a correct speed, keeping it at a certain distance from the surface will result in an even layer of weld metal called a **bead**.

For an electric current to flow, direction or **polarity** must be established. Polarity is expressed as positive (+) and negative (−). The electrical current must also have a path to follow or flow along. Conductors are used to provide this path for current flow. A conductor is a material that offers very little resistance to current flow. Metals, especially copper, are good conductors.

The cables (conductors) carry the electrical current from one terminal (positive or negative) of the welding machine to the work (the metal) and back to the other terminal of the machine. This path travelled by the electrical current is known as the electrical **circuit**.

Attached to the end of one cable is a special insulated **electrode holder**, for SMAW, or a **welding gun** in GMAW. The other cable has a clamp on the end of it which is fastened to the metal. It is usually called the **ground cable** (Figure 8-2). The cables and other parts of the conductors must be insulated to prevent the electrical current from changing path or short circuiting. Rubber, an excellent insulator, is used as a covering on the cable.

Electrical Terms

Amperage. Amperage is the unit measuring the amount of electricity flowing. It measures the amount of current moving past a given point in the circuit each second. Amperage represents the power, or heat, of an electric welding machine.

Volt (V). This is the electrical pressure or force that causes the current to flow. Voltage itself does not flow; only the current flows.

Alternating Current (ac). Alternating current is the type of current that is supplied by commercial power lines. The current changes direction or alternates back and forth as it flows through a circuit. Most commercial power supplies use a 60 cycle (Hertz) power supply, which means the current flows in 60 ahead-reversing cycles per second (120 direction reversals per second).

Direct Current (dc). This type of current is supplied by a battery or a motor-driven generator. The current flow does not alternate as it moves through the circuit as ac current does. It moves from the negative terminal through the circuit to the positive terminal; it is a "direct current."

Power Sources

Body repair shops use an ac supply from commercial power lines. The current is split and fused at the distribution panel in the shop into 110 V and 220 V circuits.

The 110 V circuits are fused at 15 A. These circuits are fused to operate the lights and plugs throughout the shop. The 220 V circuits are fused up to 40 A; they have a special "heavy duty" receptacle to carry the increased current flow.

Courtesy Canadian Liquid Air Ltd.

Figure 8-3   AC electric welder

Most SMAW and GMAW machines operate on 208/240 V, with 20, 30, or 40 A circuits. Some of the GMAW machines are designed to operate on 110 V – 15 A circuits. They can be plugged directly into the standard wall receptacle. The 208/240 V welders must be connected to the heavy circuit by special heavy duty plugs and their receptacles.

The SMAW machine receives its power supply from commercial power lines. These welders can be purchased to operate on either 208/240 V or heavy industrial 440/550 V current. (Figure 8-3).

The SMAW machine can be a motor-driven generator or an ac machine with an additional rectifier device that changes the current flow from alternating to one direction only (dc).

All GMAW machines also operate from the ac power supply. They have a rectifier to change their polarity from ac to dc.

Polarity

The direction of current flow from the welding machine through the work and back again can be further controlled by changing the polarity (current flow direction) at the terminals, since the electrical current always flows from the negative terminal to the positive terminal.

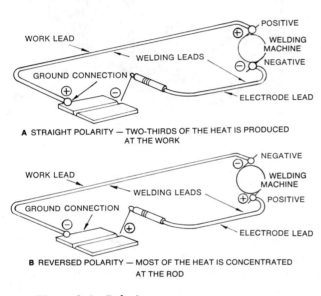

A STRAIGHT POLARITY — TWO-THIRDS OF THE HEAT IS PRODUCED AT THE WORK

B REVERSED POLARITY — MOST OF THE HEAT IS CONCENTRATED AT THE ROD

Figure 8-4   Polarity

When the electrode holder is connected to the negative side of the welding machine it is operating on **straight polarity**. The letters DCEN (direct current electrode negative) are commonly used to indicate straight polarity (Figure 8-4A). When the electrode holder is connected to the positive side of the welding machine it is operating on **reverse polarity**. DCEP (direct current electrode positive) indicates reverse polarity (Figure 8-4B).

When the polarity is DCEN (straight polarity), two-thirds of the heat is produced at the work. Reversing the polarity to DCEP (reverse polarity) most of the heat is then con-

centrated at the rod. With most of the heat concentrated at the rod, a lower amperage is needed. By controlling the polarity, the operator can control the amount of heat produced at either the electrode or the plate. This is a definite advantage for certain types of welding.

Straight polarity welds will be shallower and wider than reverse polarity welds. The heat zone of the weld area will also be wider. Reverse polarity welds will be narrow with deeper penetration. There is less heat in the weld zone. With the ac welding machine, the same amount of heat is produced at each polarity of the arc because it is alternating current.

8-4 SHIELDED METAL ARC WELDING (SMAW)

Electrodes

SMAW electrodes are often called **arc welding rods**. They can be obtained in sizes ranging from 1.6 to 6.0 mm ($^{1}/_{16}$ in. to $^{1}/_{4}$ in.) in diameter.

Steel electrodes are coated with flux. The flux melts more slowly than the steel rod and

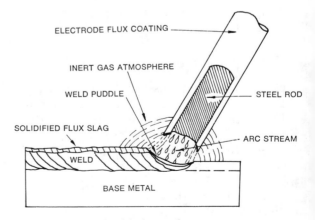

Figure 8-5   Shielded metal arc

shields the end of the rod from the oxygen in the air. As the flux melts, it flows into the puddle and cleanses it of oxides and impurities. A heavy inert gas is formed around the arc and melted puddle. This gas excludes all oxygen and nitrogen from the weld (Figure 8-5). As the weld cools, the flux forms a heavy slag over the weld puddle, protecting it from the oxygen in the air.

Because of the great variety of welding rods manufactured, a numerical classification was designated to identify the different rods. Each rod is classified by the letter E (for "electric welding") followed by several numbers, for example, E41014 or E6014. The first example is an SI classification, the second is an imperial classification. The meaning of the numbers is shown in Figure 8-6.

An E41013 electrode, for example, has the following characteristics:
1. The minimum tensile strength is 410 MPa (60 000 psi).
2. The electrode can be used in all positions.
3. An ac welder or a dc straight polarity welder can be used.
4. A weld of moderate quality is produced, with a soft arc and light penetration.

Two commonly used all-purpose SMAW electrodes are E41013 (E7014) and E48014 (E6013). The E48014 electrode is suitable for welding high-strength steels.

Heat Control

Since the current settings on machines vary, it is difficult to suggest the correct settings to be used with the various rods and different plate thicknesses. A safe rule to follow is: set the welding heat so the parent metal and electrode melt and flow together to form a good, sound weld.

Striking the Arc

There are two methods of striking the arc: the **tapping** method and the **scratching** method.

In tapping to obtain an arc, the electrode is tapped lightly against the metal and then lifted 5 mm to allow the arc to flow.

In scratching to obtain an arc, the end of the rod is scraped on the grounded base metal the same way a match is struck on a rough surface. When it has been drawn 4 or 5 cm the rod is lifted about 5 mm from the surface, and the arc is formed.

In both cases, once the arc has been established the end of the rod is brought down closer to the metal. When the arc is of the correct length, the melting rod will produce a cracking, or "frying," sound. When the rod is too far from the metal, it will produce a blowing sound. When the arc is too short, the electrode will stick, or "freeze," to the metal.

When the electrode freezes or welds to the plate, free it by quickly twisting it back and forth. If this does not release it, shut the machine off and release it from the holder. Trying to remove a frozen rod from the holder with the machine on will damage the holder.

Running a Bead

Once the arc has been established, the rod is held at approximately a 75° angle to the metal, straight in line with the joint. The welding rod is slowly dragged along the joint ahead of the puddle (Figure 8-7).

Since the rod is continually melting, the hand must be lowered to compensate for the shortening of the rod. In some cases, when a gap or V in the metal is being filled, it is not necessary to drag the rod along the seam. As

A

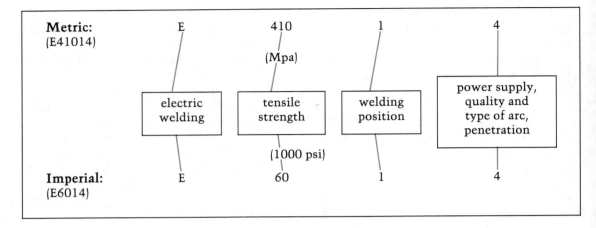

B

Digit	1	2	3
Welding Position	all positions	horizontal fillet and flat only	flat position only

C

Digit Indicating Type of Power Supply/Arc	0	1	2	3	4
Power Supply	reversed polarity	ac or dc reversed polarity	ac or dc straight polarity	ac or dc straight polarity	ac or dc straight polarity, iron powered
Quality of Arc	high	high	moderate	moderate	moderate
Type of Arc	digging	digging	medium	soft	soft
Penetration	deep	deep	moderate	light	light

Figure 8-6 Electrode classification: SI and imperial systems

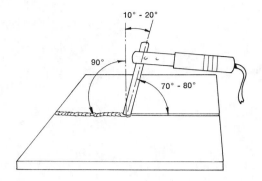

Figure 8-7   Recommended electrode position or angle

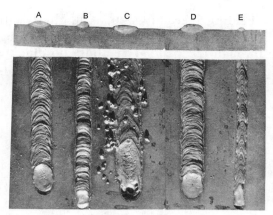

Courtesy The Lincoln Electric Company

Figure 8-9   Plane and elevation views of welds made under various conditions

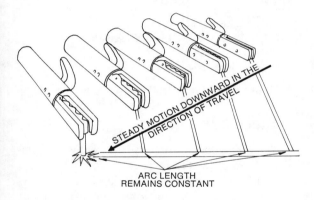

Figure 8-8   Rod is moved down to compensate for melting

the rod melts down, it will automatically move ahead, because of the angle on which it is being held (Figure 8-8). A correct bead will be uniform in height, width, and ripple (Figure 8-9).

Amperage

SMAW welders have one adjusting mechanism, usually either plugs or a dial arrange-ment, to adjust the amperage setting. The amperage can be set — the voltage cannot. The arc welder is designed intentionally to enable the voltage to fluctuate according to demand. The size of the rod being used and the distance of the arc length determine the voltage. A long arc automatically increases the voltage, thus increasing the pressure of the arc to jump the gap. Closing the arc reduces the voltage. The voltage fluctuates, but the amperage remains almost the same. The shielded metal arc welder is known as a **constant current** (CC) machine.

Low Amperage Setting. If the amperage setting is too low, the molten welding rod will not fuse into the base metal and a high, bulky weld will result. There will be little or no penetration; the arc will be hard to main-tain.

High Amperage Setting. If the amperage setting is too high, the bead will be under-cut, and burning through the plate could result. Arc splatters around the weld zone will be prevalent.

Welding Speed. Travelling too slowly will result in high build-up and possible burning through the plate. Travelling too quickly will result in an uneven, stringy weld and poor penetration.

8-5 GAS METAL ARC WELDING (GMAW)

Gas metal arc welders are also known as MIG welders or wire feed welders (Figure 8-10). They can be used to spot weld or seam weld metals, from 0.6 mm up to 8 mm thick.

The arc is shielded by a continuous envelope of gas to protect the weld from the oxygen in the air (Figure 8-11). This gas is supplied from a cylinder and fed through a hose to the end of the gun handle where it is emitted to completely surround the arc and weld area.

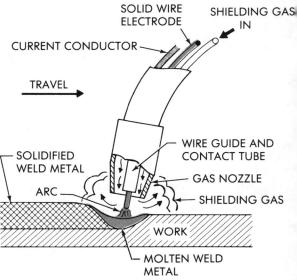

Courtesy of The Lincoln Electric Company

Figure 8-11   Gas metal arc welding

Electrode Wire

The electrode is a small solid steel wire ranging in size (diameter) from 0.6 mm (0.024 in.) to 0.80 mm (0.030 in.).

The wire is wound onto reels of various sizes, depending on the wire manufacturer and the machine size it is made for. One manufacturer's reel will sometimes not fit another manufacturer's machine. The 0.6 and 0.8 mm wires are the most common sizes used for auto body welding. The smaller 0.6 mm wire makes a very small fine weld. The larger 0.8 mm wire is better suited for making spot welds. The size of aluminum wire is larger, usually 1.0 mm (0.040 in.).

The wire is pulled off the spool at the machine by a set of two steel drive rollers which then push the wire through a conduit tube to a contact tip in the end of the gun handle. The contact tip supplies the electric current to the wire as it leaves the end of the gun. Both the wire feed and gas flow are controlled by a trigger on the gun handle.

Blackhawk Automotive Division

Figure 8-10   GMAW welder

The drive rollers, wire, and contact tip must be matched to each other, adjusted correctly, and kept clean for the machine to operate smoothly.

The wire fits into matched grooves in the rollers. These grooves must be the correct size for the wire being used. Some rollers have different size grooves machined in them for the different size wires. With other makes, the rollers have only one groove and must be changed to match the different wire sizes.

The pressure of the drive rollers against the wire must be correctly adjusted to smoothly pull the wire from the reel and push it through the conduit tube without applying too much pressure and flattening the wire. A flattened wire will tend to fishtail or snake through the conduit tube and possibly bind going through the contact tip, causing uneven wire travel. Too little drive roller pressure on the wire will cause slippage and slow or uneven wire feed problems.

The spool must turn freely on its spindle and the wire must unwind smoothly from the reel. If either the wire or reel catches or binds, the wire delivery and therefore the arc will be uneven or jerky.

The conduit tube must be kept free from kinks and pinches, and from build-up of fine metal flakes off the wire. The cable holding the conduit tube should be handled carefully. Do not allow the cable to be run over with vehicles, oxy-acetylene tank carts, or the welder wheels. Winding the cables too tightly around or over the machine can cause the conduit tube to kink where the cables leave the machine.

Wire Coating. The wire has a thin copper coating on it to protect it from oxidizing and to provide a better electrical contact as it moves through the contact tip. On some welders, the wire reel is outside the machine casing; others are mounted inside the casing. If some type of wiper is not used to preclean the wire, the small copper coating particles will, in time, completely plug the wire feed conduit causing a slow, jerky wire feed and uncontrollable weld.

Contact Tips

Contact tips are available with centre hole sizes which match the various wire sizes. The tip used should be the same size as the wire to ensure a full current flow from the tip to the wire. Eventually, through use, the tip orifice will become worn, allowing loose play between it and the wire, resulting in a poor electrical contact and uncontrollable arc.

Gases

Several different types of gases can be used — both "inert" and "active." Some are better than others for different types of metals.

Inert Gases. An inert gas is one that has no effect on the weld itself. It will not combine with or react with the products of the weld zone. Argon (A) and Helium (He) are inert gases.

The gas-shielded wire feed process was originally designed for welding aluminum and magnesium with one of the inert gases (thus, the term MIG — metallic inert gas.) The process was improved and eventually used for steel welding and it was found that an active gas such as CO_2 was better for welding steel.

Argon gas is obtained as a by-product in the manufacture of oxygen. It comprises almost 1% of the earth's atmosphere. It is used as the shielding gas for welding aluminum, magnesium, and any aluminum/magnesium alloys, as well as copper. Being inert, the gas only protects the weld and does not combine with it. Argon tends to clean the work area and aid in providing deeper penetration of the weld.

Helium is derived from natural gas. It is lighter than air and tends to dissipate somewhat from the weld area. When helium is used, the weld tends to be wider with less penetration. Helium can be used as an inert gas for welding non-ferrous metals such as aluminum, magnesium, and copper, but it is more likely to be used with other gases as part of a mixture.

Active Gases. An active gas is one that has an effect on the weld. CO_2 is a compound gas derived from carbon monoxide and oxygen. It combines with the surrounding oxygen in the arc area to super-heat the weld metal transferring from the electrode to the work. This helps to produce a narrow, deep-penetrating weld. CO_2 also has the tendency to cause a somewhat unstable arc unless the arc is kept very close. It also causes splatters — small balls of weld scattered about the weld area. These disadvantages make CO_2 rather undesirable for use with the light metals used in auto body repair. The close arc and the fact that the weld is deep-penetrating causes poor welds and frequent burn-throughs. The splatter is also very annoying because it seriously pits any glass and paint surfaces and must be ground off any bare metal areas.

> If the arc seems somewhat unstable and the weld appears "bubbly" when molten, there is likely a lean gas flow. A lean gas flow can also cause pin holes in the weld. A weld having pin holes or pores is said to have porosity. Check the end of the gun between the nozzle and tip for slag build up. Remove the nozzle and clean if necessary. If poor welds still occur increase the gas flow at the regulator.

Gas Mixtures. Most repair shops have changed to the argon-CO_2 mixture. The mixture is usually 70–80% argon/30–20% CO_2. This mixture is still considered to be some-

what "active" in that the CO_2 combines with the weld to produce a medium-penetrating weld with less burn-through. The argon from the mixture makes the arc much easier to maintain, through a greater contact tip to metal distance. A cleaner, smoother weld is produced, with little annoying arc splatter.

GMAW Machines

GMAW machines are different internally from the shielded metal arc welders. They operate on 110, 220, or 550 V commercial power and have a rectifier to change the incoming ac commercial current to direct current reversed polarity. The electrode wire contact tip is the positive terminal (DCEP) and therefore two-thirds of the heat is produced from the end of the wire. A very small penetrating weld can be quickly made.

GMAW welders have two power adjustment arrangements: one to set the voltage, the other to set the wire speed. The amperage is set automatically according to the wire speed setting. The voltage does not fluctuate. It is set by hand from either a dial or plug arrangement on the front of the machine.

MIG welders are known as **constant voltage** supply. This makes it much easier to start the arc. The wire will not stick or freeze to the work like the shielded arc machines do. The GMAW machines also react more quickly to any change in arc length, which prevents the wire from either burning back into the contact tip or stubbing onto the work.

Advantages to GMAW

The gas metal type welding process is the only method recommended for welding the high-strength low-alloy steels used in many of the vehicle panels. The small wire size provides a greater current density (defined as the amperage per wire cross section). Since the machine operates on reversed polarity, two-thirds of the heat is given off at the wire. The arc energy is concentrated on a very small area on the metal, which provides a quick, high heat at the end of the wire.

A small, fast weld can be made with good penetration. The fast welding speed is excellent for welding thin metals because a very narrow heat zone occurs. The small heat zone allows for less distortion and/or warpage and less molecular displacement along the heat zone, which is especially important with the high-strength steels. Heating high-strength steel to a temperature above 650–750°C (1200–1400°F) over a three minute period will permanently soften the metal in the heat-affected zone. The GMAW weld is so small and completed so quickly that no strength is lost.

8-6 GMAW TECHNIQUES

The wire transfer process in GMAW is different than that of SMAW. The metal from the end of the rod of the shielded arc welder is melted and forced across the arc gap. In the GMAW process, transfer of the molten weld metal takes place after the end of the rod has touched the metal.

When the trigger is pulled, the gas flow starts. The wire feeds out through the end of the gun to contact the metal and create a short circuit. The end of the wire and a very small area of the metal heat and melt together. The end of the wire melts off, breaking the circuit, and fuses into a bead. The wire continues to feed, touches the metal, short circuits, melts, and fuses to the metal in continuing cycles. This process is called the **short circuiting metal transfer process** (Figure 8-12). The short circuiting cycle can vary from a frequency of 20 to 100 Hz

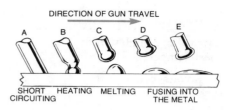

Figure 8-12   GMAW welding

(cycles per second) depending on the heat range and wire speed.

Voltage and Amperage Settings

With the GMAW machines the wire feed control sets the speed of the wire and the amperage. The amperage automatically adjusts according to the wire speed, and will change according to its need to melt the wire and make the weld, providing there is sufficient voltage to establish the arc and melt the rod.

The correct voltage and wire speed (amperage) settings will vary according to the manufacturer, the type of power supply (110 V or 220 V), the material to be welded, its thickness, the type of joint, whether the metal is rusty or painted, etc. The settings and results shown in the chart would occur when welding reasonably clean body metal.

The contact tip and nozzle positions on most welders are non-adjustable. On those that are adjustable, the end of the tip should be positioned 2–3 mm past the end of the contact tip. This produces a brighter arc, enabling the operator to see the weld area more easily.

The beginner may have trouble welding with the contact tip protruding past the end of the nozzle. If the tip is allowed to touch or come close to the metal, the molten end of the wire may freeze to the end of the tip. The drive rolls will continue to feed the wire creating a tangled knot of wire between the drive rollers and the conduit tube. This con-

Setting	Result
Low voltage, high wire speed (amperage)	• wire will stub into the metal
High voltage, low wire speed (amperage)	• wire will hit the metal, burn off, and snap back into the contact tip
Low voltage, low wire speed (amperage)	• striking and maintaining the arc is difficult
High voltage, high wire speed (amperage)	• wire consumption is very fast, weld deposit is large, and there is considerable burn-through
Correct voltage, high wire speed (amperage)	• rapid machine gunning of the wire onto the metal
Correct voltage, low wire speed (amperage)	• intermittent slow jabbing-type wire feed, high build-up weld

dition is commonly referred to as **bird nesting.**

Bird nesting conditions can also be caused by incorrect voltage/wire speed settings, excessive drive roller tension, excessive wire spool tension, or tangled wire on the spool. Should a bird nesting condition occur, all the wire from the rollers to the tip must be cut out and discarded.

> Every so often, it is necessary to remove the gas nozzle and clean the slag deposits that tend to build up between it and the tip. If the slag forms a continuous connection from the tip to the nozzle, the nozzle then becomes "live" and will short the machine out if it touches the metal. There are special pastes or sprays that can be applied to the end of the gun between the nozzle and tip to prevent slag build up.

Drive Roller Tension

The drive roller tension should be set with just enough pressure to pull the wire off the spool and push it through the conduit tube. Should the wire momentarily freeze to the tip, the rollers may slip on the wire rather than create the bird nest condition. If the wire sticks to the contact tip immediately release the trigger, wait a second for the rod to cool, and then quickly trigger the gun. The rod should then break free from the tip.

Joint Preparation

For best results in welding thin metal, the metal at the joint should be fairly clean and well fitted. Because of the small wire size, intense arc heat and thin metal combinations, it is rather difficult to make a quality weld when the joint area is either gapped, rusty, or ground thin. This is especially true for the overhead position. Welding joints are covered in Chapter 7.

Starting the Weld

Using a pair of wire cutters, cut the end of the wire off approximately 6–10 mm from the end of the contact tip. Rest the end of the wire on the weld metal. The wire is "dead"

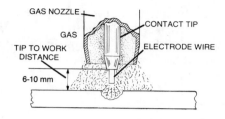

Figure 8-13   Starting the weld

until the trigger is pulled. Pull the trigger, and the gas flow and short circuit process will begin. Maintain the same distance from the work and start to move the gun as the weld is formed (Figure 8-13). Move the gun as quickly as the weld can be made. When the gun distance, voltage, and wire speed/amperage settings are correct a cracking or "frying" sound which is similar to the sound given off by the shielded arc welding process can be heard.

When the gun is too far away from the metal a "stubbing" or "roping" condition occurs. The current is passed from the tip to the wire and from the end of the wire to the metal. The extra length of wire creates an additional resistance to current flow. Instead of the current just melting the end of the wire the complete section of the wire heats up, becomes very soft, and "ropes" onto the metal. This long gun distance can be used to successfully fill a burn-through, a wide gap, or a slight thin or rusty spot along the weld. Pull the gun back, let the wire rope onto the area, then quickly close the gap and melt the rope lengths into the area.

Controlling the Gun

Similar gun control is used with the gas metal welding as with the shielded arc process, except that with SMAW the rod is always dragged away from the completed weld. With the gas metal arc process, the gun can be either dragged or pushed. For thin

metal welding it is recommended that a slightly smaller weld be made by pushing the gun. This also makes it easier to see the weld being made. The gun can be held anywhere between a 45–90° angle, and straight in line with the weld (Figure 8-14).

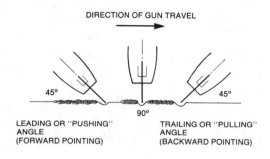

Figure 8-14   Flat position gun angles

Vertical Position Joints. The vertical down method leaves a flatter, smoother weld than the vertical up method. The gun should be held at a 45–90° angle from the metal, straight in line with the weld joint. It can be either dragged or pushed.

Overhead Position Joints. The same gun angles can be used for overhead welding. However, the push method, holding the gun on a 45–60° angle is recommended (Figure 8-15). The overhead position is the hardest to weld in because some of the molten metal from the end of the rod has a tendency to fall. If the gun is being held on a 90° angle, the molten metal will collect on the end of the contact tip and nozzle. The gas supply will

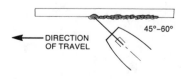

Figure 8-15   Overhead position gun angle

be partially closed off, which reduces the weld quality. If the molten metal bridges from the tip to the nozzle, the nozzle becomes "live". Should the nozzle touch the metal being welded, a "dead short" is created in the machine. Increasing the voltage will help to prevent the molten metal falling. However, if the joint preparation is poor or the metal has rusted thin, burn-throughs can then occur.

WELDING PROBLEMS AND THEIR CAUSES

Problem	Possible Cause
Feed roller rotates, but no wire feed	• not enough roller pressure on the wire • incorrect or worn rollers • dirt in wire conduit and/or contact tip
Uneven wire feed	• contact tip worn — plugged or bent end • dirt or metal particles in the feed roller track • conduit cable plugged or kinked • wire tangled on the spool • spool binding on its spindle
Arc does not strike	• poor ground contact • fuse blown • trigger switch not working
Arc is long and unstable	• voltage too high
Almost no arc	• voltage too low
Lack of fusion, no penetration (high weld bead)	• current too low in proportion to voltage • voltage too low • uneven gun movement • gun too far from metal
Porosity	• gas flow too low • insufficient gas shield due to spatter in gas nozzle • draughty work area • gun too far from metal • moist, oily, or rusty work
Insufficient deposit	• gun moving too fast and current too low
Excessive penetration (undercut weld)	• wire speed/amperage too high
Spatter	• CO_2 gas mixture being used • voltage excessively high • gas nozzle not clean
Uneven weld	• excessive wire stick-out • current too high in proportion to voltage • welding speed low and/or uneven

If the gun is tipped in any direction on too extreme an angle, the gas shield tends to dissipate, exposing the weld to the atmosphere. The arc is then hard to maintain, and the weld will be of poor quality.

Some welders are equipped with a "stitch" weld control. This is a delay control that stops the machine for part of a second on a timed interval while making a continuous weld. This allows the weld and metal to cool somewhat, to help prevent burn-through in the thin metal. Welding operators can do the same manually by quickly releasing the trigger (triggering the gun) when they suspect that the weld is becoming too hot.

8-7 SPOT WELDING

GMAW machines can be equipped with additional controls and gun nozzles which enable the machine to operate as a **consumable spot welder**. Consumable means the wire rod is melted into the two layers of metal to form the weld "spot." Spot welding commonly done by the manufacturer and some repair shops is known as **resistance spot welding**. This is one of the simplest electric welding procedures. Two pieces of sheet metal are overlapped and then two electrodes are brought in contact with the metal, one on each side. An electrical current is passed from the electrode tips through the metal. The resistance of the electrical current trying to pass through the small spot in the metals causes the area to heat and melt together. No rod is added to this type of spot weld (Figure 8-16). One major drawback is that all four surfaces of the two layers of metal must be clean of paints and rust for the electrical current to

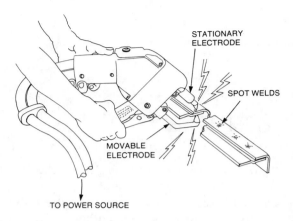

Figure 8-16   Spot welding

pass through the metals. Any dirty surface will cause the metal in that area to disintegrate in a shower of sparks.

Advantages of GMAW Spot Welding. The consumable spot welding method makes a spot weld that looks very similar to the original factory weld. It is made from the outside surface, and is made so quickly that there is very little heat spread into the surrounding metal. This is especially important with the high-strength steels since their strength is weakened in any area where the metal is overheated.

Spot Welding Nozzles

The spot welding nozzle is different from the regular type. It is usually longer and notched or shaped at the end. The extra length is necessary to distance the end of the contact tip from the face of the metal to provide for wire burn-back control.

A notched type of nozzle is used on flat surfaces. The notch cut-outs are necessary to allow the gas to escape. Nozzles with shaped ends are used to fit special areas such as corners and flanges (Figure 8-17). The end of the nozzle is bottomed against the metal and a slight pressure can be applied to the

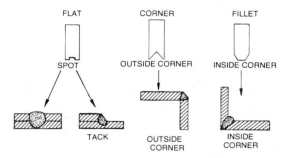

Figure 8-17   Spot welding nozzles and uses

Better spot welds are obtained by increasing the voltage setting two or three steps higher than that normally used to weld the same thickness of metal. The larger diameter wire is also better suited for spot welding since it tends to fill more easily. However, it is not necessary to change the wire to spot weld since all wires sizes will work.

area with the gun to ensure that the two metals are tight against each other.

Spot Weld Controls

There are usually two controls. One is a timer that sets the length of the weld cycle. This determines the penetration and nugget size. A setting of one-half the dial would be about one second, while a full dial setting would be two seconds.

The other spot weld control adjusts the wire burn-back. It regulates the amount of wire left sticking out from the end of the contact tip after the spot weld has been made. Too short a burn-back cycle will leave the wire frozen in the puddle. Too long a cycle will leave the wire frozen to the end of the contact tip. The ideal wire burn-back length is half-way between the contact tip and the end of the weld nozzle (Figure 8-18).

Spot Welding Procedure

1. Set the selector switch to spot weld.
2. Set the voltage two or three steps up from normal.
3. Set the weld timer control. (Try the dial set at half-way.)
4. Install the correct nozzle.
5. Adjust the burn-back control to one-third of the dial. (The higher the setting, the greater the burn-back.)
6. Hold the nozzle, using some pressure against the metal if necessary to keep the two layers tight.
7. Pull the trigger; release it when the timer has shut off.
8. Check the spot weld. It should be of a flat, uniform size, with penetration into the lower layer of metal (Figure 8-19A). For penetration, check the reverse side of the metal. A very dark blue circle or small metal lump will indi-

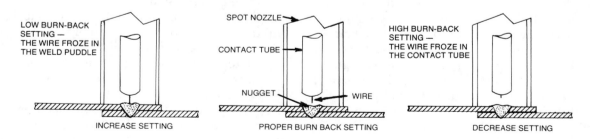

Figure 8-18   Adjusting the burnback setting

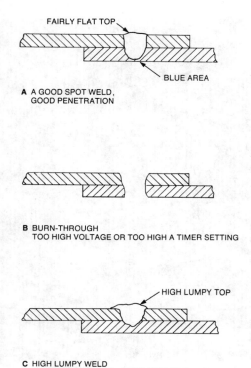

A A GOOD SPOT WELD,
GOOD PENETRATION

B BURN-THROUGH
TOO HIGH VOLTAGE OR TOO HIGH A TIMER SETTING

C HIGH LUMPY WELD
POOR PENETRATION – LOW VOLTAGE OR LOW
TIMER SETTING

Figure 8-19   Spot welds

cate a correct melting depth. The weld should have a flat, smooth, even top surface. A burn-through indicates too high a voltage or too high (long) a timer setting (Figure 8-19B). A high lumpy weld with poor penetration indicates low voltage, or a low weld timer setting (Figure 8-19C).

9. Check the wire burn-back. If the wire is frozen in the puddle, increase the burn-back control. If it is frozen to or very close to the end of the tip, lower the control setting. If the wire sticks in the weld puddle, disconnect the ground and press the trigger. The wire will feed out, allowing the gun to be pulled back and giving room for the wire to be cut. If the wire has burned

onto the end of the contact tip, it may free itself after cooling. The wire is usually just stuck to the copper tip. Sometimes unscrewing the tip a turn will break the wire free.

Plug Method

Many body repairers prefer to punch or drill a series of holes along the edge of the outer panel and then plug weld the hole. This spot welding procedure has certain advantages in that the small wire can be used. It is easier to fill the hole using standard weld procedures, and adequate penetration into the lower layer of metal is ensured. This procedure is also necessary when the welder does not have the extra spot weld controls. The hole size should be approximately 6–8 mm, large enough to actually weld around the edge, rather than just fill the hole. After the edge is welded any remaining low area in the centre is filled.

Tack Welds

Spot welds are not to be confused with tack welds. Tack welds are small, short-holding welds put at intervals along the joining area of the metals. They should not be used in place of spot welds as they do not have as much holding power. On a lap joint, for example, the tack weld is welded only to the edge of the upper layer of metal. A spot weld would have four times as much holding contact with the upper metal around the edge of the hole.

GWAM (MIG) Safety and Work Habit Review

1. **Wear protective clothing, especially when working overhead. The MIG welder tends to drop or spit small red hot balls of metal.**

2. Wear a suitable helmet with a Shade 10 lens for continuous welding.

3. Use safety glasses and a tinted face cover type shield for spot welding.

4. Do not use (to sit on) or have empty paint solvent cans in the vicinity of the weld area.

5. Do not use the machine with damaged or broken electrical plugs or receptacles.

6. The gas cylinder main valve should be turned off when the welder is not in use.

7. When the gas main valve is opened, it should be opened slowly to prevent the sudden surge of gas pressure damaging the regulator mechanism.

8. Always protect glass and painted areas close to the weld area.

8-8 PLASMA ARC CUTTING (PAC)

Advantages

Plasma arc cutting (PAC) is a cutting process which is quickly gaining acceptance in auto body repair shops (Figure 8-20). The plasma cutting method can easily cut any type of metal, both ferrous (iron based) and non-ferrous (containing no iron, such as aluminum, brass, and copper). It works well on thin metals and is especially suited for cutting the high-strength steels. The cut can be made so quickly that the paint on a body panel is only slightly burned back from the edge of the cut. There is virtually no warpage and very little heat transfer out from the cut into the metal. For example, cutting high-strength steel with the oxy-acetylene process removes the high-strength of the steel for 50–75 mm back from each side of the

Courtesy Thermal Dynamics Corporation

Figure 8-20A Plasma arc cutting machine and gun

Courtesy Thermal Dynamics Corporation

Figure 8-20B Using the plasma arc cutting machine and gun

cut. Using the plasma arc, no strength is lost. This method can also be used to pierce spot welds and "shovel" or peel away a top layer of metal spot welded to another without burning into or damaging the lower layer of metal. This process is especially useful when the damaged panel must be removed and replaced with a new one.

Principles of PAC

When a gas is super-heated under pressure it is said to become **plasma** in nature and electrically conductive. The gas is fed under pressure to the torch gun head. The electrical current passes through a small tungsten rod held in the gun head. The tungsten rod is **non-consumable** (that is, it is not melted as is the wire in the GMAW process). Its purpose is to provide the arc between it and the metal. The electrical arc charges the gas and heats it very quickly to a super-hot temperature — about five times hotter than the oxy-acetylene flame. The plasma gas after heating is forced through a very small orifice at a velocity greater than the speed of sound. The electrically charged plasma jet strikes the metal with such speed, heat, and force that a very small fine cut is made. The metal is literally melted and blown away so quickly that a smooth clean cut is produced.

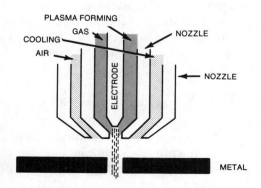

PLASMA FORMING
GAS
COOLING
AIR
NOZZLE
ELECTRODE
NOZZLE
METAL

Figure 8-21   Gun head and arc plasma jet

There is no slag clinging to the edges as is typical with the oxy-acetylene process.

A separate secondary stream of the same type of gas is emitted from the gun head to surround the plasma jet. Its purpose is to cool the cutting gun, surround the plasma jet, and help blow the melted metal away (Figure 8-21).

Gases Used for PAC

Gases such as nitrogen, argon, and hydrogen can be used to supply both the plasma (primary) and cooling gas (secondary). They would be purchased as a bottled gas.

The machine can also be operated with clean, dry compressed air supplied from an ordinary shop compressor. About 0.17–0.22 m^3 at 430 kPa (6–8 cu. ft. at 60 psi) of air input is needed to make the machine operate. The compressed air is used for both the primary and secondary supply.

Some machines are water-cooled. Water is pumped in a continuous cycle to the gun head and back to a reservoir at the machine where it is cooled before starting another cycle.

PAC Machines

The various manufacturer's machines are different. Some have only one on/off switch to operate the machine. Others have additional dial-type amperage controls to regulate the speed of the cut. Some machines must have the torch tip touching, or at best, very close to the metal to start and maintain the arc. Others can be operated in a stand-off position away from the metal, although this quickly wears the tungsten rod and tip.

PAC Cutting Procedure

1. The torch tip can be either rested directly on the surface of the metal or

held approximately 1–3 mm off the surface and free-handed.

2. The gas or air pressure must be turned on and set.

3. All other necessary switches are turned on and any controls set.

4. Triggering the torch switch starts the air flowing through the torch. After a slight delay the plasma jet starts and the cut is made.

5. When the arc and plasma jet start, the torch is simply slid very quickly over the metal along the area to be cut. If the surface is rough the torch will catch. A smoother cut can be made by holding the tip slightly off the metal.

6. The flame and arc are instantly shut off by releasing the trigger.

PAC Piercing and Shovelling Procedure

Two or more layers of spot welded panels can quickly be separated by using the torch to pierce the spot welds. Then they can be separated very easily with the air hammer cutter. To pierce the spot welds, simply hold the gun over the weld and pull the trigger; a clean hole is quickly blown through the two layers of metal. Having a hole in the lower layer of metal is often not desirable as it is the one that the new panel fits over. Leaving the holes in the lower panel might weaken it, and it is often not possible to get in behind to place the plug welds through these existing holes into the new panel.

Alternative Method. An alternative method is to use the plasma torch to shovel or peel away the outer layer of unwanted metal, leaving the lower panel with very little air hammer cleaning or grinding. By being careful, the outer layer can be quickly melted and blown away through the spot weld areas without harming the lower layer of metal. Any slag or small areas of weld can

be quickly ground clean or cleaned with the air chisel.

> The gun must be placed with the collar flat on the metal until the plasma jet is established. The gun is then carefully but quickly placed on an approximately 45° angle with the plasma jet pointing in the direction of travel. If the gun is tipped back at too flat an angle, the safety device will shut off the machine. Should this happen, it must then be repositioned flat on the metal to re-establish the flame.

Plasma Arc Safety Review

1. Always wear oxy-acetylene goggles (Shade 4 or 5) and protective clothing — especially a good pair of leather gloves. Remember the flame is four to five times hotter than the oxy-acetylene flame.

2. Extremely high output voltage is used with the machine. Do not touch any live parts of the machine.

3. Do not use the machine with cut or defective cables, hoses, electrical plugs, etc.

4. Protect the vehicle parts such as the fuel lines and tanks, glass, plastic parts, upholstery, etc., from the after-cutting stream.

REVIEW QUESTIONS

1. Why should the eyes and skin be protected while arc welding?

2. Zinc coated metals should not be welded for a prolonged period in enclosed areas. Explain why.

3. a) Define the terms SMAW and GMAW.
   b) Explain the differences between the two processes.
4. Explain how an electric current is used to fusion-weld metals together.
5. Define the terms polarity and circuit.
6. a) What two types of current are used in arc welding?
   b) Explain the differences between these current types.
7. What is meant by "straight" and "reversed" polarity?
8. What purpose does the flux coating on the rods serve?
9. What type of SMAW rod is recommended for welding high-strength steels?
10. Explain the two methods that can be used to strike the arc.
11. What procedure must quickly be followed should the rod freeze to the plate?
12. Explain the results of (i) a low amperage setting, (ii) a high amperage setting.
13. What type of current and polarity do most GMAW machines use?
14. What two adjustments must be made on most GMAW machines?
15. Explain how the GMAW arc is protected from the atmosphere while the weld is being made.
16. a) List the three common sizes of wire used.
    b) Which is the smallest?
17. How is the electric current passed into the wire?
18. Explain the possible results when there is (i) too much drive roller pressure on the wire, (ii) not enough drive roller pressure on the wire.
19. a) Define the terms "inert" and "active" gas.
    b) Name one gas of each type and briefly explain how it affects the weld.
20. List three advantages of a constant voltage supply.
21. Briefly explain the short circuiting metal transfer process.
22. What distance should the gun be kept from the metal?
23. What happens when the distance between the metal and gun is excessive?
24. How should the gun be held and moved while welding in the overhead position?
25. Briefly explain the purpose of the stitch weld control.
26. Explain the difference between resistance and consumable spot welding.
27. Explain the purpose of the two spot weld controls.
28. What voltage setting is recommended for spot welding, compared to the normal bead welding?
29. Explain the procedure to unstick the wire should it freeze to the puddle while spot welding.
30. Explain the difference between a tack weld and a consumable spot weld.
31. Briefly explain how the plasma arc cutting equipment operates.
32. Why can a very fine cut be made quickly?
33. What is the purpose of the secondary stream of gas?
34. What type of electrode is used with the plasma arc equipment?
35. List three safety rules that must be observed while using the plasma arc equipment.

9 EXPANSION, CONTRACTION, HEAT DISTORTION, AND SHRINKING

9-1   Effects of Heat on Metal
9-2   Expansion and Contraction Forces in Sheet Metal
9-3   Welding Patches and Repair Panels
9-4   Shrinking

9-1 EFFECTS OF HEAT ON METAL

When heat is applied to metal, the metal **expands**; that is, it becomes larger in every dimension. As the metal cools it **contracts** (returns to its original size and shape). Metal is made up of many small, vibrating molecules. As heat is applied to the metal, the molecules vibrate more quickly and move further away from each other, thus causing the complete area of heated metal to expand. As the metal cools, the particles vibrate more slowly and the distance between them decreases until the metal has returned to its original size.

In areas of the world where there is considerable temperature change with the seasons, allowances must be made in structures to compensate for expansion and contraction. For example, gaps between railroad rails and expansion joints in bridges allow for expansion and contraction as the temperature increases and decreases.

Expansion and contraction in sheet metal are not as easily controlled. Since only a small area of a panel is heated at one time, the rate of expansion and contraction is usually uneven. Even if the complete panel were evenly heated, its movement would still be partly restricted by heavier, reinforced members and adjacent panels. In some cases, expansion is greater than the subsequent contraction; in others, contraction is greater than expansion.

> The greater the difference between expansion and contraction, the greater the chance of buckling and warping occurring in the panel.

These problems cannot be ignored during welding or heating operations on sheet metal. Because no one set of rules can be applied to every repair operation requiring heat, an understanding of expansion and contraction effects can best be acquired by considering a number of specific examples.

By doing this we will learn how to prevent, or at least lessen, panel warpage.

Example 1: If a bar of steel is freely supported and its temperature is uniformly increased, the length, width, and thickness of the block will all increase in size. If the bar is now allowed to cool evenly until it reaches its starting temperature and is again measured, it will be found that the dimensions are the same as they were at the start (Figure 9-1). Therefore, when a freely supported piece of metal is evenly heated and cooled, expansion and contraction are equal.

Example 2: Now suppose that the ends of this same bar are held so that there is no possibility of the length increasing, and sup-

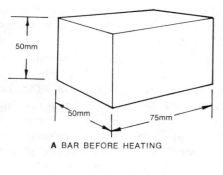

A BAR BEFORE HEATING

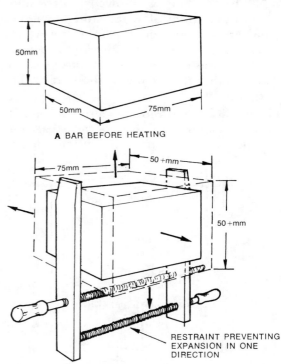

A BAR BEFORE HEATING

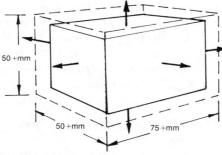

B BAR EXPANDING DURING HEATING

RESTRAINT PREVENTING
EXPANSION IN ONE
DIRECTION

B EXPANSION OCCURS IN TWO DIMENSIONS ONLY

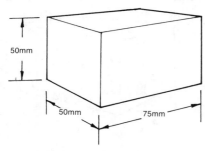

C BAR CONTRACTED AFTER COOLING

Figure 9-1   Free expansion and contraction

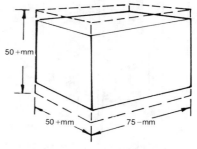

Figure 9-2   Expansion — one dimension restricted

pose that it is again uniformly heated. In this case, the expansion in the two free dimensions has to be greater than before to make up for the restriction on the third dimension (Figure 9-2). When expansion is prevented in one dimension, the rate or amount of expansion is increased in the other two.

If the specimen is allowed to cool uniformly to its original temperature, it will be found that the two dimensions that were allowed to expand are still larger than before and that the third, restricted dimension is now smaller than it was at the start of the experiment.

Example 3: Expansion can also be stopped in two dimensions with all of the expansion taking place in the third dimension (Figure

9-3). When the metal cools back to its normal temperature, the two restricted dimensions will be smaller than before and the third dimension will be larger.

Therefore, when we heat a piece of metal while restricting it in one or more dimensions, the metal's shape is permanently changed. In the dimensions allowed to expand, expansion is greater than contraction. Although the restricted dimensions do not expand when the metal is heated, they do contract as the metal cools back to its normal temperature.

Example 4: The opposite results will occur if the same specimen is uniformly heated to the high temperature and the ends of the bar are forcibly retained, so that, during cooling, contraction of the length of the bar during cooling is impossible. When the bar is completely cooled, the length will be greater than it was originally, while the other two dimensions will be smaller (Figure 9-4). Thus, contraction in one or even in two directions may be stopped, causing increased contraction in the other dimensions. In this case, contraction is greater than expansion in the unrestrained dimensions.

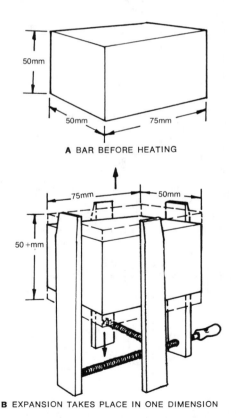

A BAR BEFORE HEATING

B EXPANSION TAKES PLACE IN ONE DIMENSION

Figure 9-3   Expansion — two dimensions restricted

We can control expansion and contraction in one (or two) dimensions, but always at the cost of the other two (or the third) dimension.

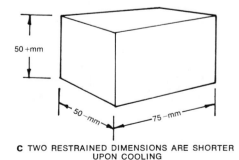

C TWO RESTRAINED DIMENSIONS ARE SHORTER UPON COOLING

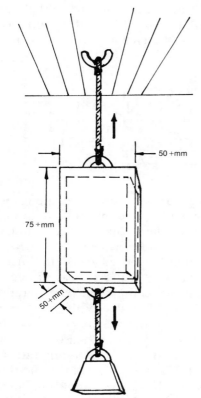

A SPECIMEN FULLY EXPANDED — ENDS RESTRAINED
DURING COOLING

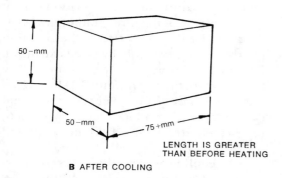

LENGTH IS GREATER
THAN BEFORE HEATING

B AFTER COOLING

Figure 9-4   Contraction — one dimension
restricted

Heat and Metal Strength

When heat is applied to metal, the heated area becomes soft and loses strength. The ductility of the heated metal is increased and its elasticity is decreased. It takes less force to bend, stretch, or twist the metal. Heated metal has little or no ability to resist bending, nor does it return to its original size and shape after it has been bent.

Example 5: Suppose, then, that a section of the face of a steel bar is heated. As the temperature of the area increases, the heated metal tries to expand in all three dimensions (Figure 9-5). However, the surrounding cooler metal exerts a restraining pressure against the expanding metal. At first, expansion forces will try to push the cooler metal back. These forces might be strong enough to actually bend the bar backward a small amount. Some of the expansion forces will be relieved in the directions of Arrows 2 and 4. As the temperature of the heated area increases, the metal becomes softer and weaker. The heated metal loses its ability to force back the cooler metal. All the expansion occurs in the area of the heated metal. The soft expanding metal piles up in the heated area. A bulge or convex crown is created along the face of the bar (Arrow 3). When expanding metal is forced to pile up in an area because of the restraint of the surrounding cooler metal, an **upsetting** condition exists.

If the bar were to return to its original size and shape, the metal that was piled up during heating would have to be unpiled or levelled off during cooling.

As the metal cools the heated area starts to contract, making the bulge smaller. As the bulge cools the metal in it also becomes stronger and more resistant to any further contraction forces. The surrounding cooler metal is not strong enough to resist the contraction forces, so instead of the bulge being

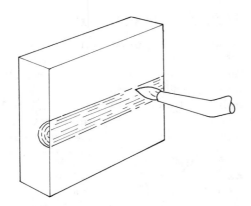

A SMALL SECTION IS HEATED ALONG THE FACE OF A STEEL BAR

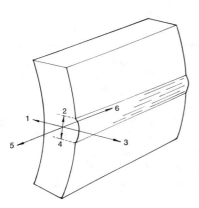

B UPSETTING CONDITION

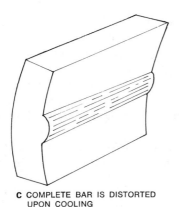

C COMPLETE BAR IS DISTORTED UPON COOLING

Figure 9-5   Expansion and contraction in a section of a steel bar

completely removed, the contraction forces will pull the ends of the bar toward the heated area. As a result, when the metal has cooled, the whole bar will be pulled out of shape — the ends bowed toward the still-visible bulge.

9-2 EXPANSION AND CONTRACTION FORCES IN SHEET METAL

Example 6: Suppose an area along the edge of a piece of sheet metal were heated to a bright red then allowed to cool slowly back to room temperature (Figure 9-6A, B). A strip along the heated edge would expand the most because that area was heated to the highest temperature. The temperature of the metal would gradually decrease from the hottest edge toward the cooler metal. The expansion forces would also lessen proportionately to the metal temperature. The heated area would expand in the three dimensions, but the cooler metal along the back side would act as a vice, preventing free lengthwise expansion. Most of the expansion would take place in the directions in which there was no restraint. The majority of expansion would be in the directions of Arrows 1, 3, and 4, with no expansion in the direction of Arrow 2. There would be some expansion lengthwise through Arrows 5 and 6. The front edges of the metal would be slightly fan shaped (Figure 9-6C). Because the metal cannot freely expand in directions 5 and 6, the heated area would become wavy and warped.

In the cooling process, the contraction forces would reduce the width and thickness close to their original size. Since the cooler metal prevents full lengthwise expansion, a slight upsetting condition would occur in

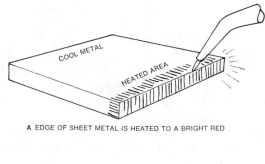

A EDGE OF SHEET METAL IS HEATED TO A BRIGHT RED

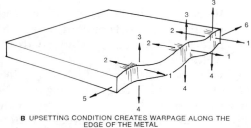

B UPSETTING CONDITION CREATES WARPAGE ALONG THE EDGE OF THE METAL

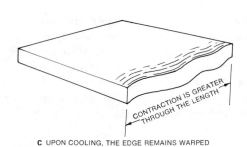

C UPON COOLING, THE EDGE REMAINS WARPED

Figure 9-6   Expansion and contraction along the edge of sheet metal

Example 7: When heat is applied to the centre of a sheet metal panel, the expansion forces from the heated area are restricted in two dimensions — length and width. All the expansion must take place in the third dimension. As the temperature in the heated area increases, the expansion forces push against the surrounding cooler metal. The cooler metal resists the expansion forces.

As the temperature increases, the heated metal becomes softer (Figure 9-7). The soft metal loses its strength to bulge outwards

SURROUNDING COOLER METAL PUSHES INWARD

HEATED AREA PUSHES OUTWARD

Figure 9-7   Surrounding cooler metal prevents normal expansion of the heated area

the heated area. At the first stages of contraction this extra metal would start to unpile as the area cooled. It would become stronger, resisting further unpiling. The contraction forces would tend to pull on the area of cooling metal offering the least resistance. This final contracting would likely create a greater amount of warpage along the edge. The length would be slightly longer, contraction and expansion in the width and thickness would be practically even.

and all the expansion forces are relieved by the metal piling up in the centre of the heated area to create an upsetting condition. The thickness of the metal increases and a noticeable bulge is formed (Figure 9-8A). So that the bulge may contract as the metal cools, the contraction forces must even out the metal that has piled up during heating. However, as the area cools it becomes stronger and resists the pull of contraction forces. When the area has cooled back to

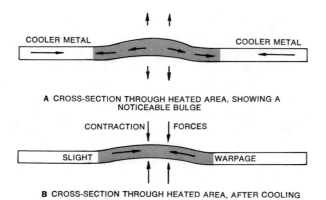

A CROSS-SECTION THROUGH HEATED AREA, SHOWING A NOTICEABLE BULGE

B CROSS-SECTION THROUGH HEATED AREA, AFTER COOLING

Figure 9-8

room temperature, the bulge will not have disappeared completely. If the surrounding area is not strong enough to resist the contraction forces, a slight warp or buckle will result (Figure 9-8B).

Summary: Effects of Expansion and Contraction

From the preceding examples, it can be seen that the results of expansion and contraction forces vary with every case. There are many factors that determine the amount and therefore the effect expansion and contraction forces will have on sheet metal. Some of these are:

1. Temperature. The higher the temperature of the metal heated, the greater the possibility of distortion occurring.
2. Size and location of the heated area. When a large area of metal is heated distortion will be greater.
3. Shape of the area of metal being heated. Heat usually has less damaging effects on work-hardened areas of the panel. The forces affect the high-crowned areas very slightly compared with low or reverse-crowned areas.
4. Unequal expansion and contraction,

caused by the surrounding cooler metal and the fact that only a small area is heated at one time.

5. The metal is not massive enough in all directions to resist the expansion and contraction forces, and therefore the metal surrounding the heated area is warped or bent out of shape.
6. When sheet metal is welded, the heat is not applied evenly to the complete weld zone.
7. When sheet metal is fusion welded, welding rod that is molten, and therefore fully expanded, is added to the weld puddle.

(When a continuous weld is made in a sheet metal panel, Factors 6 and 7 will influence the amount of distortion caused by the expansion and contraction forces set up by the heat.)

To illustrate these conditions, suppose that two pieces of sheet metal are butt welded together. As the weld progresses across the plate, the heat entering the metal along the edge of the sheets starts to expand the metal ahead of the weld puddle. The colder metal prevents the heated edge from expanding sideways into the plate. The

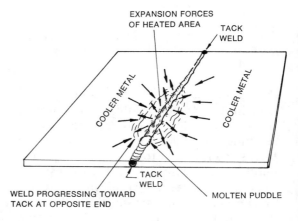

Figure 9-9 Expansion forces when welding sheet metal

edges are prevented from expanding length-wise by the weld at one end and the tack at the other end. The restraints of the colder metal, the tack, and the weld cause the expansion forces to concentrate along the edge (Figure 9-9).

The edge of the heated sheet becomes thicker and usually bulges up or down, creating a warp or buckle in the metal. The rest of the expansion forces are relieved by expanding the edges of the sheets toward each other (Figure 9-10). If an insufficient gap is left between the two edges, they will overlap. Since most of the expansion forces were relieved by piling up the metal along the edge of the sheets, and since fully expanded welding rod was added to the weld puddle, a build-up, or bulge, of molten, fully expanded metal is produced in the weld area. As the surrounding metal cools, contraction forces are set up that pull or tighten the weld build-up along the weld zone. However, as the weld cools, the metal in it becomes stronger and more resistant to the contraction pull. Because the surrounding metal on either side of the weld is not massive enough to resist the forces of contraction, the sheet itself is pulled out of

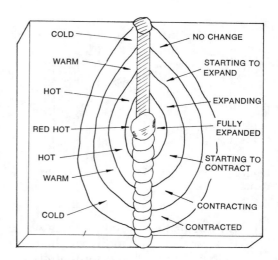

Figure 9-11   Uneven expansion and contraction forces cause distortion

shape. This distortion is further increased because the complete length of the weld is not evenly heated and cooled (Figure 9-11). Therefore, the expansion and contraction forces are uneven.

Methods for Preventing Heat Distortion

The following are methods to prevent distortion by controlling the expansion and contraction forces:

1. Leave a gap between the two edges of metal to be welded. The gap should be at least as wide as the thickness of the welding rod. The two edges will expand toward each other, closing the gap. This prevents the expansion forces from piling up in the weld zone and distorting the complete panel.

2. Clamp the two pieces of metal together and then tack weld them at intervals along the joint. This holds the two metals in alignment and prevents the expansion forces from warping the edges (Figure 9-12).

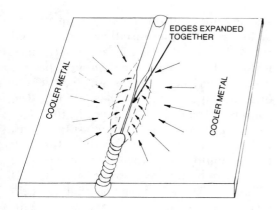

Figure 9-10   Edges of the sheets expand toward each other relieving expansion forces

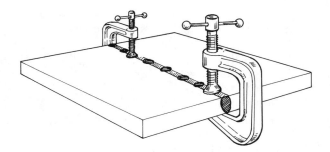

Figure 9-12   Tack welding two pieces of metal together

3. Do not make one continuous weld; make short welds and space them out by hopping back and forth along the weld joint. Allow each weld to cool somewhat before making the next. A wet rag or sponge is also often used to cool the weld but not until all red heat has left the weld area. These procedures help to keep the complete area as cool as possible. Only a very small area is actually heated at one time.

4. Do not preheat the area. Quickly bring the point of the cone down close to the metal, make the weld, and then remove the flame from the panel. Never move a cone back a short distance in an attempt to control the heat. This allows the heat to spread over a larger area of the panel.

5. Do not attempt to weld the metals together if the edges are not aligned properly. Tack weld them together and dolly the edges back to the correct alignment.

6. Lightly tap the weld as it is cooling. This helps it to contract and prevents the hot weld metal from exerting a pull on the cooler surrounding metal.

7. Forge the weld as it is cooling. **Forging** is a method of relieving the contracting forces in the weld area by using on-dolly blows. The dolly is held under

the weld and the hammer blows are directed on top of the weld. The weld area is flattened to approximately the same thickness as the rest of the metal.

8. Lay water-soaked rags around the area to be welded. This stops the heat from travelling into the surrounding cooler metal.

9. If the metal warps either as it is cooling or after it has cooled, the warpage is usually caused by the pull of the weld on the surrounding metal. This can be controlled by dollying the weld.

Repairing Heat-Distorted Sheet Metal

The easiest way to remove warpage once it has occurred is to use hard, on-dolly blows to stretch the weld, and then to use the off-dolly method to lower the high spots and raise the low spots. The dolly is held under the low spots, and the hammer blows are directed at the high spots.

9-3   WELDING PATCHES AND REPAIR PANELS

The amount of distortion created in a patch or in a repair panel installed over a rusted area will depend on the location of the tack welds and on the sequence in which they are made. When a patch is to be welded over the original panel, a lap joint is formed. The corners of a patch should always be rounded. A greater amount of distortion results when a weld is made on a sharp corner. The tack welds should start in the centre of each side of the patch and work toward the corners (Figure 9-13). Tacking the patch in the centre of the sides allows the heat to work out to the corners, thus preventing the top layer of metal from lifting away from the original

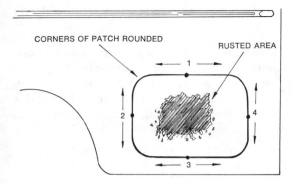

Figure 9-13   Tack welding a patch over rust

panel. The heat is free to expand the edges toward the corners. The metal is "ironed out" toward each corner.

When a repair panel or patch has to line up to an edge (for example, a lower, quarter repair panel that has to line up with the quarter-panel edge to provide an even door gap), the tacks must be started at the edge and the metal ironed out toward the opposite end (Figure 9-14). If the tacks were started in the middle and worked toward each end, the repair panel would not fit tightly to the edge of the quarter panel, and the door gap would be lost. The same procedure is used when the panel is being fastened with rivets or metal screws, even though there is no heat involved.

Figure 9-14   Tack welding a repair panel beside a "fitted" edge

Crack or Rip in a Fender or Panel

Start the tacks at the inner end of the crack or rip and work toward the outside edge (Figure 9-15). Keep the two edges lined up and flush with each other by dollying the edges both before and after tacking. This process allows the heat to move toward the edge. If the tacks are started at the edge and worked toward the inside of the panel, a bulge can result at the end of the crack.

If the panel has been ripped, the metal along the rip will have stretched. By working the tacks toward the edge, you can keep the two edges flush and can work some of the stretched metal out of the edge. Then dolly the edge into shape and tack it. When the tacks have been completed, use the outlined methods to control the distortion, and make the weld.

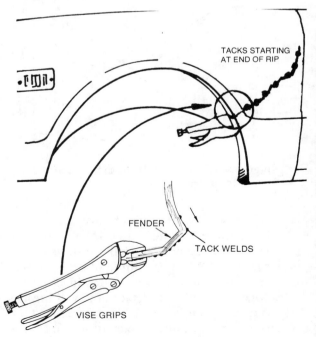

Figure 9-15   Tack welding a rip

If the metal along each edge actually stretched before the rip occurred, the two edges will not be easily butted together. In order to bring the edges together an outward bulge will have to be formed in that area of the panel. If the edges are welded in this position the extra bulge in the metal will then have to be shrunk down into position.

An easier solution is to trim some metal off each edge until the two fit. This way there won't be a bulge in that area of the panel. Make sure a slight gap is left between the two edges for expansion. Tack and weld the rip as previously explained.

When the edge of a fender or panel has to be welded, always weld in from the edge of the panel for at least 12 mm. If the weld is made toward the edge, the heat will concentrate at the edge and a portion of the edge will burn away (Figure 9-16).

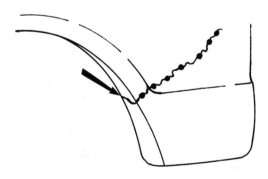

Figure 9-16   Weld in from the edge of the panel for at least 12 mm

The weld itself should have little or no build-up. When the weld is thicker than the metal itself, a new crack often starts beside the weld. When the automobile is driven, the panels vibrate a certain amount along the edges. The thicker metal at the weld resists the vibrations, causing a new crack. Vibration can also cause a crack to start from the weld crater at the edge of a panel.

9-4 SHRINKING

When metal is severely damaged in a collision it is often stretched in the badly buckled areas of the ridges and channels. These same areas are sometimes stretched slightly during the straightening process. Most of the

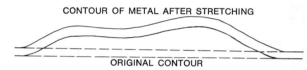

Figure 9-17   Stretched metal

stretched metal will be found along the ridges, channels, and buckles in the direct damage area. When there are stretched areas of metal present in the panel, it is impossible to correctly straighten the area back to its original contour. The stretched area can be compared to a bulge on a tire. There is no place for the stretched metal surfaces to fit within the correct panel contour (Figure 9-17).

When an area of metal is stretched, the molecules of metal are moved further away from each other. The metal is thinned and work-hardened. **Shrinking** is the method used to bring the molecules back to their original position and thus to restore the metal to its proper contour and thickness. The object of shrinking is to remove the stretched metal without disturbing the relatively undamaged elastic metal in the surrounding area.

Basic Shrinking Procedures

Before any shrinking is attempted, the damaged area must be dollied back as close to its original shape as possible, with the stretched areas bulged outward. Only then can you accurately determine whether there is any stretched metal in the damaged area and, if so, where shrinking should be done.

> Always remove the sound-deadening material from the underside of the metal before attempting to shrink an area.

To shrink an area, a small spot in the centre of the stretched area, or bulge, is heated to a range between a light red and a cherry red colour. A flat-faced dinging hammer is then used to drive, or compress, the molecules in the heated area closer together. A dolly having the same shape as the metal is held lightly under the "shrink" to help support the metal. The dolly is usually not used until after the "shrink" redness has disappeared (Figure 9-18). The "shrink" is placed in the highest spot of the stretched area, then in the next highest spot, and so on, until the stretched area has been shrunk back to its proper position (Figure 9-19).

The size of the "shrink," or "hot spot," is determined by the amount of excess metal in the area to be shrunk. The "shrinks" can be anywhere in size from a silver dollar down to the head of a thumb tack. The larger the hot spot, the harder the heat is to control. An average-size "shrink" is usually about the size of a quarter. Small shrinks should always be used on flat panels, as such panels tend to warp easily.

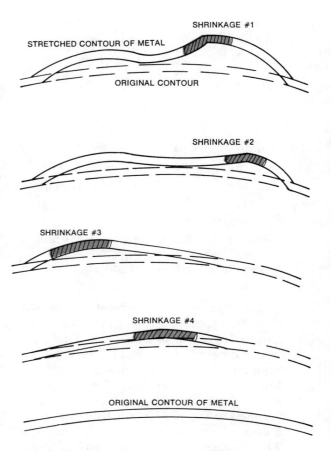

Figure 9-19   Each shrinkage is placed in the highest spot of the stretched area

A very small hot spot would be used to take an **oil can** out of a flat panel. The term "oil can" is used to describe an area of a panel that is stretched very slightly. It can be pushed in. As soon as the pressure is released, the area will pop back out again, just as the bottom of an oil can does.

A neutral flame and the tip used for welding sheet metal are used to heat the hot spots. The point of the cone is brought straight down to within 3 mm of the metal and held steady until the metal starts to get red. The torch is then slowly moved outward in a circular motion until the complete hot spot

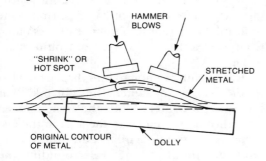

Figure 9-18   Shrinking stretched metal

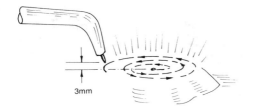

Figure 9-20   Preparing a "hot spot"

is between a light red to a cherry red (Figure 9-20).

> Do not heat the metal past a cherry red. It will start to melt and a hole may be burned through the metal.

As the heat from the torch enters the small spot in the panel, the heated metal expands. The cooler metal surrounding the hot spot resists the expansion forces. As the temperature increases, the heated metal becomes softer. This soft metal piles up and forms a bulge in the hot spot (Figure 9-21). The metal usually bulges up instead of down because the top of the metal is heated first. When it starts to bulge, the rest of the metal in the hot spot follows.

Several sharp hammer blows are directed around the edge of the hot spot, driving the molecules of metal closer together (Figure

9-22). During this procedure, it is not necessary to support the metal with the dolly unless the metal collapses. If it is necessary to support the panel, the dolly should only be held lightly under the metal. As soon as the redness disappears, off-dolly blows and light, on-dolly blows are used to smooth and level the area around the hot spot.

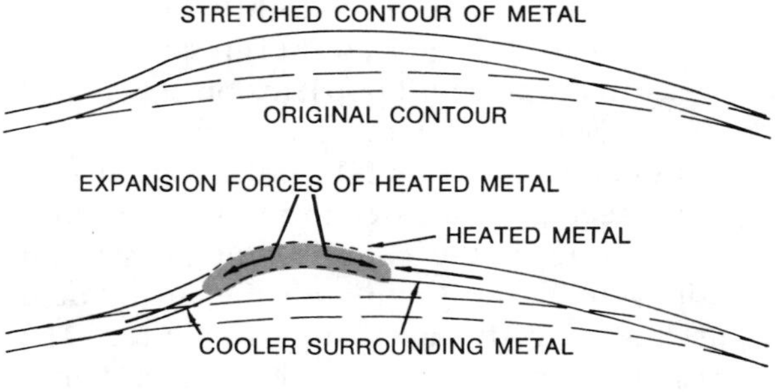

> Do not use heavy, on-dolly blows to level the area. This will restretch the area of metal.

Once the redness has disappeared and the area has been dollied smooth, the "shrink" can be cooled with a wet rag or sponge. When this is done, a greater degree of contraction occurs, and a slight amount of distortion could result. The warpage should be straightened before the next "shrink" is attempted.

> Do not shrink another spot in the area until the last one has completely cooled. As the metal cools, it contracts. You cannot determine where the next "shrink" should be placed or if another is even needed until after the panel has cooled and contracted.

It is very hard to determine accurately the amount each "hot spot" will shrink. One "shrink" may remove far more excess metal in one area than the same size would in another.

It is not uncommon to find that an area has been overshrunk when the "shrink" has completely cooled. When the area has been overshrunk, the metal in the area of the last "shrink" is usually collapsed or pulled flat and sometimes the metal surrounding the "shrink" area can even be pulled out of the

STRETCHED CONTOUR OF METAL

ORIGINAL CONTOUR

EXPANSION FORCES OF HEATED METAL

HEATED METAL

COOLER SURROUNDING METAL

Figure 9-21   Soft, heated metal bulged up

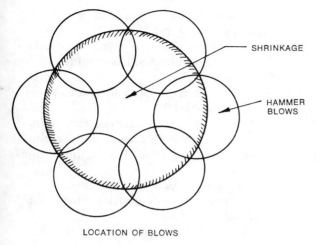

Figure 9-22   Hammering the hot spot

proper contour. Overshrinking is corrected by using hard, hammer on-dolly blows to stretch the last "shrink." The last shrunken area is usually the direct cause of overshrinking.

Shrinking a Gouge

A gouge in a panel is usually caused by a small, sharp object that severely creases the metal. The metal in the gouge area is badly stretched and work-hardened (Figure 9-23).

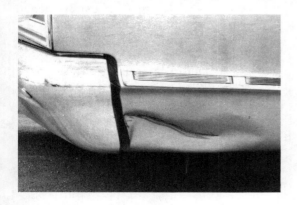

Figure 9-23   Gouge-type damage

One method of repairing gouge-type damage is to work the metal out to form an outward bulge along the crease and then shrink the excess metal. Start to shrink the gouge at the end with the least amount of stretched metal, and work toward the point of greatest stretching. Keep the "shrinks" small, and place them directly along the crease. Dolly each hot spot smooth. Wait for the metal to cool completely before applying the next "shrink".

Some body repairers prefer to straighten a severely gouged area by first heating it then bumping and/or prying it out and shrinking it all at the same time. Only a small area is done at a time.

Tap around the edge of the gouge with a hammer while lifting or pushing outward with the dolly. Quickly use both off-dolly and light on-dolly blows to smooth and level and shrink the area.

When the area has cooled repeat the process in the next section of the gouge, and so on, until the whole gouge has been removed. If any additional shrinking is necessary, it should be performed by the regular method.

Shrinking an Edge

When the edge of a fender or panel has been stretched, straightening will usually pro-

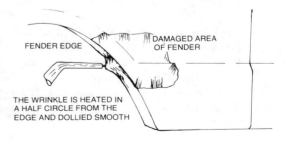

Figure 9-24   Shrinking an edge

duce wrinkles along the edge. These wrinkles can be shrunk. Heat each wrinkle to a light red, moving the torch in a semi-circle from the edge. Then use light, on-dolly blows to dolly the wrinkles smooth (Figure 9-24).

> If any of the metals are high-strength steel, the amount of heat used must be closely controlled.

REVIEW QUESTIONS

1. Why does metal expand when it is heated?

2. When heat is applied to a sheet metal panel, the expansion and contraction are often hard to control. Why?

3. Explain the end result of expansion and contraction on a freely supported bar of metal, when it is evenly heated and cooled.

4. a) What is the result of heating when expansion is prevented in one or two directions?
   b) What is the final effect, after the metal has contracted, on the dimension that is prevented from expanding?
   c) What is the final effect on the dimensions that are allowed to expand?

5. Explain why a bar of metal that has been evenly heated along one side and then evenly cooled does not return to its original size and shape.

6. a) In what direction does the least amount of expansion occur when the edge of an area of sheet metal is heated? Why?
   b) What is the final result when the sheet-metal edge has contracted?

7. What is the result of heating a small area in the centre of a sheet metal panel to a red heat? Why?

8. List five important factors that determine the effects expansion and contraction forces will have on sheet metal.

9. Why must a gap be left between two pieces of sheet metal that are to be butt welded together?

10. a) List the reasons that sheet metal panels warp, or distort, when they are fusion welded together.
    b) How can the warpage caused by a fusion weld be removed from the surrounding sheet metal?

11. a) In what order should the tack welds be placed on a patch that is to be welded over a rusted area?
    b) Explain why the tack welds should be made in this order.

12. When welding a ripped or cracked fender, the tacks are started at the end of the rip and worked toward the fender edge. Why?

13. When a crack is welded, the weld should have little or no build-up. Why?

14. Why is the damaged area straightened before stretched metal is shrunk?

15. In what area of the stretched metal should the "shrinks" be placed?

16. What factor determines the size of a "shrink"?

17. When being shrunk, the heated metal usually bulges outwards. Why?

18. Where and how hard should the first hammer blows be placed on the "shrink"?

19. When should the dolly first be used under the "shrink"?

20. Why should the next "shrink" not be placed until the previous one has cooled?

21. If water is to be used in the shrinking operation, when should it be used?

22. When an area of metal has been over-shrunk, how may it be straightened?

23. Where should the "shrinks" on gouges or sharp creases be started?

24. Explain how the stretched edge of a fender or panel should be shrunk.

10 PANEL-FORMING TECHNIQUES

10-1   Bending Right Angles
10-2   Bending a Flange Along the End of a Curved or Crowned Panel
10-3   Forming Rolled Flanges
10-4   Forming Straight-Line Curves
10-5   Forming Straight Ridges or Creases in Sheet Metal Compound Curve
10-6   Shaping a Flat Sheet Over a Double or
10-7   Forming a Partial Door Panel

Although manufacturers can supply both complete and partial panels for the repair of damaged and rusty areas, rebuilders often need to hand form complete panel sections, fenders, and other body parts in their repair and restoration work. One-of-a-kind custom or race car builders actually hand form the complete body. Aluminum is often used in race car building because it is light and easily worked and shaped. Sheet metal is harder to shape because it is tougher.

In Chapter 4 considerable time was spent discussing panel shapes. A panel may have flanges along the edges and pressed creases through the panels as well as single, reversed, and/or compounded crowns. A single- or reverse-crown shape, or an edge or bend running through a panel in a straight line, can be easily shaped over a metal or even a wooden form. However, almost all panels have some degree of compound curve in them — usually very little from front to rear, with varying amounts from very high to very low crown running from top to bottom. Highly-compounded crown panels are the hardest to duplicate because the metal must be shaped from both directions.

10-1 BENDING RIGHT ANGLES

A regular **sheet metal break** is used by sheet metal shops to make straight-line bends (Figure 10-1). However, many body shops do not have such a break. As a substitute, they bend flanges and edges over a heavy piece of angle iron or I beam. The use of the break and other heavy iron backing

Figure 10-1A   Sheet metal break

Figure 10-1B   Wheeling machine

Figure 10-1C   Close-up view of wheels

Bending a Straight-Line Right Angle Flange

Place the metal on the support. The flange to be bent should stick out past the edge of the bending support. Clamp or steady the metal and use a flat-faced hammer to hit the edge of the metal. Use forceful, direct blows. As the flange bends, continue to direct the hammer blows along the length of the edge of the metal (Figure 10-2A). Once the crease at the bend point has been started, use the hammer to tap along the actual bend line (Figure 10-2B). This sharpens the bend and allows the flange to bend more easily to a 90° angle. Then direct the hammer blows along the edge of the metal again. Once the flange has been brought around to the 90° angle, use light hammer blows to further sharpen and square the bend. Tap along each side of the bend (Figure 10-2C).

methods is limited to making a straight-line bend. The body hammer and a dolly or a beading machine are used to bend edges and flanges that are not straight-line. The **beading machine** can also be used to make different-shaped flanges along the edge of a panel and to duplicate originally pressed ridges or beads on a panel.

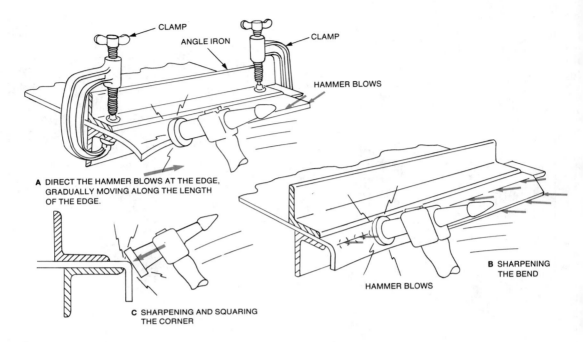

A DIRECT THE HAMMER BLOWS AT THE EDGE, GRADUALLY MOVING ALONG THE LENGTH OF THE EDGE.

B SHARPENING THE BEND

C SHARPENING AND SQUARING THE CORNER

Figure 10-2   Bending a right angle flange over an angle support

All the hammer blows are directed along the edge of the metal and on the bend. Do not hammer the metal on either side of the bend as hammer marks will be left in the metal.

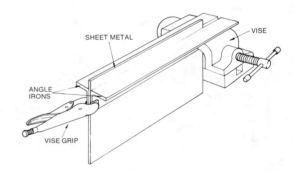

Figure 10-3   Straight line bend between two angles

Alternative Method: Bending a Straight-Line Right Angle Flange

A straight-line right angle bend can also be made by clamping the metal between two angle irons as shown in Figure 10-3. A vise and vise clamp are used to clamp the metal between the two angle irons. The hammer blows should be directed at the edge of the metal. As the flange bends, the angle of the hammer blows should be increased (Figure 10-4). When the flange has been bent to a right angle, one piece of angle iron is removed so the bend can be sharpened. Lightly hammer close to each side of the bend.

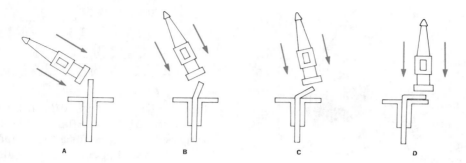

Figure 10-4   The direction of the hammer blows is changed as the flange bends

Bending a Straight-Line Right Angle Flange with the Hammer and Dolly.

Scribe a line on the inside of the panel at the location of the bend. Place the panel upside-down on the edge of a bench or other solid support and hold the dolly tightly against the metal, beside the scribed line (Figure 10-5). Direct the hammer blows against the edge of the flange. Change the angle of the hammer blows as the flange bends over, as shown in Figure 10-6.

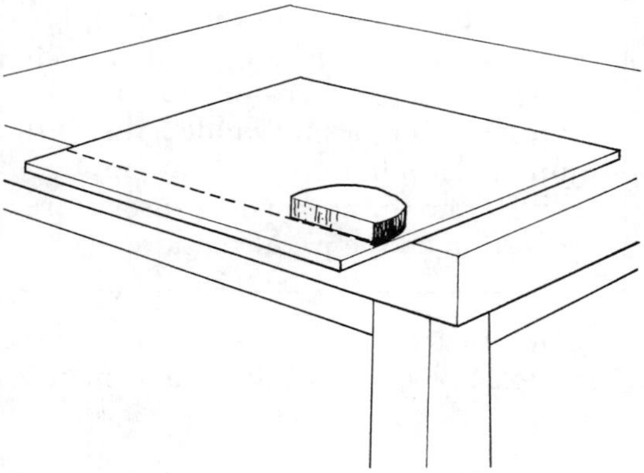

When the flange has been formed to a right angle along the length of the dolly, move the dolly approximately half its length further along the scribed line (Figure 10-7). Keeping the rear portion of the dolly against the previously formed flange makes it easier to hold the dolly along the scribed line. Bend the next section of the flange up along the dolly. Continue the process until the complete flange is formed.

Turn the panel over and using the hammer and dolly sharpen the bend. Hold the dolly tightly against the inside corner and direct the hammer blows at each side of the bend.

Figure 10-5   Hold the dolly tightly against the metal, beside the scribed line

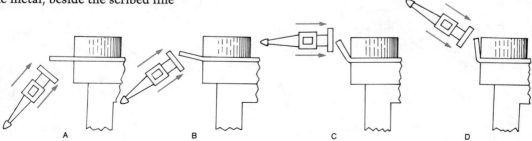

Figure 10-6   The direction of the hammer blows is changed as the flange bends

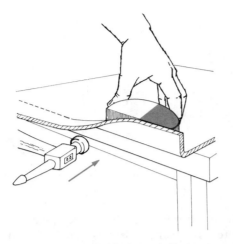

Figure 10-7   Keep half of the dolly against the formed flange while bending the next section

The same procedure is used to bend a scrolled or curved flange, although more pressure must be applied against the dolly to hold it along the scribed line. More dolly control can be gained by keeping slightly more of the dolly against the part of the flange previously bent. Smaller sections are bent up at a time, especially in tightly curved areas. (Figure 10-8).

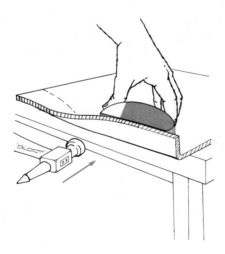

Figure 10-8   Bending a scrolled flange

10-2 BENDING A FLANGE ALONG THE END OF A CURVED OR CROWNED PANEL

With the hammer and dolly, use the above procedure to form the flange. As the edge is being bent inward to form the flange, bulges or wrinkles will occur in the metal because there is actually too much metal in the flange. This extra metal is removed by shrinking the wrinkles while they form as the edge is being gradually bent around. Shrinking is explained in Chapter 9. When the flange is formed and the wrinkles have been removed, the bend is sharpened with the hammer and dolly.

> Do not cut notches in the flange, because a ridge will be created at each notch in the panel (Figure 10-9). Also, unless the notches are welded, rust will quickly form in the cracks. Attempting to weld the seams usually causes more distortion on the panel surface.

Shops that do a large amount of panel forming have different machines made es-

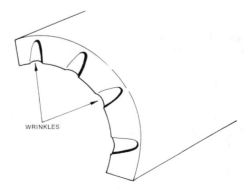

WRINKLES

Figure 10-9A   Bending a flange along the edge of a curved or crowned panel

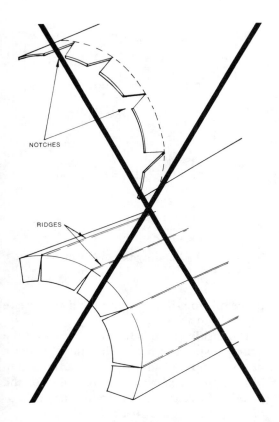

Figure 10-9B   Notches will create ridges in the metal

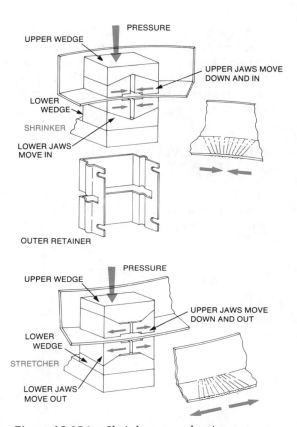

Figure 10-10A   Shrinker-stretcher jaws

pecially for either shrinking or stretching flanges. These machines have four jaws: two upper and two lower. Prying the hand lever downward moves the two upper jaws down to pinch the metal between them and their matching lower jaws. Further downward movement of the shrinking-machine lever forces both the upper and lower jaws to move inward, to shrink the metal. With the stretching machine, the levers move outward to stretch the metal in the flange. The molecules in the metal between the two sets of jaws of the shrinker are actually squeezed in closer together. With the stretcher, they are pulled farther apart. With either of these

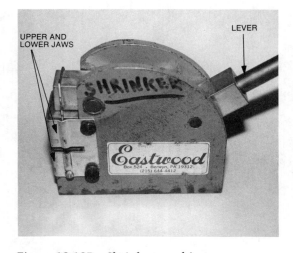

Figure 10-10B   Shrinker machine

two machines a flange can be bent in the break and then altered to create the correct shape. Figure 10-10 illustrates a right-angle edge first bent in a break and then formed into an inner and outer curve by the shrinker and stretcher machines.

10-3 FORMING ROLLED FLANGES

A rolled flange (Figure 10-11) can be formed with the hammer and either a dolly or a short

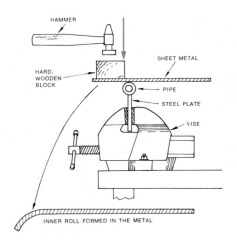

Figure 10-12   Bending the inside curve over a piece of pipe

piece of pipe that is welded to a steel plate and held in a vise.

The inside curve is formed first. Hold the panel upside-down over the pipe. Using a heavy bumping hammer and a hard wooden block, drive against the outer edge of the panel to force the metal around the contour of the pipe (Figure 10-12).

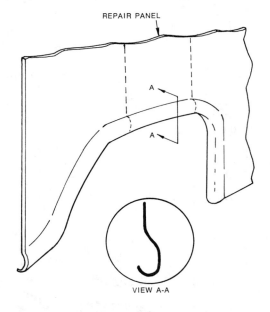

Figure 10-11   A rolled flange

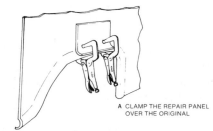

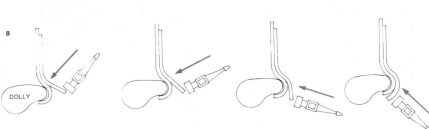

Figure 10-13   Using the hammer and dolly to bend the outer curve

Figure 10-14   Bending the inner roll with the hammer and dolly

Fit the new panel to the old panel. When the correct contour of the inner roll has been obtained, clamp the new panel over the original. Holding the dolly behind the old panel to provide support, hammer the edge of the new panel to form the outer lip around the original panel. Direct the hammer blows at the edge of the panel, as shown in Figure 10-13.

A dolly also can be used to form the inner roll. Place the dolly on the outside of the panel, as shown in Figure 10-14. Apply pressure on the dolly and direct the hammer blows at the edge of the metal. This forces the metal to curve upward around the dolly. Clamp the new panel over the original panel and bend the remaining part of the flange as previously explained.

10-4 FORMING STRAIGHT-LINE CURVES

Straight-line curves are easily formed by bending the metal around a pipe. The metal is clamped between a pipe and a heavy angle iron (Figure 10-15). With the hands flat against the edge of the metal, forcefully pull and roll the metal up and around the pipe. Over-roll the metal somewhat to allow for spring-back. Using a pipe slightly smaller than the required curve also helps to obtain a better curve. Bend a small scrap of metal first to test the curve's radius and the position of the curve in the new panel. Devise a measuring system from the test piece to locate the position of the curve in the new panel.

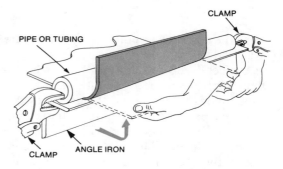

Figure 10-15   Rolling a straight line curve

10-5 FORMING STRAIGHT RIDGES OR CREASES IN SHEET METAL

Slight ridges or creases can be formed in flat, sheet metal panels with a simply constructed jig, such as that shown in Figure 10-16. Clamp the jig in the vise and place the sheet metal over the jig at the required location. Place another angle on top of the metal and clamp it to the first angle, as shown in Figure 10-17A. Place both hands flat on the panel and carefully bend the panel over the pipe to the desired curve. Turn the panel over and clamp it on the jig at the other side of the ridge. Roll the metal over the pipe

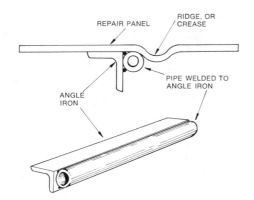

Figure 10-16   A jig

until the correct contour is obtained (Figure 10-17B).

A sheet metal beading machine is excellent for forming both straight and curved right angles or contoured flanges along the edge of a panel. It can also be used to duplicate pressed creases or ridges through the centre of a panel. The edging machine consists of two shafts, two gears and many interchangeable matching rollers. A cranking handle is connected to the end of one shaft. The metal is placed between two rollers. As downward pressure is applied to the top roller and the handle is turned, the metal is pulled through the rollers, forcing their shape into the metal. Usually at least three passes are needed, with the pressure gradu-

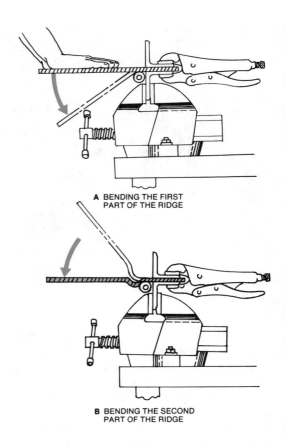

A BENDING THE FIRST PART OF THE RIDGE

B BENDING THE SECOND PART OF THE RIDGE

Figure 10-17A, B   Bending a ridge

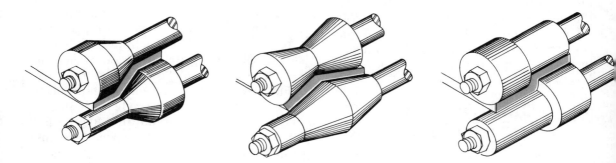

Figure 10-18A   Roller shapes

ally increasing on each pass. A variety of different-shaped rollers can be made by a machine shop to duplicate any type of flange, beads, and angles. Figure 10-18A illustrates some of the roller shapes available and Figure 10-18B shows a beading machine.

> Always push the metal through the rollers. This makes it much easier to keep the rollers aligned to the scribed line. When one pass has been made, remove the panel and reposition it in the rollers at the original starting location. Add more pressure to the roller and make another pass. Most machines have an adjustable guide that can be used to align the metal. However, the edge of the metal must be very straight and smooth — if there is a slight wave in the edge, it will be transferred into the rolled shape.

Figure 10-18B   Beading machine

10-6 SHAPING A FLAT SHEET OVER A DOUBLE OR COMPOUND CURVE

When flat sheet metal has to be formed or shaped in more than one direction, either the centre of the panel must be stretched or the outer areas must be shrunk. As has previously been explained, all the panels for mass-produced vehicles are stamped into shape. One-of-a-kind custom car builders and antique and classic car restorers actually hand form their panels using a wheeling machine to shape the flat sheet metal.

Wheeling machines are hand-operated. These consists of a C-shaped framework holding a flat-faced upper-mounted wheel and a lower V-notched support, both connected to a vertically mounted threaded shaft. Turning a lower hand-crank raises or lowers the shaft and V support. Two smaller interchangeable lower wheels are used. One is quite flat, while the other is highly crowned. The wheels are fastened to a short cross-shaft with very smooth turning bearings. The cross-shaft sits in the lower V support.

The flat sheet of metal is put between the upper and lower roller and a slight pressure is applied by the lower crank. The metal is slowly worked by hand back-and-forth through the two wheels. The molecules are forced to move and the metal is thinned and stretched. As the metal thins, more pressure is added to the lower wheel. Long, even, back-and-forth strokes must be used to shape the metal evenly. The direction of travel through the metal determines the direction of stretch. The high-crowned lower roller is used when a very high-crowned shape is to be made. The flat roller is used when a very slight crown is added to a large flat panel.

The body repairer patching a rusted area

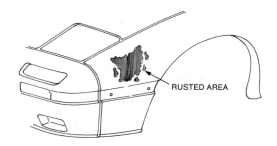

Figure 10-19A   Rusted area in a compound curve

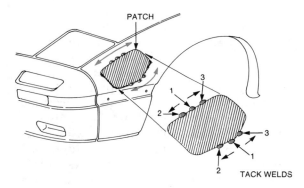

Figure 10-19B   Start tack welds in the middle of each side and work outward

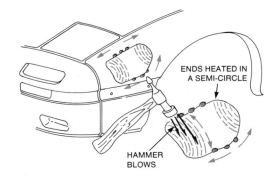

Figure 10-19C   Shrinking the excess metal to the outside edge

would have to shrink the outer areas to make the compound shape if a wheeling machine were not available. Figure 10-19A illustrates a rusted area in a compound curve for which a repair panel must be hand formed. The sheet metal is cut to the correct shape and formed to fit over the highest crown on the original panel.

The panel is tack welded at the two sides that fit flush with the original panel. The tack welds should start in the middle of each side and work outward (Figure 10-19B). The other two sides must be shrunk flush with the contour of the original panel. They can be shrunk by using the oxy-acetylene torch with a large tip (number 4 or 5) and a neutral flame. One side at a time is heated to a cherry red in a large semicircle.

The heated metal is tapped flat carefully with a flat-faced hammer. The hammer blows are started on the inside edge of the heated semicircle and worked back and forth around the circle toward the outside edge. The excess metal around the edge of the heated circle is driven into the centre of the heated area. The complete bulge is gradually moved toward the outside edge where, eventually, it can be shrunk (Figure 10-19C). The shrinking process can be speeded up by cooling the heated area quickly with a water-soaked sponge or rag.

It is not necessary to back up the heated area with a dolly, because the original panel provides the necessary back-up support. When the excess metal has been shrunk tightly against the original panel, the edges are then tacked and welded in the usual manner.

10-7 FORMING A PARTIAL DOOR PANEL

When the bottom of the outer door panel rusts through, it is often faster and easier to

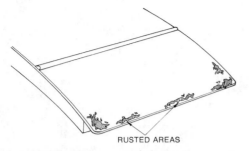

Figure 10-20   Door rusted through around
the lower edges

make a complete or partial outer replacement panel then to patch and fill the rusted
area. Normally, the original panel is removed before a new one is installed.
However, in a case such as this, it is often
better to leave the original panel in place, to
provide support and to hold the new panel
in its correct contour.

Leaving the old panel also makes it easier
to bend the edges of the new panel around
the door frame and to keep the edges
straight. If the old panel is removed and a
handmade panel is used, it usually has a
tendency to be flat or hollow through the
centre. If it can be put through the wheeling

machine to give it a slight compound curve,
it would hold itself in shape. Then the old
panel would be unnecessary, and it would be
better to remove it.

A new panel that is to be installed over the
original should be painted on the inside before installation to prevent rust from forming. Moisture may collect between the two
panels.

The size of the replacement panel depends on the contour of the door and on the
moulding location. The new panel should be
made large enough to fasten under existing
mouldings. If there are no mouldings on the
door, the replacement panel should be
brought up to the point of highest crown,
because a high-crowned area is less likely to
warp than a low-crowned area when the
panel is welded.

Figure 10-20 illustrates a door rusted
through around the edges. A new panel must
be made to cover the door from the moulding down.

Procedure

Using the portable grinder, grind down the

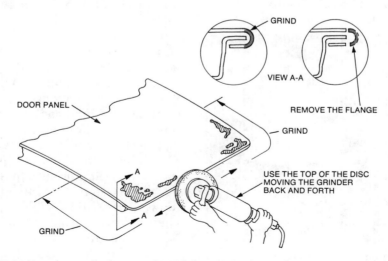

Figure 10-21   Grinding down the lower edge of the original panel

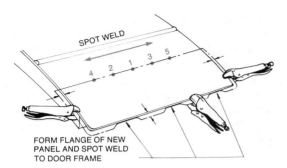

Figure 10-22 Spot weld the bottom flange and upper edge

edge of the original panel by approximately 3 mm, or until the panel separates from the bent lip (Figure 10-21). Grinding down the edge makes room for the flange of the new panel, so that no door gap is lost. Remove the inner flange of the original panel from the door frame, clean off any rust along the door frame and repair it if necessary.

Clamp the new sheet of metal over the original panel and mark the required size around the edge. Remove the sheet, and trim off the excess metal 9 to 12 mm out from the scribed mark. Use the break or angle-iron procedure to bend the flange along the lower edge of the panel. Bend it as far as possible past 90°.

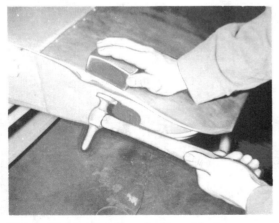

Figure 10-23 Bending the lip with the hammer and dolly

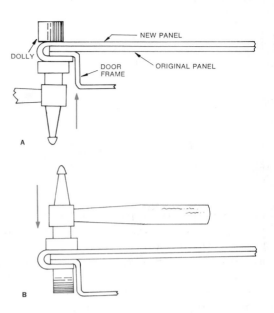

Figure 10-24 Use on-dolly blows to flatten and sharpen the new lip along the edges of the door

Place the new panel on the door, hook the lower flange over the bottom of the door frame, and clamp it. Use steel straps or wood strips between the new panel and the clamps to prevent the new panel being marked or dented. Using the hammer and a flat-faced dolly, bend the lower inner lip tightly against the door frame in three places only — at the centre and at each end along the bottom. These flattened areas need only be 75 mm to 100 mm long.

Make sure the panel is tight against the lower edge of the door and properly centred. Spot weld the new panel to the door frame at the three dollied areas. This prevents the panel from slipping out of position as the top is being fastened. Should the panel slip down there will be no door gap between it and the rocker panel when the door is installed (Figure 10-22).

Clamp the two panels tightly together along the sides. Make sure that the new panel

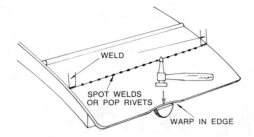

Figure 10-25 Removing slight snakes in the edge of the new panel

is pressed tightly against the original panel throughout the centre section of the door. Spot weld the two panels together along the top edge. Work from the centre toward each side to prevent the new panel from buckling. Finish bending the lip along the sides and bottom (Figure 10-23).

Use on-dolly blows to flatten and sharpen the edges, as shown in Figure 10-24. Slight snakes along the edges of the panel can be removed by dollying more on the innermost part of the warp (Figure 10-25). The more an area is dollied, the flatter the edge becomes and the more it spreads.

Weld the upper, outer edges of the panel where they join the old panel. Sometimes it is also necessary to weld a bead to the edge of the panel at this joint to help even up the edge. This should be fusion-welded as it can be ground or filed without cracking.

Spot weld the rolled lip to the door frame along the sides and bottom. Metal finish the outside edges of the face of the new panel, and lightly "true up" the edges with the body file.

REVIEW QUESTIONS

1. Which type of crown is the hardest to shape into a handmade panel? Why?

2. Where should the first hammer blows be directed when starting to bend the flange?

3. Why is it recommended to tap along the bend line once the flange has started to bend?

4. Why is it necessary to tap along each side of the bend once the flange is bent?

5. Why are the hammer blows directed at the edge of the metal when bending a right-angle flange?

6. Explain, in your own words, the procedure for bending a flange with the hammer and dolly.

7. When bending a curved flange with the hammer and dolly, what two dolly techniques are especially helpful?

8. Why should notches not be cut in the metal of a flange that is being formed along the edge of a curved or crowned panel?

9. Briefly explain how a shrinker or stretcher machine operates.

10. Which curve should be formed first when making a rolled edge? Why?

11. Why is it sometimes necessary to place a hand-formed panel over an existing panel?

12. Why is it always advisable to fasten a repair panel either under a moulding or on a high-crowned area?

13. Explain how the door gap is not lost when a hand-formed panel is placed over an existing panel.

14. Why is the bottom of the replacement door panel tack welded before the top is fastened?

15. The top edge of the replacement panel is welded from the centre working to each end. Explain why this procedure is used.

16. Explain how a slight warp along the edge of the door panel can be removed.

11 FITTING METHODS

11-1   Methods of Aligning Parts
11-2   Deck-Lid Fitting Adjustments
11-3   Hood Fitting
11-4   Bumper Adjustments
11-5   Door Fitting

Fitting refers to the correct spacing and aligning of the various panels, units, and sections of the vehicle. Although this chapter deals mainly with the theories involved in fitting the deck lid, hood, front fender assembly, and doors, the same methods apply to any other parts of the vehicle that may require fitting.

The correct fit of these different units has a direct bearing on the finished vehicle, especially if it has required collision damage repairs. Customer satisfaction depends on the overall fit and ease of opening and closing of these units.

A poorly fitting hood, door, or trunk lid will often vibrate, squeak, or rattle as the vehicle is driven. A misaligned door or trunk lid will leak water and will allow wind and dust to seep into the vehicle. Improperly adjusted doors are a safety hazard to passengers and driver.

Misalignment of the various units is usually the result of collision damage, misuse, and wear through normal use of the vehicle. In some cases, the units were not properly fitted and aligned before the vehicle left the factory. An incorrectly fitting unit can be caused by any one, or a combination, of three different factors:

1. The unit itself is not correctly fitted to its opening.
2. The body opening's shape will not permit the unit to fit.
3. The lock mechanism and lock catch are not properly aligned.

11-1 METHODS OF ALIGNING PARTS

Any part or section of a vehicle can be moved forward (toward the front of the vehicle), back (toward the rear), up or down, and in or out. "In" refers to movement toward the centre of the vehicle, "out" means away from the centre (Figure 11-1).

Four methods are used to make the various units fit correctly: **adjusting, shimming, bending or straightening,** and **jacking.**

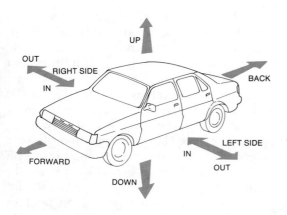

Figure 11-1   Fitting directions

Adjusting

Almost every part that bolts to the vehicle has elongated or over-size holes so that the parts can be shifted to obtain the proper fit. Some parts are bolted through these holes to "tapped cage plates" or "nuts" that can be shifted when the bolts are loosened. The metal cage holds the threaded plate or nut in place while allowing it to move with the shape of the elongated holes. Door striker catches are usually fastened to the lock pillar in this manner (Figure 11-2).

Shimming

Shims are spacers that are inserted at the bolts between two bolted parts to change the position or fit of the unit. Shims usually are made of steel, although fibre or rubber materials can be used. The shape and thickness of the shim depend on the part to be shimmed

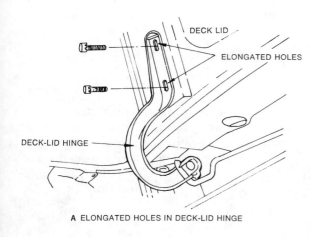

A ELONGATED HOLES IN DECK-LID HINGE

Photo by B. Robinson

Figure 11-3   Shimming the upper rear corner of the fender

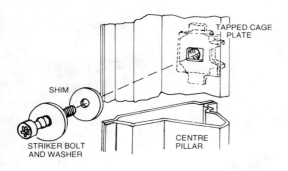

Figure 11-2   Adjusting parts

and the amount the part is to be moved. Figure 11-3 illustrates a typical shim application: to move out the upper, rear corner of the fender. Adding a shim separates the two parts. Removing a shim brings the two parts closer together.

Bending or Straightening

Bending or straightening is used to correct misalignment that has occurred as a result of a collision. If the hinge or hinge-mounting area of the unit has actually been bent out of its proper position, it is necessary to bend back or straighten the damaged area.

Jacking

Jacking is the use of hydraulic jacks to fit a misaligned part. Although jacks are often used as the corrective pressure for bending back or straightening a damaged part, they are also used as a separate means of moving a complete panel or section into position. Welded parts and body sections cannot be adjusted but often can be jacked into position. Jacking is also used to align and hold new panels or sections that are being replaced. The panels must be held in proper alignment while the welding is performed. Hydraulic or mechanical jacks are also used to correct improperly aligned door and trunk openings.

The method used to fit a unit depends very much on the causes of the misalignment. Before attempting to fit a part or panel, carefully inspect and consider the misalignment problems. Try to determine the probable cause and a method of repair. A misaligned part on a new vehicle would likely need only minor adjustments, or the removal or addition of a shim. For example, sagged doors on an older vehicle could be caused by worn hinge pins or worn bushings, or both. They would need to be replaced and the door then adjusted. Weakened hinge-mounting metal

could also cause misfitting problems. Maybe the door could be adjusted to fit, or perhaps the metal in the door mounting areas would need to be straightened to obtain the proper door fit.

A vehicle which is structurally rusted could sag enough to force the door opening out of shape. The body would have to be pulled or jacked back into position and held there while the rusted areas were repaired.

Collision damage is the main cause of misalignment problems. If the parts had fit correctly, it's likely that something bent or moved in the collision to cause the misalignment condition. The bent areas should be restraightened. The adjusting and shimming methods would only be used to "fine fit" the unit.

11-2 DECK-LID FITTING ADJUSTMENTS

Figure 11-4 illustrates a typical deck lid-to-hinge mounting design. The deck lid can be moved forward and back or from side-to-side in the body opening. The adjustments are

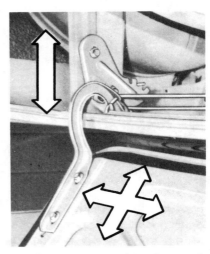

Courtesy Ford Motor Company of Canada, Limited

Figure 11-4   Deck-lid adjustment locations

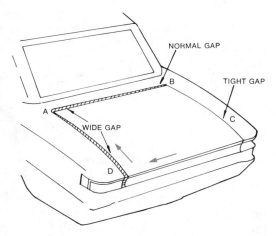

Figure 11-5   Deck lid is moved forward at the left hinge

made at the hinge-to-deck lid mount. When the lid has to be adjusted forward or backward, adjust one side at a time because it is easier to control the movement of the lid.

When the lid has to be moved sideways, it is advisable to loosen one hinge slightly and to give it a sharp blow with the hammer. Snug the bolts and repeat the procedure on the other hinge. Push the lid in the direction it is to be moved and drive the hinges in the opposite direction. This method gives easier control of the lid movement, and the forward and backward adjustments are not lost which is what would happen if all the bolts on both hinges were loosened at once.

The deck lid should be adjusted so that the gap between the body opening and the deck lid is even. To properly centre the lid in the opening, it is often necessary to adjust the lid forward or back at one side only (Figure 11-5).

> Moving the lid ahead or back from one hinge pivots the complete lid, changing the side gaps of the back section of the lid.

The vertical adjustment of the front end of the deck lid is accomplished by one, or both, of two adjusting methods. On some designs, the deck-lid hinge itself can be adjusted vertically. However, on some automobiles the hinges are welded directly to the body and no vertical adjustment is possible at the mounts. With this type of design, the vertical adjustment is obtained by adding shims between the deck lid and the hinge. Adding a shim between the lid and the hinge at the front bolt will raise the front of the lid; adding a shim between the lid and the hinge at the rear bolt will lower the front of the deck lid (Figure 11-6).

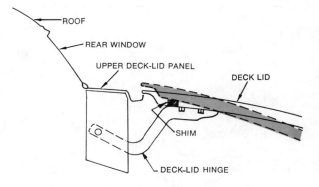

A RAISING THE FRONT OF THE LID

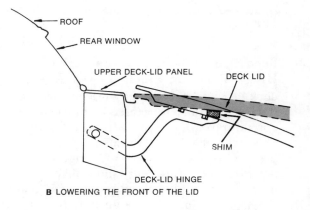

B LOWERING THE FRONT OF THE LID

Figure 11-6   Shiming the deck lid

Figure 11-7 illustrates a deck lid-to-hinge mounting design where the forward, backward, and vertical movements are made from the same locations. Both bolts must be loosened to move the lid ahead or back. Only the front bolt need be loosened to move the front of the lid up or down.

When both bolts are loosened to move the lid ahead or back, the correct up and down adjustment is lost. The usual procedure is to set the ahead/back adjustment, snug the bolts, check the lid fit, and then set the front vertical adjustment by the front bolt.

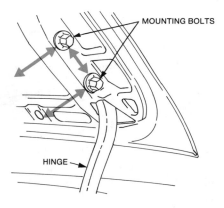

Figure 11-7   All adjustments are made at the deck lid mounting bolts

Bending or Straightening the Deck Lid-to-Hinge Mounting Panel. Suppose that the deck lid were forced shut while an obstruction in the trunk prevented or blocked the normal travel of one of the deck-lid hinges. This action would pull the metal of the deck-lid inner panel away from the hinge around the front mounting bolt, and collapse the inner panel at the hinge around the rear hinge mounting bolt (Figure 11-8). This same condition could also be created by a

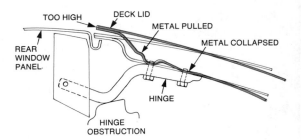

Figure 11-8   Deck lid inner panel bent

rear-end collision. When the hinge mounting metal of the inner panel bends in these locations, the front end of the lid is raised above the surrounding panels.

By reversing the bending action of the inner panel at the hinge bolts, the directly opposite condition is created. This type of deck-lid misalignment is created if, through misuse or collision damage, the inner panel around the front bolt is collapsed and the metal at the rear bolt is pulled away from the hinge (Figure 11-9). As a result, the front of the deck lid fits lower than the surrounding panels. Either of these conditions usually can be corrected by adjusting or by shimming. However, the logical method would be to straighten the inner panel.

For example, if the front of the lid were higher than the surrounding panels, it could be lowered by forcing the back of the lid up past the normal hinge location. With some automobile models it is necessary to block

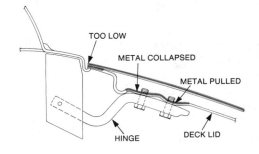

Figure 11-9   Front of the lid too low

the hinge in a partially open position to prevent the deck lid from hitting the rear window (Figure 11-10). To raise the front of the lid it is necessary to block the hinge (with a hydraulic-jack extension tube or a block of wood) in a partially closed position and to press down on the back of the lid (Figure 11-11).

Bending the Deck-Lid Hinge. In some cases, the deck-lid hinges themselves may bend from a severe rear-end collision (Figure 11-12). The hinges' bending in this man-

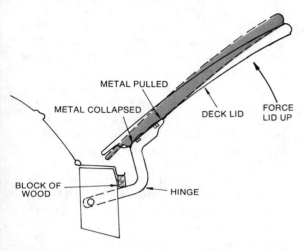

Figure 11-10   Lowering the front of the lid

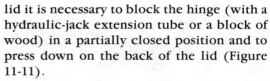
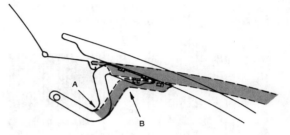

Figure 11-12   The deck-lid hinge has bent at A and B

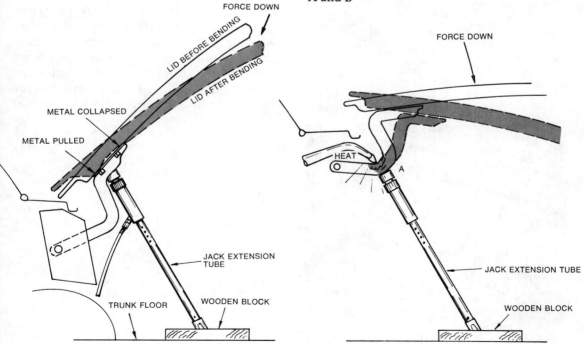

Figure 11-11   Raising the front of the lid

Figure 11-13   Bending the deck-lid hinge at A

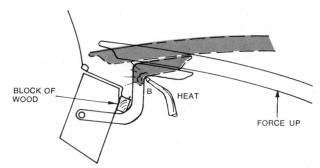

Figure 11-14   Bending the deck lid hinge at B

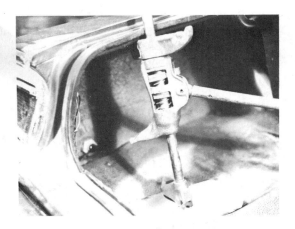

A. Courtesy Guy-Chart Sales Limited
B. Photo by B. Robinson

Figure 11-15   Jacking the trunk opening

ner would force the lid up and over the rear window panel. In order to straighten the hinges, block them up from the trunk floor, as shown in Figure 11-13. Heat the hinges at A, and slowly apply downward pressure on the rear of the deck lid. As the hinge straightens, the complete lid is moved back and the front of the lid is moved up.

To lower the front of the lid, open the lid until the hinges are against the opening stops (Figure 11-14). Apply heat at B and slowly force up the back of the lid. Continue to check the fit by closing the lid. Do not overheat or bend the hinge.

Hydraulic or mechanical jacks are used to shape the deck-lid opening. Figure 11-15 illustrates two typical examples of the jacking operations.

Deck-Lid Lock and Striker Catch. The deck-lid lock and striker catch control how the vertical rear section of the lid fits the sealing rubber. The hinges control the front vertical position of the lid. Provision is always made in either the lock or the striker so that one of them can be adjusted up or down and the other from side to side. Using the example in Figure 11-16, lowering the lock loosens the fit of the rear of the lid and makes

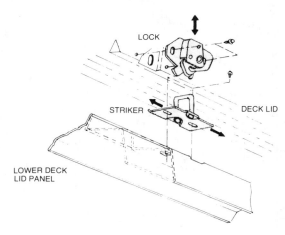

Figure 11-16   Typical deck-lid lock and striker catch adjustments

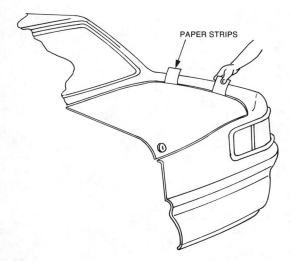

Figure 11-17 Testing the seal of the deck-lid weatherstrip

the lid easier to close. Raising the lock pulls the lid closer to the body. The catch, as indicated, can be moved from side to side.

The lock and striker catch should be perfectly aligned with one another. They should be adjusted so that they engage smoothly, without binding. If they are not properly aligned (for example, if the striker is off to one side) the lid will be pushed to one side as the lock engages with the striker catch.

> Before attempting to adjust a lock, study its design to determine the adjustment locations. They differ between automobiles.

The sealing rubber between the lid and the body opening should be compressed sufficiently so that the lid, when locked, is not loose. Check the seal of the rubber by inserting a piece of paper between the lid and the body and then closing the lid. Slowly pull on the paper. If the rubber is tightly compressed, there will be a considerable drag on the paper (Figure 11-17).

11-3 HOOD FITTING

Although the style of hood hinge varies with different manufacturers and from year to year with each manufacturer, provision is usually made for the vertical, forward-and-back, and side-to-side adjustments of the hood. The location from which these adjustments are made depends on the way in which the hood is mounted to the hinge, and the hinge to the body.

Many hood hinges are similar to deck-lid hinges. Some vehicle hinges are equipped with torsion bars or springs to hold the hood open. Other vehicles use a simple independent support rod to hold the hood up. When torsion bars or springs are used the hinge must be strong enough to withstand the additional hold-open twist on the hinge. Figure 11-18 illustrates a heavy side-mounted hinge. It is spring-loaded to hold the hood in the open position. Another typical hinge uses a front support rod. The hood can be adjusted forward and backward and from side to side at the hinge-to-hood mounting

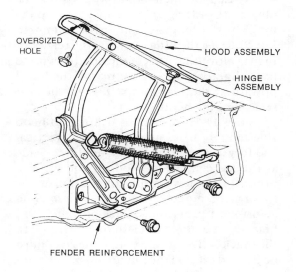

Figure 11-18 Heavy spring loaded side-mounted hinge

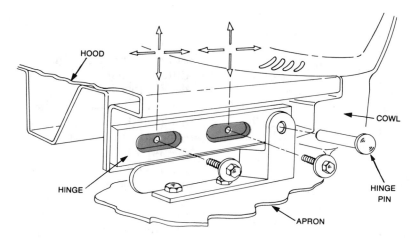

Figure 11-19   Hinge to hood side mount design

location in the same way that most deck lids are adjusted.

The hinge area of the hood can be raised or lowered by adding shims between the hood and the hinge. Adding shims at the rear bolt will raise the back of the hood from the cowl. Adding shims at the front bolt will lower the back of the hood.

Vertical movement of the hood also can be obtained by lifting or lowering the complete hinge at the hinge-to-fender baffle mounting. Rotating the hinge down at the rear bolt, in turn moves the back of the hood down and back slightly. Rotating the rear of the hinge upward at the rear bolt will raise the rear section of the hood.

Figure 11-19 illustrates a hinge-to-hood side-mounted design where both vertical and forward-and-back adjustments are made at the same hinge-to-hood mounting location. Slight sideways adjustment is made by forcing the hinges to the side. There is no adjustment provision at the hinge-to-cowl bracket. The hinge pin is actually riveted to the bracket. The staked end of the rivet must be ground off, and the pin driven out, when a new hinge is being installed.

Bending. Collision damage may bend the

hood's inner panel at the hinge mounting, the hinge itself, or the metal at the hinge-to-cowl mount. When the back of the hood sits high to the cowl and fenders as a result of a collision, the cause can be in any of those three areas. The newer style strap-type hinges are more easily bent than the stronger spring-loaded type.

The most common cause of hood misalignment after an accident is bending of the hood inner panel at the hinge mountings. The metal around the rear bolt will have pulled out, and the metal around the front bolt may have collapsed. Either or both conditions will cause the hood to sit high at the cowl (Figure 11-20). To correct this misalign-

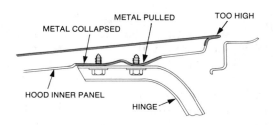

Figure 11-20   Hood inner panel metal has bent at the hood to hinge mounting bolts

ment, the hood is forced open while the metal of the hood inner panel is heated around the bolts. If the opposite condition occurs, that is, if the hood is low at the cowl panel, the hinge is blocked open and downward pressure is applied on the front of the hood while the inner panel is heated around the hinge mounting bolts as illustrated in Figures 11-10 and 11-11.

> Use the heat sparingly. Do not bring the metal to a red colour, since it may be high-strength steel. It is often possible to correct the hood fit by bending the metal without using heat. Heat should only be used if the hood has to be repainted because of the collision damage.

The lighter strap-type hood hinges can also bend in a similar manner to the deck-lid hinges. The procedure for straightening them is the same as that used for deck-lid hinges.

Fitting the Front of the Hood

The hood hinge, regardless of its style, controls the fit of the back part of the hood. The rest of the hood fits to the top of the fenders and is controlled by fixed rubber bumpers in the fenders along the hood opening and by adjustable rubber bumpers located on each end of the radiator support (Figure 11-21). The hood is held tightly against these rubber bumpers by the hood lock and striker. Either the hood catch or the lock-assembly mounting holes, or both, are slotted to provide an up-and-down and sideways adjustment. In this example, the hood lock is adjustable for both vertical and sideways alignment (Figure 11-22).

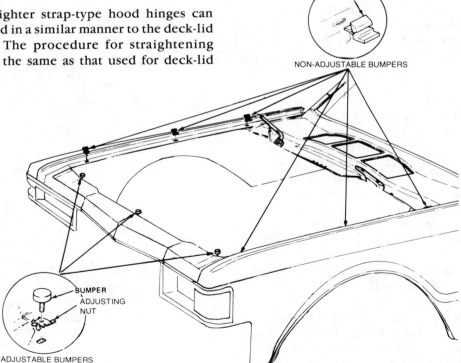

Figure 11-21   Position of the non-adjustable and adjustable rubber bumpers

The lock should be adjusted so that opening and closing the hood is reasonably easy and so that the hood alignment, as obtained by the hinge and rubber bumper adjustments, is maintained when the hood is closed. The hood lock and striker catch should be adjusted so that the catch is perfectly aligned with the lock opening. The hood lock vertical adjustment should be set so that the hood bumpers are slightly compressed when the hood is closed. If the hood is not held tightly against the rubber bumpers, it will tend to flutter when the vehicle is driven.

> The main purpose of the hood lock is to hold the hood closed tight against the rubber bumpers. It is not designed to correct basic hood alignment faults. If the hood lock is not properly aligned with the catch, the hood will be pushed sideways as the catch enters the lock opening.

The shape of the hood opening can be changed by adjusting or repositioning the front fenders. However, some unitized vehicles have the front fenders and inner splash panels welded both to each other and to the body. With this type of construction, the size and shape of the hood opening can be changed only by pulling or jacking the opening into position. Specialized body- and frame-straightening equipment are used to correct this type of condition. Chapters 12 and 13 deal in greater detail with body-straightening procedures.

Most unitized vehicles are designed to allow the front fenders to be adjusted; this provides for limited changing of the hood opening. The conventionally-built vehicle is designed with all the front end panels bolted together. Each panel has some adjustment allowances and the hood opening shape can

be changed by adjusting the parts. Mechanical or hydraulic jacks are often needed to move the fenders into different positions, and then to hold them in position while their connecting bolts are tightened.

The standard procedure for fitting a front end, especially on a conventional vehicle, is to first fit the hood to the cowl. The gap should be even between the two panels. The front fenders are then fitted to the hood. This fitting procedure ensures that the centre line of the hood and front end are in line with the corresponding centre line of the body.

This method doesn't work as well with vehicles that have an open area between the windshield and the end of the hood or for those vehicles that have the hood hinged from the radiator support.

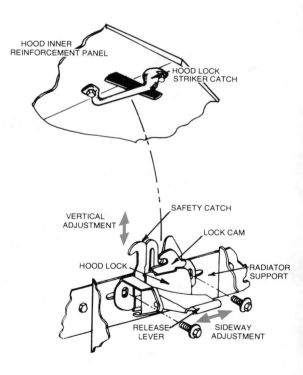

Figure 11-22   Typical hood lock adjustment

Front Fender Assembly Adjustments

The method used to adjust front fenders depends on the design and position of their mountings. All bolt-on fenders can be adjusted forward and back, in and out, up and down at the front door, cowl area, and at the radiator support. The fenders are adjusted through over-size or elongated holes or by adding or removing shims between the fender and mountings.

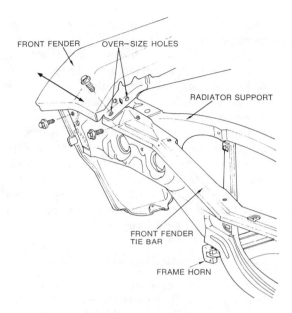

Figure 11-24 Front fender, in-and-out adjustments

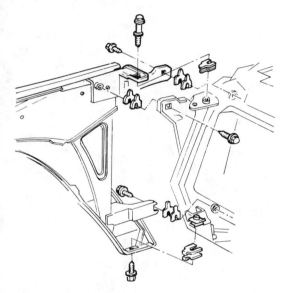

Courtesy General Motors Corp.

Figure 11-23 Typical fender-to-cowl mount adjustments

Figure 11-23 illustrates a typical fender-to-cowl mount, showing the possible adjustments and shimming locations used to adjust the fender. The forward-and-back fender movement is achieved through the use of over-size holes and by adding or removing shims at the proper connecting points. The vertical adjustment is controlled by adding or removing shims at either the top fender-to-cowl mount or the lower fender-to-rocker

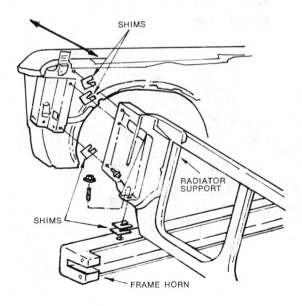

Figure 11-25 Adjusting the hood gap by adding or removing shims between radiator support and fender

panel mount. The fender can be moved away from or closer to the cowl by means of the over-size hole in the bottom fender mount. The in-and-out movement of the top of the fender is controlled by adding or removing shims between the fender and cowl at the mounting point.

The front of the fender can be moved to adjust the hood gap either by the over-size holes at the radiator support mounting locations (Figure 11-24) or by adding or removing shims (Figure 11-25). The method used depends on the construction design of the fenders and the radiator support.

Radiator Cradle Adjustments

With unitized vehicles, the radiator support is not adjustable because it is welded to the inner wheelhouse panels and to the frame rails. On conventional vehicles, provision is made for the radiator support to be adjusted forward and backward, from side to side, and up and down.

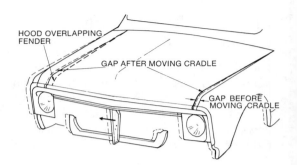

Figure 11-27   Moving the radiator support from side to side to adjust the hood opening

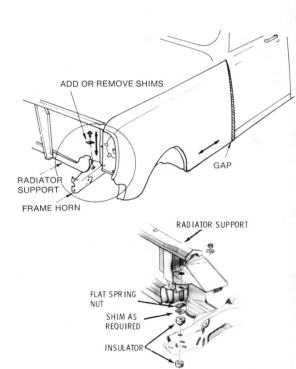

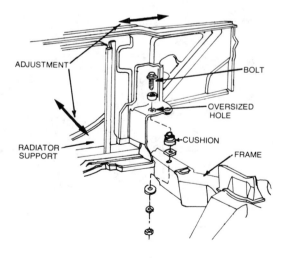

Figure 11-26   Conventional radiator support to frame rail mounting

Figure 11-28   Shimming the radiator support

The support can be moved forward and back and from side to side through the over-size holes at the support-to-frame mounting points (Figure 11-26). The correct spacing between the door and fender and the radiator and fan is obtained by the forward-and-back adjustment. The side-to-side movement of the support adjusts, or corrects, the shape of the hood opening (Figure 11-27).

The vertical movement of the support is controlled by adding or removing shims between the support and frame. Adding shims will increase the gap between the front door edge and the bottom rear edge of the front fender. Removing shims will close the gap between the door and bottom fender edge (Figure 11-28).

When the radiator support is bolted on each side to the frame rails, the front of the fender assembly can be twisted slightly by adding or removing a shim on one side. This adjustment puts the top of the fenders flush with the hood and changes the gap between the hood and fender edges.

> The radiator support should be shimmed only a limited amount. The depth of three shims is the most which the radiator support normally should be changed from its original setting. When more than two shims have to be added or removed to fit the front end assembly correctly, this is usually an indication that a further misalignment condition is present in the frame itself.

Suppose there was a slight sag in the frame under the cowl on the right side. The front fender assembly would not fit the body correctly, in that there would be a wide gap at the bottom between the door and the fender edge (Figure 11-29). Although this condition could possibly be corrected by removing shims from the radiator support-to-frame mount, this practice is not recommended. The front bumper would not line up with the fender and grille, and the correct wheel

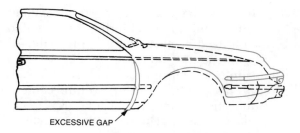

EXCESSIVE GAP

Figure 11-29 Excessive gap caused by sag in the frame

alignment could not be obtained, because the frame would still be bent. It is very poor practice to fit one unit at the expense of another. When it becomes necessary to file the over-size holes even larger or to add more than the regular number of shims to fit a part correctly, this is usually an indication that the surrounding parts have been straightened incorrectly.

There is some adjustment provided in the fenders and hood of unitized vehicles. However, when many of these same misalignment conditions are present in a unitized front section, the front superstructure itself is likely twisted or bent out of position. It must be straightened and aligned with body- and frame-straightening equipment covered in Chapters 12 and 13.

11-4 BUMPER ADJUSTMENTS

Most bumpers can be adjusted vertically (up and down), forwards, backwards, and sideways. The location from which these adjustments are made depends on the design of the bumper attachment to the arms or energy absorbers and their attachments to the frame or body mountings.

In a bumper energy-absorber attachment assembly, the energy absorber is fastened to the unitized frame rail with no provision for adjustment. The vertical (up or down) and side-to-side adjustments are made at the energy absorber to bumper reinforcement mounting. Forward and backward adjustments are made by adding or removing shims at the same location. Adding a half shim between the support and bumper reinforcement at the top or bottom of the bumper will tip the end of the bumper down or up, respectively.

11-5 DOOR FITTING

Door removal and/or fitting adjustments are made at the hinge-to-hinge pillar and door-to-hinge mounting locations. In most cases, provision is made at these two locations for the door to be moved up and down, in and out, and forward and back (Figure 11-30).

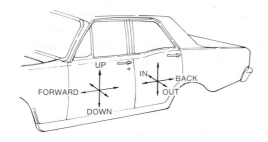

Figure 11-30   Door adjustment directions

Door Hinge Designs

Some manufacturers, on certain models, are welding or rivetting the hinges to the body pillar, the door frame, or both. In this system there is no provision for any adjustments to be made other than by bending. To remove the door the hinge pins must be driven out. (One manufacturer recommends drilling or cutting the pin into two pieces so it can be removed more easily.) The procedure for removing and replacing welded-on hinges varies greatly between manufacturers. Some have replacement hinges that are designed to be bolted on. With others, replacement hinges should be welded. Whenever it is necessary to change a welded-on hinge, it is advisable to consult the vehicle service manual for the correct hinge replacement procedure.

Although there are many different hinge styles, their operating principles are all similar. Door hinges consist of two halves connected at the pivot point by the hinge pin. Where the various hinges differ is in their mounting design and adjustment location. With some hinges, the adjustments are made at the hinge-to-hinge pillar mounting; with other styles, the adjustments are made only at the door-hinge mounting; and still other designs allow adjustment at both mounting locations.

Bolt-on hinges have the holes of the hinge and/or the hinge attachment points enlarged or elongated to provide for hinge movement. The bolts tighten into a tapped cage plate in the pillars and doors.

One of the more common hinge and mounting designs involves the in-and-out adjustments made at the door-to-hinge mounting location. The forward-and-back and up-and-down adjustments are made from the hinge-to-hinge pillar mount.

Figure 11-31 illustrates a slightly different version. Both forward-and-back and up-and-down adjustments can be made from either mounting location. Note that the strap part of the hinge fits into openings in the end of the door frame. The hinge is bolted to the reinforced part of the inner panel. This type

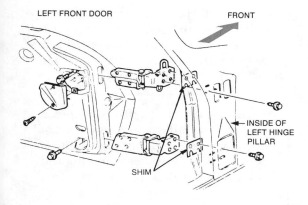

Figure 11-31   Door hinge style

of hinge-to-door mounting is more commonly used on larger vehicles with heavy doors. The in-and-out adjustments are made by adding or removing shims.

Some vehicles use a strap-type hinge design that makes no provision for any forward-and-back adjustment of the door.

Some up-and-down and in-and-out adjustment is provided on one of the mountings. In another mounting design the door side of the hinge is welded to the door. The forward-and-back and vertical adjustments are made at the hinge-pillar mount. The in-and-out positioning of the front of the door is changed by adding or removing shims.

The preceding examples describe only a few of the many different hinge-mounting designs used on different vehicles, it is suggested that before attempting any door removal or adjustments, the hinge design and the misalignment problems should be studied. Then check to see if the door can be adjusted and, if so, in what direction and from what mounting location. Before loosening any bolts it is a good idea to mark the original hinge position by scribing a line around the hinge. This provides an original reference location.

> The hinge pin, being the pivot point of the hinge, is the key to any door adjustment. Whichever direction the hinge pin (pivot point) moves, so goes the door.

Fitting Techniques

The following examples illustrate the various fitting techniques and results. Notice how the door gaps change in the illustrations.

Raising or Lowering the Door. When the whole door has to be raised or lowered, the connecting bolts of both hinges at either the pillar or the door must be loosened at the same time. To control the door movement, the front of the door is held with the knees or a floor jack, as shown in Figure 11-32. When the bolts are loosened, the door can be moved to the proper position. One bolt in each hinge is tightened, and then the door is closed carefully so that the door gap can be checked.

Figure 11-32   Raising or lowering the door with the aid of a floor jack

Forward-and-Back Adjustments. Figure 11-33 shows the results of adjusting the door forward or backward at one hinge only. When the whole door must be moved forward or backward, the adjustments are made on one hinge at a time. Figure 11-34 illustrates a forward adjustment of the whole door.

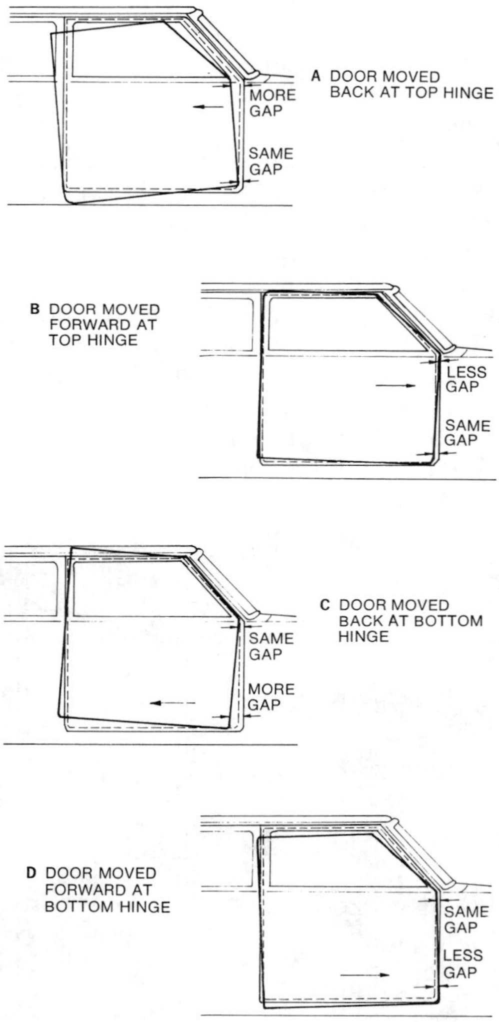

A DOOR MOVED BACK AT TOP HINGE
MORE GAP
SAME GAP

B DOOR MOVED FORWARD AT TOP HINGE
LESS GAP
SAME GAP

C DOOR MOVED BACK AT BOTTOM HINGE
SAME GAP
MORE GAP

D DOOR MOVED FORWARD AT BOTTOM HINGE
SAME GAP
LESS GAP

Figure 11-33 Forward and back door adjustments

Shims could be used with a strap-type hinge to move the door either forward or backward. The door could be moved back by placing a shim the same size as the hinge strap between the pillar and the hinge.

> When a small shim is placed between the hinge and pillar on the inside end of the hinge strap, the hinge pivot point is moved ahead. The pivot point, in turn, moves the door ahead. In the same way, a shim placed between the hinge and pillar on the outer end of the hinge strap moves the door back (Figure 11-35).

In-and-Out Adjustments. The in-and-out adjustments control the fit of the door against the body door opening frame. The sealing rubber weatherstrip between the body and the door must be sufficiently compressed to eliminate wind noises and to prevent drafts, dust, and water from entering the vehicle. The outer door panel must be flush with the other surrounding panels.

When the door is moved in or out by an equal amount at both hinges, the change in door alignment takes place mainly at the front of the door, gradually decreasing along the top and bottom toward the rear of the door. The rear of the door is not affected because its in-and-out position is controlled by the lock and striker plate.

When the door is adjusted in or out at one hinge only, the opposite corner of the door is also affected. For example, moving the door out at the top hinge moves the top front section of the door out and the rear bottom corner of the door in. If the door were moved in at the top hinge, the top section of the door would move in and the lower rear corner would move out. The top rear corner of the door will be affected in a similar manner when the lower hinge is moved in or out.

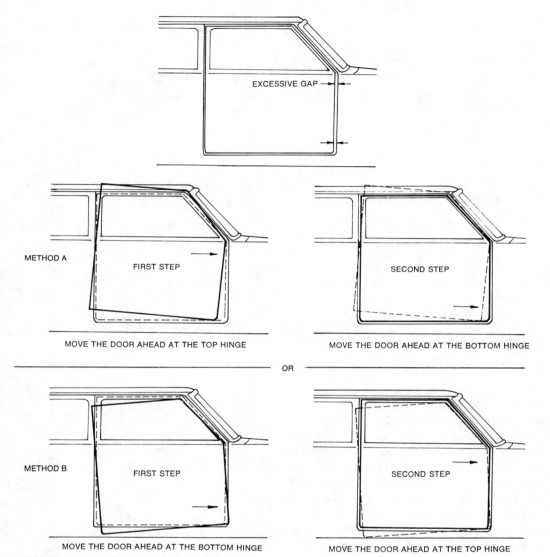

EXCESSIVE GAP

METHOD A

FIRST STEP

MOVE THE DOOR AHEAD AT THE TOP HINGE

SECOND STEP

MOVE THE DOOR AHEAD AT THE BOTTOM HINGE

OR

METHOD B

FIRST STEP

MOVE THE DOOR AHEAD AT THE BOTTOM HINGE

SECOND STEP

MOVE THE DOOR AHEAD AT THE TOP HINGE

Figure 11-34   Moving the door forward

Suppose that the lower rear corner of the door were not flush with the rocker panel and centre post. This condition should be corrected either by moving the door out at the top hinge or by moving it in at the bottom hinge. In some cases, it would be necessary to move the door slightly at both hinges to bring the rear corner in flush with the surrounding panels.

Any in-and-out adjustments should be made from only one hinge at a time since, most of the time, the vertical adjustments are made from the same locations. If the door were loosened at both hinges at once, the vertical adjustment would be lost.

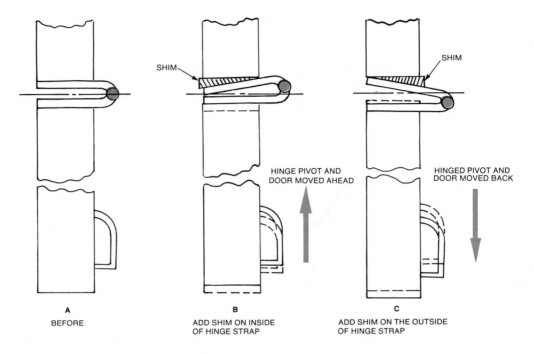

A
BEFORE

B
ADD SHIM ON INSIDE
OF HINGE STRAP

C
ADD SHIM ON THE OUTSIDE
OF HINGE STRAP

Figure 11-35   Shimming a strap-type hinge

Bending. When a door has become misaligned through direct collision damage, or when the hinges are of the weld-on type, bending is the only method that can be used to fit the door. It is seldom the hinge itself that must be bent to refit the door. Usually, the hinges are much stronger than either door or pillar hinge-mounting surfaces. It is this metal at the hinge mounts that bends to cause the misalignment. Figure 11-36 illustrates a typical door hinge-mounting design.

Suppose that a vehicle has been involved in a front-end collision and that the fender has been driven back into, and under, the front edge of the door. This could produce a misalignment condition where the complete door has been pushed back and the front of the door has been shifted out away from the body (Figure 11-37).

Note that the door has been pushed back and out because the metal at the door and

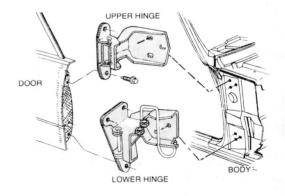

Figure 11-36   Front door hinge mounting

cowl hinge-mounting locations has bent. Figure 11-38 represents a typical cross section view of a hinge and its cowl-to-door mounting design.

The damaged condition is shown in detail in Figure 11-39. At the hinge-to-pillar mount-

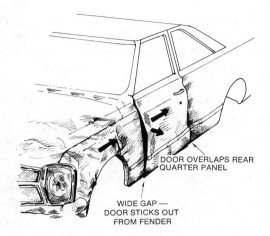

Figure 11-37 Door misalignment caused by front end collision

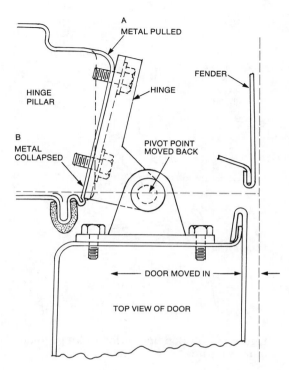

Figure 11-39 Bending action of hinge to hinge pillar mounting area

ing, the metal at A has been pulled and the metal at B has collapsed. As the hinge pivot point moved back, the whole door moved back. At the hinge-to-door mounting, the metal at C has been pulled and the metal at D has collapsed (Figure 11-40). This causes the front of the door to move out away from the door jamb. To correct this condition, the metal at both hinge mountings should be bent back in the reverse order to that in which they were bent out of shape.

The bent metal at C and D sometimes can be straightened by locking the hinge with a steel block, socket, or pry bar and forcing the door open. The hardest part of this procedure is to find some method of locking the hinge while pressure is forced against the back of the door. Pressure should be applied

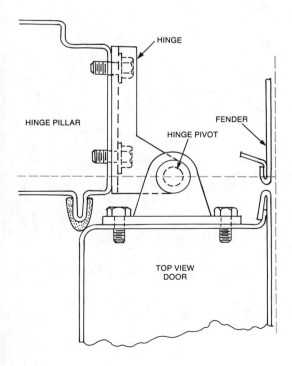

Figure 11-38 Hinge cross-section — top view

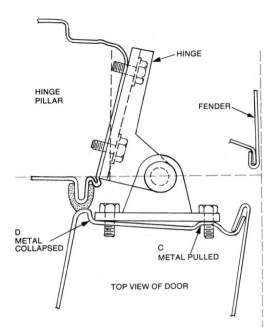

Figure 11-40 Bending action of hinge to door mounting area

very sparingly and with caution. Slowly apply the pressure to one hinge and then the other. The hinge-to-cowl mounting area often can be straightened by driving the hinge with a bar.

> If the hinges are the bolt-on type, it is often easier to remove the door and hinge and then straighten the metal.

The opposite misalignment condition is created when the door is either forced open or driven ahead, as might happen when a door is snagged while the car is backing up.

In this situation, (Figure 11-41) the metal at A of the hinge-to-pillar mount collapses while the metal at B is pulled. This bending action causes the hinge pivot point to move ahead which, in turn, moves the complete door ahead. The metal at the hinge-to-door

mount will collapse at C and be pulled at D. This causes the door to move ahead slightly and the front edge of the door to move in tight against the door opening frame.

The door can be realigned by placing a socket tied to a welding rod or block in the hinge. Close the door against the block, and then carefully apply inward pressure at the back of the door. This action realigns the hinge on the cowl and the door. The metal on the cowl would be pulled back at A and would collapse at B. The metal on the door would be pulled back at C and would collapse at D. The door would be moved back and the front out to its original position. Apply the pressure to the back of the door very slowly. Apply only enough pressure to bend the mounting metals a small amount. Then remove the block and check the door fit. Do one hinge a little bit and then the other.

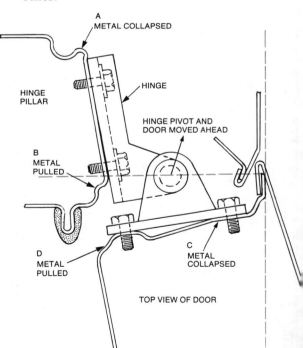

Figure 11-41 Result of the door being swung open

When applying pressure on the back of the door, always keep the hands on the outside of the door so that, if the block slips, the fingers will not be pinched between the door and the door opening frame.

The bending method should be applied to only one hinge at a time, although it should be noted that it is necessary to bend the metal the same amount at each hinge in order to move both the top and the bottom of the door through the same distance. When the metal at one hinge is moved more than the metal at the other, the up or down fit of the door at the striker plate is affected.

Bending is used with the strap-type hinge to move the back of the door up or down and to move the complete door back. There is no provision made for these door adjustments. By placing a block between the hinge straps of the bottom hinge and applying inward pressure against the back of the door, the hinge pivot point is moved back. This in turn moves the bottom of the door back and the back of the door up (Figure 11-42). When the block is placed between the straps of the top hinge and the back of the door is forced inward, the top of the door is moved back and the back of the door is moved down.

Be very careful not to bend the hinge too far when using this method, because it is very difficult to reverse the bending action to move the door forward.

Note that the illustrations have been exaggerated to make the misalignment conditions easily understood. In actual fact, the metal at both hinge mounting locations moves only a very slight amount to cause door misalignment. There are seldom any creases or marks present in the metal to indi-

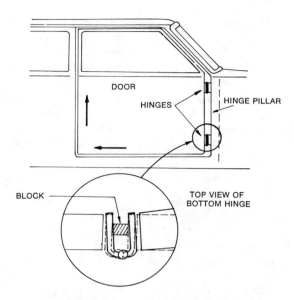

Figure 11-42 Bending the strap-type hinge

cate that the hinge has changed position. As each type of hinge-mounting design can create different misalignment problems, it is important to apply only slight bending pressure and then to check the door fit to determine whether the bending method is correcting the misalignment.

A door slightly low in relation to the striker catch can be lifted by using a length of board or bar as a lever from the top of the sill. Use it to pry up on the bottom of the door. Place a short piece of wood under the door and on the top of the sill. This spreads the force from the lever and prevents the bottom of the door and the step plate from being damaged.

Carefully lift on the lever and slowly raise the back of the door. Keep checking to see how the door fits to the striker. The one problem with this method is that there is little control as to where the actual bending takes place. Suppose for example, that the door is low to the striker and the door gap is too wide through the top hinge area and an attempt is made to close this gap by prying up on the back of the door, thus moving the top of the door ahead. However, if the metal around the lower hinge is weaker, the door may move back from that hinge. The back of the door will be at the correct height to the striker, but the gap along the front would be excessively wide, with a tight gap along the rear of the door to the quarter or centre pillar.

Constantly check the door fit when using this method. Carefully lift the door in small amounts and frequently check the fit.

Misaligned Door Openings

Door misalignment can also be the result of an improperly aligned door opening frame. The shape of the door opening can be corrected by jacking, pulling or, with conventional-design vehicles, by adding or removing shims between the body and the frame at the various body mounting bolts.

Jacking. Figure 11-43 illustrates a situation in which the top of the cowl and the hinge pillar have been driven back as a result of collision damage to the front of the vehicle. Because the cowl moved back, the back of

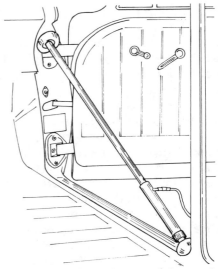

Figure 11-44   Jacking the top of the cowl ahead

the door has dropped and is low at the striker plate. This condition is corrected by jacking the opening, as shown in Figure 11-44. Note the use of rubber bumpers on each end of the jack to prevent the door frame from being damaged.

This type of condition is more commonly found in conventional vehicles, especially those involved in a head-on impact and/or those having large, heavy doors. Unitized vehicles are much stronger through the cowl area. This type of damage in a unitized vehicle would indicate major front section damage. Checking and straightening conventional and unitized vehicles and their body openings is covered in greater detail in Chapter 13.

Shimming the Body Mounts. When the vehicle is of conventional design, the shape of the door openings can be changed by adding or removing shims between the body and frame at the mounting locations.

When shims are added between the body and the frame at mount #1 (Figure 11-45), the cowl is tipped back. The cowl, in turn, moves the top of the door back and the back

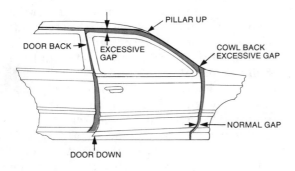

Figure 11-43   Door misalignment caused by the top of the cowl and hinge pillar being driven back

of the door down. Adding shims at mount #2 moves the cowl up and ahead. The door is moved up at the back and ahead at the top. When the cowl is moved back by collision damage, it usually can be jacked ahead. However, with a new vehicle, or one that has been subjected to extreme driving conditions, it may be necessary to use shims to correct the misalignment problem.

Figure 11-46 illustrates an incorrect door gap in the area of the centre post. Adding shims between the body and frame at mount #3 raises the centre section of the body to correct the uneven gap. Note that the gap at the top and bottom of the back of the rear door would also change slightly, as a result of raising the rear-door hinge pillar. Both door striker catches would have to be readjusted to align with the door locks.

In Figure 11-47, the rear-door lock pillar is high. There is too wide a gap between the rear of the door and the roof rail and too tight

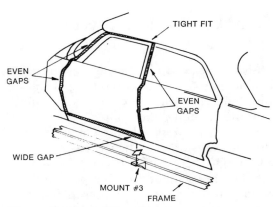

Figure 11-46 Adding shims at mount #3

a gap between the rear of the door and the rocker panel. Removing shims from mount #4 will lower the lock pillar and correct the door gap.

This method of shimming the body mounts to change the door gap can be used only when the location of the body mounts is such that these methods are effective. In each of the examples given, the opposite movement can be obtained. After placing shims at any body mount, the adjacent mounts should also be shimmed, in decreasing amounts, to support the body and to keep it in a straight line.

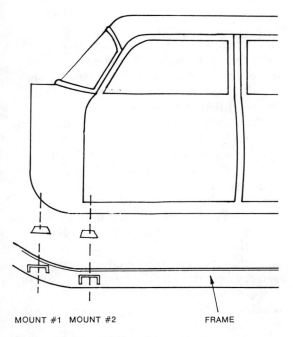

Figure 11-45 Adding shims at mounts #1 and #2

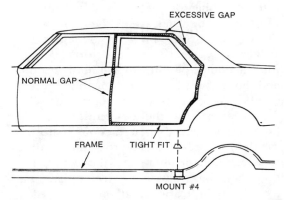

Figure 11-47 Removing shims at mount #4

Door-Lock Striker-Catch Adjustments

The striker-catch should never be adjusted to compensate for, or to correct, a poorly fitting door. The striker-catch serves a two-fold purpose: it holds the door closed, and it prevents any vertical vibration of the door as the vehicle is driven. The striker should be adjusted so there is no vertical movement of the door as the door lock engages with the striker. When the door is locked into the second catch of the striker, the door weatherstrip should be sufficiently compressed so that there is no loose in-and-out play of the door against the lock pillar.

The striker should be aligned with the door lock, provided the door is correctly aligned with the door frame. Some body repairers prefer to remove the striker plate before making the necessary door adjustments, and then to replace and align the striker plate with the correctly fitting door. This is a matter of choice, as it is not necessary to remove the plate first as long as the correct procedure is followed.

Checking and Adjusting the Door Fit, and Positioning the Lock Striker. Hold the door handle in the open position and slowly close the door. As the door lock engages with the striker, check for any up or down movement of the door. If there is no vertical movement, release the handle plunger and continue to close the door. Then check the door gap. If the gap is correct, both the door and the striker are correctly adjusted. However, an uneven door gap indicates that both the door and the striker plate need adjusting.

When the door lock does not line up with the striker plate as the lock engages but the door gap is correct when the door is closed, the door must be adjusted to align with the striker. When the door gap is distorted as the door lock engages with the striker plate, it is usually an indication that only the striker needs to be adjusted. The striker plate should be adjusted to align with the door lock, and then the gap can be rechecked for door misalignment.

> Remember that, of the four methods used to fit a part or unit, the quickest and/or easiest method is not always the best. The method chosen should depend entirely on the circumstances that caused the condition of misalignment.
>
> When using the bending method to align or fit a part, be very careful not to damage other surrounding parts.

Testing the Door-to-Weatherstrip Seal

Under certain conditions — with the windows closed, the fresh air vents open, and/or the heater on — the cabin interior can become pressurized. When this happens a low pressure area is created on the outside at the side windows while the vehicle is moving. The air enters the cabin faster than it can leave. This pressurized air is forced through any small gap, which usually creates an irritating whistling noise.

The weatherstrip seal against the door can be checked by rubbing a soft carpenter's chalk along the sealing surface of the rubber. Chalk the complete length of the rubber (not just sections). Close the door and then reopen it. The chalk will transfer to the metal surface in a continuous unbroken line if the seal is correct. Blue chalk works better with light colours; white works well with dark colours. If the chalk does not seem to transfer onto the metal, apply a thin film of body wax to the metal surface where it touches the weatherstrip. The wax tends to pick up the chalk and leave a clear surface. Once the door is closed and the wax has touched the rubber, it is hard to add more chalk to the rubber without first cleaning it.

To correct a poor seal, it may be necessary to change the fit of the door or shim out the weatherstrip. Water leaks can be found by lightly playing a water hose over the suspected area while someone watches from the inside.

REVIEW QUESTIONS

1. When a unit or part does not fit correctly, there are usually three possible causes. List and explain them.
2. List the four different methods employed to fit, or align, the various parts of the automobile.
3. Explain what is meant by "tapped cage plates" or "nuts."
4. Why are the forward-and-back deck-lid adjustments usually made from only one side at a time?
5. a) Explain how the front of a deck lid can be raised when no vertical adjustment is provided for at the deck-lid hinge.
   b) Where should a shim be placed to lower the front of the deck lid?
6. Using Figure 11-5, explain the procedure to correct the deck lid fit if the gap A–B is excessive and all other gaps, i.e., A–D and B–C, are even.
7. a) Explain the procedure for lifting the front of the deck lid, using the bending method.
   b) What part of the deck lid actually bends, and in what way does it bend?
8. Why must the deck-lid lock and catch be aligned correctly?
9. What adjustment must be made to the striker catch adjustment, if the deck lid must be slammed to close it?

10. Explain how the seal of the deck-lid rubber can be checked.
11. List the adjustments that can be made to fit or align most hoods.
12. Explain the procedure to lower the back of the hood when a side-mounted hinge is used.
13. What adjustments control the flushness of the front of the hood with the top of the fenders?
14. How should either the hood catch or hood lock be adjusted to pull the front of the hood tighter against the rubber bumpers?
15. What two fitting methods are used to adjust, or reposition, bolt-on front fenders?
16. What adjustments usually can be made to the radiator supports used with conventional-design vehicles?
17. Explain why an excessive number of shims should never be removed or added around one mounting point.
18. What allowances usually are made for bumper adjustments?
19. In what directions can doors be moved by the adjusting method?
20. Is it necessary to loosen the bolts at both hinges to raise or lower the door? Give reasons for your answer.
21. List the changes in door gaps that take place when the door is moved back from the bottom hinge.
22. List two ways in which the lower rear corner of the door can be moved out from the body by the adjustment method.
23. When the bending method is used to align a misfitting door, the bending pressure should be applied very lightly. Why?
24. Explain how a door with strap-type hinges can be moved back by the bending method.
25. What two methods can be used to cor-

rect improperly aligned door frames on conventional-design vehicles?

26. When shims are added to a body mount, it is sometimes necessary to add shims, in decreasing numbers, to the adjacent mounts. Why?

27. When the centre pillar is shimmed up, which way should the front door striker catch be adjusted?

28. What are the two purposes of the striker plate?

29. Explain the procedure for checking and adjusting a door striker plate.

30. Explain one method of checking the seal of the weatherstrip against the door.

12 CONVENTIONAL FRAME AND UNITIZED BODY DESIGN

12-1   Frame Design and Construction

12-2   Conventional Frame Construction

12-3   Unitized Construction

12-4   Space Body Shell Construction

12-5   Repairing Frame or Unitized Body Damage

12-6   Types of Damage

12-7   Control Positions

12-8   Frame Gauges

12-1 FRAME DESIGN AND CONSTRUCTION

This chapter deals with the methods used to check and correct the alignment on the conventional vehicle's frame, the complete unitized body, and the new space body shells. Automotive vehicles are dependent on the underbody structural members to provide the necessary strength to support the body, engine, running gear, and suspension units. These structural members can be a separate frame, as in the **conventional** design or they can be welded to the body floor pan, as in the **unitized** design (Figure 12-1).

Figure 12-2 illustrates some of the different structural shapes used for constructing conventional frame rails, unitized subrails, crossmembers, and other reinforcements. The **channel shape** is strong, yet flexible. It is used in truck frames and in areas of conventional vehicles where both strength and some degree of flex is needed. The **box** design is used in many of the separate or conventional frames, especially when extra strength is needed. Note that the box is constructed from two channel shapes.

The **closed box** design is used in unitized construction to make the lower rails. These are made by spot welding a flanged, channel-shaped rail to the body floor or inner wheelhouse panel.

I beam shapes are used for truck front axles. Both **tubular** and I beam shapes are also found in various crossmembers.

Conventional vehicles are heavy and costly to build. Therefore the use of conventional frames is limited to heavier vehicles such as pick-ups, off-road vehicles, large trucks, and some vans. The frame, being the

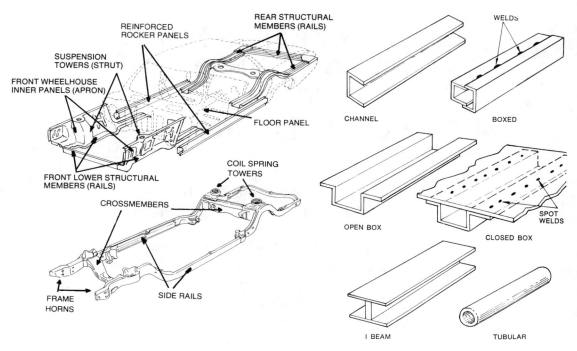

Figure 12-1   Conventional and unitized frame construction

Figure 12-2   Various shapes of frame rails and crossmembers

backbone of the vehicle, must support all the weight and stresses of each of the vehicle's components, as well as any load carried by the vehicle. The separate body/frame design allows the frame to flex or twist with the load. For example, a truck can handle a heavy load even when driven over uneven ground on a construction site.

12-2 CONVENTIONAL FRAME CONSTRUCTION

The frame structural members, or **side rails** as they are often called, are joined together with crossmembers. The strongest crossmember is mounted at the front of the frame to support the engine and front suspension

units. Each crossmember is either rivetted or welded to the side rails.

All frames, whether of conventional or unitized design, are narrower at the front than at the back. The narrow front section allows the front wheels to be swung from left to right for steering and still keep their tracking width approximately the same as that of the rear wheels. The frame width at the back distributes the body load closer to the rear wheels, providing better stability.

Over the years a variety of frame designs have been used. Two of the more common are the ladder and perimeter designs. The **ladder** type has always been used for large trucks (Figure 12-3A). The **perimeter** type is used for conventional vehicles because its "perimeter" shape provides the greatest protection to both the body and passengers from broadside collision (Figure 12-3B).

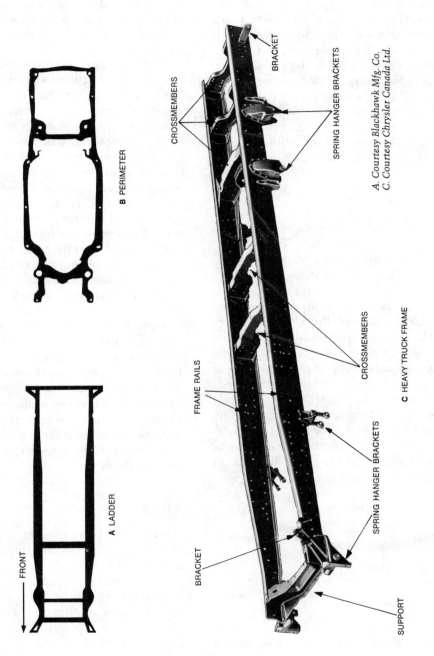

B PERIMETER

A LADDER

FRONT

BRACKET

CROSSMEMBERS

SPRING HANGER BRACKETS

CROSSMEMBERS

FRAME RAILS

SPRING HANGER BRACKETS

BRACKET

SUPPORT

C HEAVY TRUCK FRAME

A. Courtesy Blackhawk Mfg. Co.
C. Courtesy Chrysler Canada Ltd.

Figure 12-3A, B, C   Frame designs

Somewhat greater vehicle stability is also obtained with this wider style frame. The centre section of the car and light truck frames between the front and rear wheels is dropped to obtain a lower centre of gravity and a lower vehicle profile. This creates better vehicle stability. Ladder and perimeter type frames look the same from the side (Figure 12-4). Note how the frame rails are "kicked up" over the front and rear suspension areas. The heavy truck frame (Figure 12-3C) has no front or rear kick up.

·3 UNITIZED CONSTRUCTION

The unitized vehicle is not "frameless." Automotive engineers and designers simply took out the centre section of a conventional frame and designed the front and rear frame sections to fit and weld directly to the lower body. The reinforced rocker panels, floor panels, and complete body shell provide the necessary **centre** body support. The rear section of the body is strengthened by spot welding an inverted flanged U- or C-shaped frame rail directly to the floor panel. The frame rails have a kick up which is very similar to the rear of the conventional frame as shown in Figure 12-4. The rear suspension system bolts to the frame rails.

Courtesy Blackhawk Mfg. Co.

Figure 12-4 Side view of the conventional frame

The front frame rails are also shaped in a similar way to the front section of a conventional frame; both have a kick up area at the front of the cowl (Figure 12-5). The rails are also a flanged U-shape and the inner wheelhouse panel (apron) is spot welded to the flanges of the rail to form a strong boxed member.

The wheelhouse panel is commonly referred to as the **inner apron** (Figure 12-5). This is the key panel that is very necessary to the front section of a unitized vehicle as it provides the extra support to the front section of the vehicle. Without this inner apron, the front frame rails and lower cowl/floor panels could not support the vehicle's weight and endure road stresses. The vehicle would collapse at the cowl. The rails are welded to the bottom of the floor and cowl area. The apron is welded to the rails, the cowl/floor area at the back, and the radiator support at the front (Figure 12-6). The rails, radiator support, and inner aprons become strongly twist-resistant when welded together and to the cowl/floor panel.

Suspension mounting towers are built into the inner aprons. The front suspension units bolt to the towers. All the weight of the front of the vehicle and from the road forces must travel through the suspension system into these towers. The position of the towers controls the front wheel alignment. They must be set in the correct position and held solid for the front suspension to mount and operate from.

Metal

Heavier metals are used to manufacture the conventional frames than those used for unitized members.

The lighter structural members can be used with the unitized design because the vehicle gains it strength through the complete body being welded into an integral unit. Any critical mounting locations are reinforced by adding extra fish plates or layers of metal to that particular area.

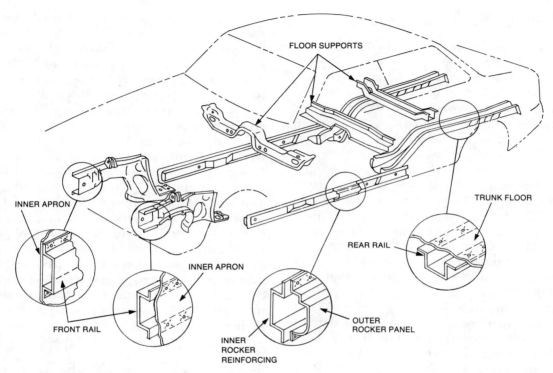

Figure 12-5   Unitized vehicle frame supports

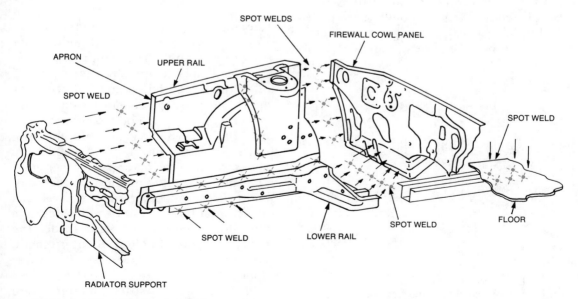

Figure 12-6   All welded unitized front section

Design Features

Unitized vehicles are not new; they have been used by some manufacturers since the 1930s. However, the type of unitized or uni-coup vehicle now being made is considerably different. These newly designed vehicles have been developed for a lighter, more fuel efficient, and safer vehicle. In order to reduce the weight and still maintain the necessary strength, these vehicles are designed so that every part and panel adds strength to the complete body. Even the front windshield and rear window are urethane bonded to their openings to add additional strength to the upper part of the vehicle and the passenger compartment. The windshield pillars are purposely set at a low **rake** (angle) so there is less drag (less wind resistance) around the windshield area (Figure 12-7). More importantly, set at a low angle the pillars and windshield can resist a far greater impact force from a front-end collision. The all-welded unitized vehicle is designed to absorb most of the damaging forces from a collision in the front or rear sections. The damage tends to travel through the vehicle leaving the passenger compartment intact and, one hopes, the passengers unhurt.

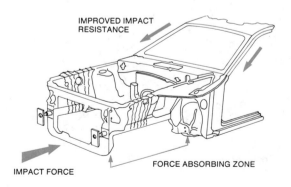

IMPROVED IMPACT RESISTANCE

IMPACT FORCE

FORCE ABSORBING ZONE

Figure 12-7   Newly designed unitized vehicles have low windshield rake and front crumple zones

The steel used in many key locations throughout the vehicle is "high strength," up to three times stronger than steel used in past years. The many metal stampings in the **direct damage** areas tend to bend, buckle, fold, and wad as the force is absorbed. Special convolutions (indentations or wrinkles) and accordion-formed sections are purposely designed into the front and rear section of the unitized vehicle so that upon impact the metal at these areas will actually start to fold and buckle. As the metal folds, it also work hardens to create an additional resistance to further bending. The combination of the metal work hardening, and folding and crushing is designed to absorb the damage force before it reaches the passenger compartment. The front and rear sections are designed to fold down under the body rather than directly back into the passenger compartment.

12-4 SPACE BODY SHELL CONSTRUCTION

Automotive engineers have refined designs for the unitized vehicle into the new **space frame body shell**. The main rails, pillars, posts, and inner reinforcing panels provide all of the structural strength of the body shell. The passenger compartment is surrounded by this main body framework (Figure 12-8). The outer panels are not load-bearing as they are on a unitized vehicle. The only purpose of the outer panels on a space frame body shell is to provide the outer cosmetic shape and covering to the vehicle. This type of body could be compared to a wire bird cage or a wire lamp shade. The wire framework supplies all the strength; the outer covering provides the outer "look."

The outer panels of space frame bodies are often plastic. The lower panels are soft and

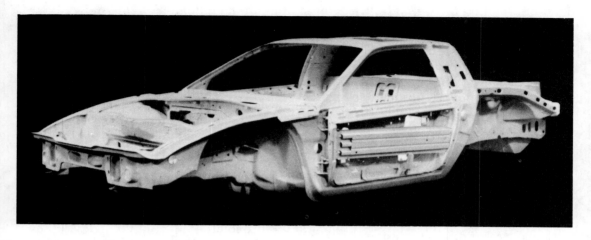

Figure 12-8   Space frame body shell

Courtesy General Motors of Canada Limited

flexible to take light hits and scrapes and still be able to bounce back. The upper panels are made of the rigid type of fibreglass reinforced plastic. Both types are either bonded, clipped on, or screwed to the metal framework.

12-5   REPAIRING FRAME OR UNITIZED BODY DAMAGE

The conventional frame vehicle is the easiest to repair of the three differently constructed vehicles. Damage is usually localized in one rail or section which can be easily identified and located. Although the unitized and space body shell have similar damage characteristics, they are harder to repair than a standard or conventional frame, because the damage tends to spread through the vehicle. It is not uncommon for a vehicle that has been hit hard on the front (direct damage) to have some degree of **indirect damage** in the rear section. This indirect damage might not be visible on the outer panels; the

damage may be hidden in the body floor or rear suspension towers.

Both the separate frame and the unitized body must be sufficiently strong not only to support all the vehicle's weight and road stresses, but also to hold the other units in correct alignment. A collision of sufficient force to bend the frame or unitized body rails will cause misalignment in any of the following: bumpers, body and front fender assemblies, suspension, steering, or running gear assemblies. In order to ensure proper body alignment, and vehicle steering, handling, and roadability, damaged frame rail or body section must be restored to its original shape and tolerances. Manufacturers strive to keep any section of the body or frame rails aligned to within 3 mm to the rest of the vehicle.

Since the frame or unitized frame rails provide the main support and alignment for all the other units, it would be impossible to align or straighten any of the attached units before correcting the lower frame damage.

When both the frame rails and other reinforcing body panels are bent, the damaged body will prevent the frame members from returning to their original shapes. In this case, it is necessary to apply corrective measures to both frame and body panels at the same time. This is especially the case in unitized vehicles where the front frame rails are spot welded to the wheelhouse inner aprons and radiator support as illustrated in Figure 12-6.

With conventional vehicles, the body is bolted to the frame through rather large over-size holes. Usually the damaged frame is first pulled straight. The movement is possible because of the oversize holes. After the frame damage is corrected, the body is straightened to fit the frame.

In many cases damage to a frame rail or other supporting panels can be considered indirect or hidden damage. Often, they were not in actual contact with the impact object. Therefore, one of the first rules to follow before attempting collision-damage repair is to inspect the rails, crossmembers, inner aprons, lower cowl areas, and floor panels thoroughly for visible damage. Look for stress or flex marks in these areas. These marks will be identified as any "clean" areas where mud, undercoating, or rust scale has been cracked or knocked off. These clean marks do not necessarily mean actual damage. The metal may have just flexed at these points as it absorbed the impact force, without taking a permanent bend or the complete section may have been moved out of its alignment. Check these areas closely for any bulges on the sides and/or kinks on the top of the frame rails. Any bulges, wrinkles, kinks, and torn metal areas definitely indicate frame or body misalignment. If any of these tell-tale signs are visible on the frame rails or other supporting members, then one must determine how much and in what direction the conventional frame or unitized rails or section has actually bent or moved out of position.

12-6 TYPES OF DAMAGE

Whether a vehicle has a conventional (separate), a unitized, or a space body shell frame, depending on the direction from which the vehicle was hit, the frame or unitized-body distortion will usually follow one, or some combination, of six basic patterns:

- sag
- front or rear kick down
- sway
- mash
- diamond
- twist

Sag

Sag, one type of misalignment, is caused by an impact force hitting one end of the conventional frame rail. As the force travels through the frame the kick up area drops at

A FRONT-END COLLISION

B REAR-END COLLISION

Courtesy Bear Manufacturing Company

Figure 12-9A, B   Sag

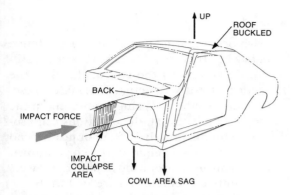

Figure 12-10   Sag in a unitized body

The ends of the front and rear sections of the rails are purposely designed to roll down and back under the vehicle (Figure 12-11A, B). The engine and sheet metal are carried away from the passenger compartment on impact. The kick down is always created first. If the impact is severe, the unitized vehicle will then, after kicking down, begin to sag at the cowl area.

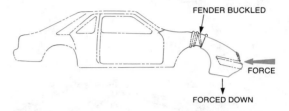

Figure 12-11   Unitized front kick down

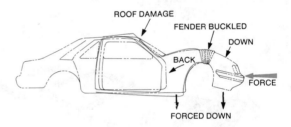

Figure 12-11B   Kick down and cowl sag

either the cowl or rear door area, depending on whether the vehicle was hit from the front or the back (Figure 12-9A, B). Definite evidence of a sag condition are bulges on the sides and wrinkles on the top of the frame rails at the area of bend. With a sag condition on a conventional frame, the engine and sheet metal are actually carried up and back into the passenger compartment. A sag condition can also be referred to as a **front or rear rail kick up**.

Conventional vehicles tend to sag much more easily than unitized or space body shells. With the unitized design, the frame sub-rails are strongly reinforced in the front by the inner apron, cowl, windshield pillars and roof rails, and in the rear by the rockers, quarters, inner wheelhousing, and roof rails. The frame rails do not sag unless the vehicle has been severely impacted. When they do sag, the roof usually buckles in the area of the centre or rear quarter pillar area (Figure 12-10).

Front or Rear Kick Down

Front or rear kick down is a damage condition that is common on unitized vehicles.

Sway

Sway can occur in the front, rear, or centre section of the frame or unitized vehicle usually as a result of an impact to the corner or the centre of the vehicle (Figure 12-12A, B, C). The impact forces one section to move sideways. Usually the rail closest to the point of impact moves the farthest, although both side rails can bend sideways by the same amount. Figure 12-13 illustrates sway in a unitized vehicle.

Centre sway is caused from a broadside

collision force. The centre is pushed in and each end of the vehicle is pulled toward the point of impact.

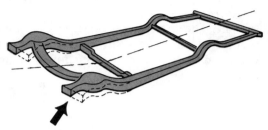

A FRONT-END COLLISION

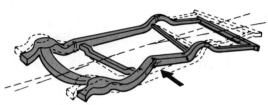

B SIDE COLLISION

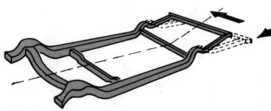

C REAR-END COLLISION

Courtesy Bear Manufacturing Company

Figure 12-12A, B, C   Sidesway

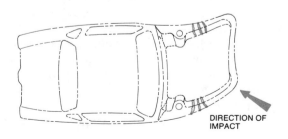

DIRECTION OF IMPACT

Figure 12-13   Unitized sway

Mash

Mash occurs in the outer areas of the frame rails when there is a direct front or rear collision force against the end of the rail. The section of rail will actually wrinkle, or accordian together, causing shortening in the length of the rail. Mash conditions can usually be found directly in front or just behind the front crossmember on the conventional frame and just in front and behind the towers on a unitized vehicle (Figure 12-14A, B).

With unitized vehicles special convolution and accordion sections are purposely built into the rails. Collision forces are absorbed as the metal in the sections fold and mash together. Due to their lighter gauge of metal and all-welded design, unitized vehicles tend to have more frontal or rear mash collision damage. The radiator support, inner apron, and frame rail all tend to absorb the force, by folding and wadding together. The force is gradually absorbed as it moves through the vehicle. A unitized vehicle hit

A FRONT-END COLLISION

B REAR-END COLLISION

Courtesy Bear Manufacturing Company

Figure 12-14A, B   Mash

hard in the front could sustain not only front area mash, but also a very noticeable wrinkle in the rear section of the vehicle.

Diamond

A diamond condition occurs when an impact has forced one side rail back further than the other throughout the complete length of the conventional frame. The crossmembers are pushed "out of square" with the side members. The impact usually occurs at one corner, either front or rear (Figure 12-15). Unitized vehicles seldom assume a diamond

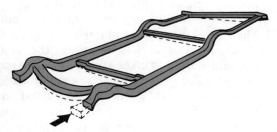

Courtesy Bear Manufacturing Company

Figure 12-15   Diamond

shape through the complete lower length of the frame rail platform area, although one front rail could be pushed back into the cowl, making only the front section appear diamond.

Twist

Twist has occurred when the centre section of the frame rails or the unitized rocker panels are not level with each other through the horizontal plane (Figure 12-16A, B). A common cause of twist is a vehicle rolling over while all the vehicle's weight is on one wheel. Twist conditions are often caused in trucks by the load shifting as the vehicle pitches and rolls. Unitized vehicles twist. When this happens the twist is also present through the upper body areas.

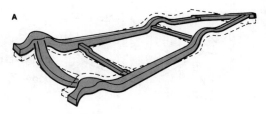

Courtesy Bear Manufacturing Company

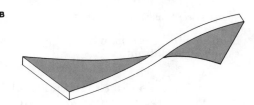

Figure 12-16A, B   Twist

A twist condition should not be confused with a front or rear section being kicked up or down. The frame or body may appear twisted when in fact only one section of rail is kicked up.

12-7 CONTROL POSITIONS

To understand these misalignment conditions, consider the frame or unitized body to be divided into three separate sections as shown in Figure 12-17. The conventional frame has four main **control positions** through these three sections (Figure 12-18).

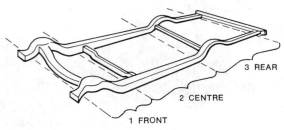

Courtesy Bear Manufacturing Company

Figure 12-17   Concept of three sections

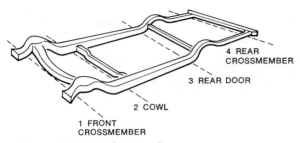

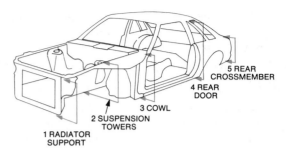

Courtesy Bear Manufacturing Company

Figure 12-18 Four main control positions on a conventional frame

Figure 12-19 Five main control positions on a unitized or space shell

The unitized and space shell body each have five (Figure 12-19). These four or five positions are the normal controlling points for the front and rear suspension mountings, the engine support, as well as for the body and front fender assembly.

In order for the vehicle to steer, drive, and track correctly, each control area must be in its correct alignment to the others.

> The unitized and space shell have a suspension tower area in place of the conventional frame crossmember as well as the additional front radiator support control position.

Both the conventional frame and unitized bodies are assembled and welded in jigs to tolerances of within plus or minus 3 mm. The bodies are made symmetrical. Each half, slicing lengthwise, will be exactly the same size and shape and in the same position as the opposite side (Figure 12-20). Some unitized bodies may have a rail, part, section, or mounting hole "offset" from the centre line compared to its other side. For example, a rear frame rail may be offset to provide room for the gasoline tank. One strut tower may be offset to help set the wheel alignment. Any offset area is said to be **asymmetrical** (not the same). The complete overall body is always **symmetrical**, while one part of it may be asymmetrical.

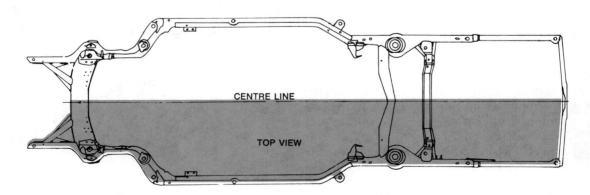

Figure 12-20 Symmetrical design for a conventional frame

Datum Plane

The contour of the side view of both the frame rails and/or lower unitized platform must also be the same. Their contours can be checked by measuring from various points on the rails and unitized body floor to a common **datum reference plane.** This datum plane is a horizontal plane running under and parallel to the length of the frame or unitized platform. It is an imaginary plane set at a fixed distance from the frame by the vehicle manufacturer (Figure 12-21). Various measurements from different positions are shown on frame dimension reference charts either supplied by the vehicle manufacturer or by frame and body straightening equipment manufacturers. The measurements on one side can be compared to a similar measurement taken from the same position on the opposite side, and both can be compared to those shown in the reference chart (Figure 12-22). The datum plane can be raised or lowered by subtracting or adding an equal amount to all the datum measurements.

Figure 12-23 illustrates a reference chart typical for a conventional frame. Note the side view datum measurements, the top view

centre line, and diagonal corner-to-corner measurements, as well as the rail length measurements. The length measurements are especially necessary for checking the length of the rails through the kick up areas.

By using the information in the reference chart, the conventional frame can be checked for the length of the rails, the width of each side of the frame from the centre line to the rail, the squareness of each section, the height contour, datum measurements, and the horizontal plane of the two side rails to each other (twist).

Figure 12-24 illustrates a unitized reference chart. Note the symmetrical measurements made through the lower section of the body. Also important in the unitized body are the upper body super structure measurements which must have matching height and squareness in each of the five control positions in relation to the lower floor/frame platform (especially through the inner apron suspension tower area). Because the upper body pillars, rails, and panels are load-bearing, they move out of position and alignment from each other as the collision forces move through the vehicle. When straightening a unitized body, the width, length, height, and squareness of the platform and

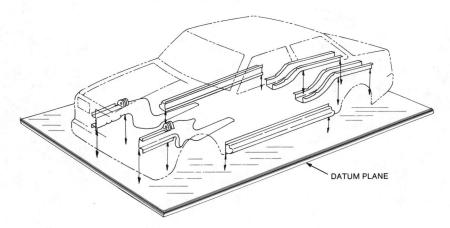

DATUM PLANE

Figure 12-21   Datum plane and typical measuring locations

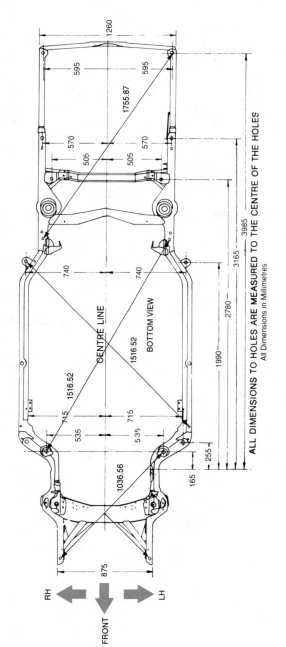

ALL DIMENSIONS TO HOLES ARE MEASURED TO THE CENTRE OF THE HOLES

All Dimensions in Millimetres

Figure 12-22   Typical frame dimensions chart

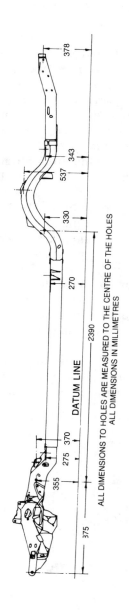

ALL DIMENSIONS TO HOLES ARE MEASURED TO THE CENTRE OF THE HOLES

ALL DIMENSIONS IN MILLIMETRES

Figure 12-23   Datum-line reference chart

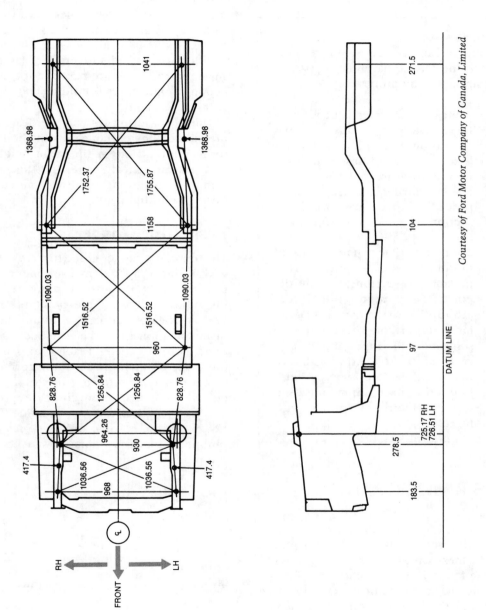

Courtesy of Ford Motor Company of Canada, Limited

Figure 12-24 A unitized body reference chart

each of the control sections in the upper super structure must be checked and straightened at the same time.

Regardless of the type of vehicle or amount of damage, there are three necessary operations that must be part of the straightening process.
1. Evaluate the extent of the damage. Some means of measuring is necessary. This is done first to find out what sections are out of alignment and in which direction. A measuring devise is also needed during the straightening procedure to indicate when the section is back in its correct position.
2. There must be some means of holding the vehicle "solid" in the undamaged section(s) while the corrective straightening forces are applied to the damaged area.
3. Most important, there must be some method of applying the corrective force to the damaged area while the vehicle is being held. Hydraulic jack equipment is used to apply a corrective push or pull force.

12-8 FRAME GAUGES

For years the conventional frame was measured with relatively simple equipment such as a measuring tape, tramming and self-centring frame gauges. Slight "out of alignment" in the frame could be compensated for through the many adjustments in the suspension system and front fender assembly where they bolted together and to the frame.

With the unitized vehicle being a completely welded integral load-bearing shell, every part, rail, panel, and section must fit and align correctly. Improved checking and measuring devices were needed for better accuracy. The measuring tape and tram gauge is still used along with various mechanical, dedicated, universal, or laser measuring systems that are part of a specialized bench or platform rack holding and straightening equipment.

These measuring systems are designed to measure the lower frame rails and body platform width and length, the datum height, the body's symmetrical shape, and the suspension tower locations. Some also measure the upper body alignment.

Tramming Gauge

The tramming gauge is used to check length, width, and diagonal measurements. This gauge is made of square or round telescoping tubes and adjustable pointers (Figure 12-25). The pointers can be set and clamped in any position along the tram body, as well as adjusted for their "reach out" from the tram. The pointers are set at the correct distance either by referring to the measurements on the chart or by comparing the undamaged length to the damaged side. Figure 12-26 illustrates some of the typical measurements that can be made with the tram and pointers.

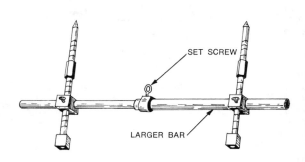

Figure 12-25   Adjustable tramming gauge

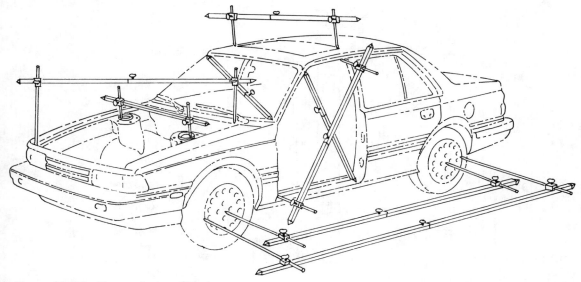

Figure 12-26   Tramming applications

The tram gauge can be used without the pointers for direct point-to-point measurements. The pointers are used when it is necessary to "reach" the measuring points.

The length of each pointer should be either the same or the pointers must be set to keep the tram bar as parallel as possible with the item being measured (Figure 12-27). Either method can be used when the distance of one side is being compared to the opposite side. When the length of the distance being measured is being compared to measurements in a reference chart, then it is important that the gauge be used as it was shown on the chart or a false reading will be obtained. Sometimes it may be necessary to compare both methods of measurements to those listed in the chart.

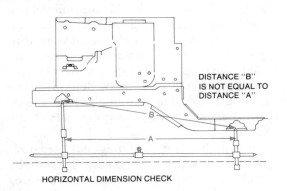

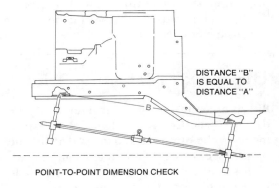

Figure 12-27   Horizontal and point-to-point dimension checks

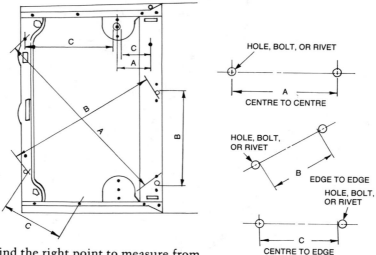

Figure 12-28   Find the right point to measure from

Carefully note the location of the point of the measurement arrows shown in the chart in relation to the hole, edge, dot, etc. Some points are to the centre, others to the edge, either front or rear (Figure 12-28). Many manufacturers are pressing small dimples or notches into the metal at various centre and other reference locations. Usually there is some type of identical seam, spot weld, or edge that can be used as a reference measuring point. Some pointer sets are equipped with a large slip-on tapered end that will centre itself in any size hole.

Upper Body Measuring Points

By comparing the measurements of the damaged section with identical measurements of the opposite undamaged areas, the parts or section out of alignment can be readily located. The measurements can be made with a tramming, a measuring bar, or a tape measure.

Diagonal measurements can also be made to check for body squareness. Diagonal measurements must be taken between points which are exactly opposite each other, with the ends of the measuring bar contacting the identical points.

All measurements should be made from the metal. This sometimes necessitates the removal of the interior trim.

It is difficult to obtain correct aligning measurements when a body is damaged on both sides. In these cases, measurements can be taken from a body of the same model and body style. Figures 12-29 A–D show the locations of the horizontal and vertical measuring points. Once these basic dimensions are established on the damaged body, the misalignment conditions can be determined by making diagonal measurements from the established measuring points, shown in Figure 12-29 E–H.

When the opposite diagonal measurements are not the same, the body should be forced out along the short diagonal. The area at the end of the short diagonal must be moved out slightly more than half the dif-

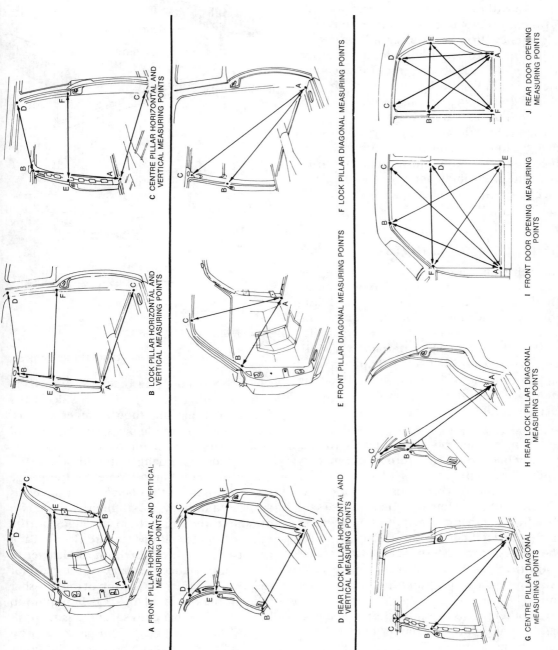

A FRONT PILLAR HORIZONTAL AND VERTICAL MEASURING POINTS

B LOCK PILLAR HORIZONTAL AND VERTICAL MEASURING POINTS

C CENTRE PILLAR HORIZONTAL AND VERTICAL MEASURING POINTS

D REAR LOCK PILLAR HORIZONTAL AND VERTICAL MEASURING POINTS

E FRONT PILLAR DIAGONAL MEASURING POINTS

F LOCK PILLAR DIAGONAL MEASURING POINTS

G CENTRE PILLAR DIAGONAL MEASURING POINTS

H REAR LOCK PILLAR DIAGONAL MEASURING POINTS

I FRONT DOOR OPENING MEASURING POINTS

J REAR DOOR OPENING MEASURING POINTS

Figure 12-29   Upper body measuring points

ference between the two diagonals. The extra push will compensate for "spring-back."

Do not attempt to correct any serious misalignment with one jacking or pulling operation. This is particularly important if other sections of the body also require aligning. Each section should be aligned in proportion to the damage in that area, until the proper dimensions are obtained.

The shape of the door openings can also be checked by comparing the measurements on one side of the body to those on the opposite side. The horizontal, vertical, and diagonal checking points are shown in Figure 12-29 I and J.

Self-Centring Gauges

Self-centring gauges have been used for years to check conventional type frames. They can be used for unitized vehicles; however, other types of newer equipment have gained favour. The self-centring gauges used with a conventional frame are still worth an explanation because knowing how they operate helps in better understanding the theory behind the newer types of measuring equipment.

Self-Centring Frame Gauges. These are self-centring devices that connect to the frame or body lower structure. There are two types. One type consists of two sliding crossbars which can be adjusted in or out to the width of the frame members. An **adjustable hanger** that can be raised or lowered clamps to each end of the sliding crossbar. The middle of the crossbar housing contains a **sighting pin** which always remains centred. The sighting pin can be adjusted up or down (Figure 12-30A).

The other type is a simpler centring device that is hung from the frame or body by two light chains (Figure 12-30B).

The adjustable hangers or chains are hung from identical points, such as factory-formed

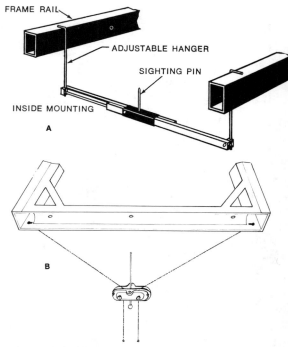

Courtesy Blackhawk Mfg. Co.

Figure 12-30A, B   Self-centring frame gauges

holes, body-mounting brackets, or suspension mounting points, on each side of the frame. The gauges should never be suspended from movable parts, such as control arms, springs, or torsion bars.

Three or more gauges should be used to check for frame misalignment. One gauge should be hung at the control position that is suspected of being misaligned. At least two others (three are better) are hung at the other control positions (Figure 12-31). Each crossbar must be adjusted on the hanger to the datum distance indicated on the chart for that control position. The top of the crossbar is set at the datum plane. It is important to have both crossbar ends set at the same position on the two hangers. If one gauge must be lowered to clear an obstruction, the other gauges must all be lowered an equal amount at each hanger to maintain the same datum

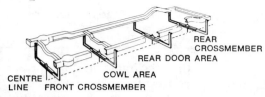

CENTRE LINE FRONT CROSSMEMBER COWL AREA REAR DOOR AREA REAR CROSSMEMBER

Courtesy Bear Manufacturing Company

Figure 12-31   Gauge locations for four frame-centring gauges

plane. The frame sway misalignment is checked by looking down the centre sighting pins. If the frame is not distorted, the pins should all be aligned as shown in Figure 12-32. When the pins will not line up, a side-sway condition is present in one or more sections of the frame.

Sag and twist conditions can be checked by sighting along the top of the gauge crossbars at their outer ends. If the crossbars are still in line with each other, the height contour of the rails is correct.

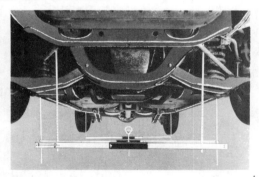

Courtesy Blackhawk Mfg. Co.

Figure 12-32   Sighting along the centre pins for frame misalignment

Checking for Sag. A sag condition in both rails would be indicated by the front gauge crossbar appearing higher than the crossbars of the other gauges (Figure 12-33). A sag in one rail would be indicated by the crossmember gauge appearing **cocked** (not parallel to the gauge under the cowl control

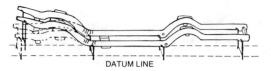

DATUM LINE

Figure 12-33   Gauges indicate that both side rails are sagged

position). The sag is located under the cowl at the side of the high corner of the first gauge. One side rail can go down as much as 150 mm without affecting the other rail (Figure 12-34).

The gauge crossbars at the cowl and rear door may line up while the front gauge looks cocked. This happens because the frame usually remains in line back from the cowl. As the cowl sags, the frame pivots over the front wheel like a teeter-totter. The front section of the frame kicks up, preventing the first two gauges from lining up. The same results occur with rear sag damage.

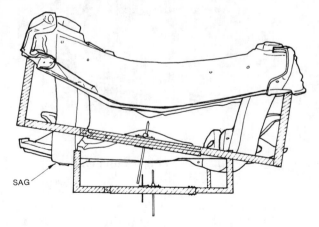

SAG

Figure 12-34   Sag in one side rail

Checking for Twist. Twist is checked by sighting the gauge crossbars at the cowl and rear door control positions. If the crossbars

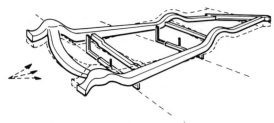

Courtesy Bear Manufacturing Company

Figure 12-35   Checking for twist

are cocked or twisted from each other, a twist is present through the centre section of the vehicle (Figure 12-35).

Checking for Diamond. A diamond condition in a conventional frame is checked by making diagonal cross-checks with the tram gauge as illustrated in Figure 12-36.

Courtesy Blackhawk Mfg. Co.

Figure 12-36   Checking for diamond

Mash. A mash condition cannot be checked with self-centring gauges. However, mash is usually so noticeable that it can be determined by just looking at the rails. Since mash is a shortening of the rail or section, the length of the rail is checked with the tram gauge by measuring lengthwise along each

side rail or by taking diagonal measurements of the section (Figure 12-37).

> The width of the frame must be correct for the self-centring gauges to work correctly. If only one rail is pushed in or out in the area where the gauge hangs, then the centre pin will appear off to one side, indicating a sway condition when there actually is not one.

The self-centring gauges do not check or measure any upper body areas, especially the important front section unitized body suspension towers. They are also somewhat hard to accurately sight along the centre pins and crossbars.

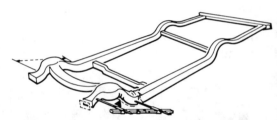

Courtesy Bear Manufacturing Company

Figure 12-37   Using a tram gauge to measure mash

REVIEW QUESTIONS

1. What is the purpose of the underbody structural members?
2. List the names given to the various shapes of the underbody structural members, and draw a cross-sectional diagram of each to help explain them.
3. List two advantages of using the perimeter design frame.
4. Why is the channel design usually used for truck frames?
5. Why are the frames designed to be narrow at the front and wide at the back?

6. Why is the centre section of the automobile frame dropped between the front and rear wheels?

7. With a unitized vehicle, the centre section of the frame is not needed. Why?

8. Define the term "kick up" as it is used in describing a section of the frame rails.

9. Explain how the front section of a unitized vehicle is strengthened.

10. Why can lighter metals be used for the structural members of a unitized vehicle rather than for a conventional frame?

11. Why are the windshield pillars set at a low "rake"?

12. Define the term "convolutions."

13. Explain the difference between a space frame body and an ordinary unitized body.

14. a) Why is a bent frame often considered indirect damage?
    b) What are the visible signs indicating frame damage?

15. List and briefly explain the six basic distortion patterns that frame rails usually follow when they have been damaged.

16. The unitized rails are purposely designed to kick down. Explain why.

17. Why do unitized vehicles usually tend to have more frontal or rear mash?

18. a) Draw a diagram to illustrate the three sections and five control points of a unitized vehicle.
    b) Which control point does the conventional frame not have?

19. Define the terms symmetrical and asymmetrical.

20. Define the term "datum line."

21. List the three operations necessary to check and straighten a damaged section in a unitized vehicle.

22. What is the purpose of a tramming gauge?

23. Explain how the tramming gauge is used.

24. Why are the tram pointers needed?

25. What type of condition is usually indicated by unequal diagonal measurements through a section of the body?

26. a) Why should the self-centring frame gauges never be suspended from movable parts?
    b) From what points on a frame should the self-centring gauges be suspended when three gauges are used to check frame damage?

FRAME STRAIGHTENING: SUSPENSION AND STEERING SYSTEMS

13-1 Portable Body-Frame Straighteners
13-2 Bench Equipment Systems
13-3 Frame Straightening Methods
13-4 Suspension Systems
13-5 Steering Linkage

The operating principle of any straightening operation is to firmly anchor the vehicle at the undamaged area while the damaged area or parts are pulled back in a reverse direction from which they were damaged by the impact force. New types of equipment gradually evolved over the years as certain needs

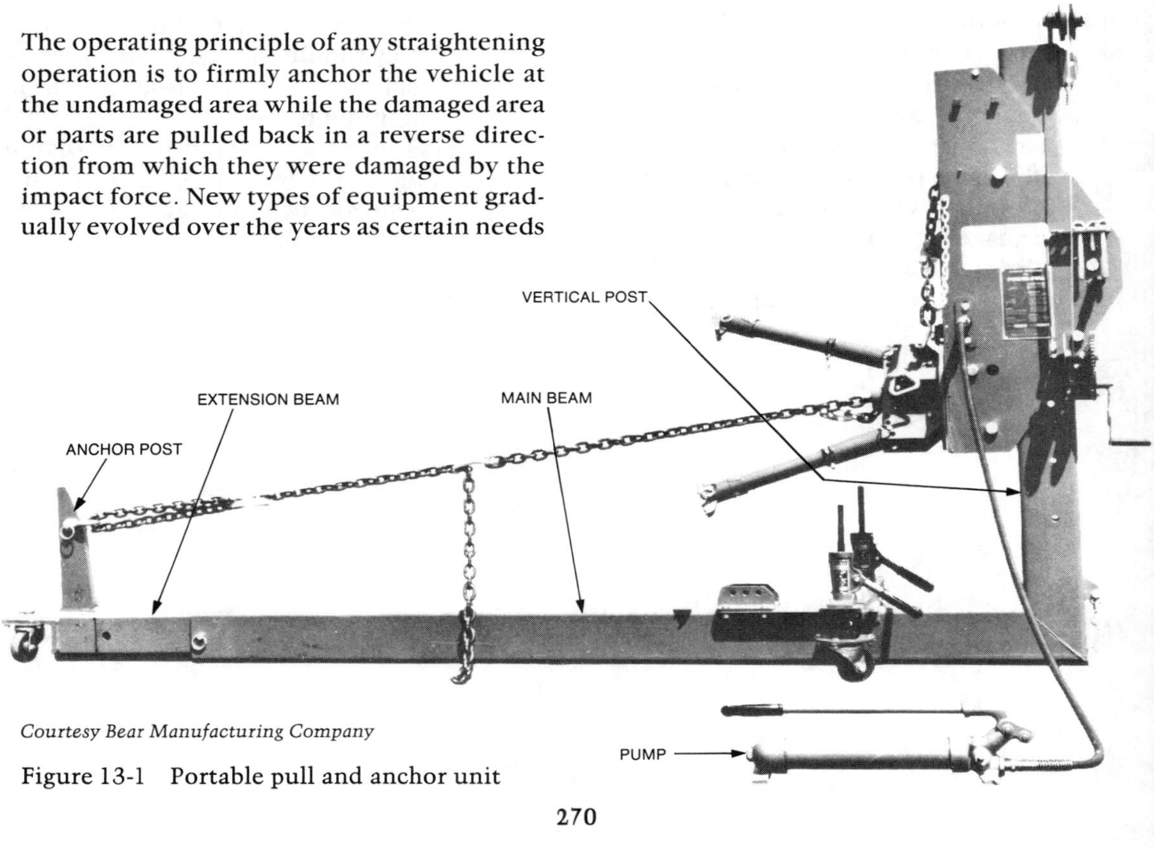

Courtesy Bear Manufacturing Company

Figure 13-1   Portable pull and anchor unit

270

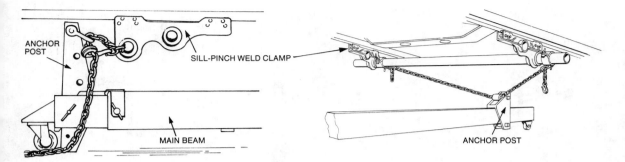

Figure 13-2   Anchoring methods

Courtesy Blackhawk Mfg. Co.

developed. Straightening equipment ranges from very simple portable pull-only units, portable pull and hold systems, and stationary rack to various types of bench systems. Whether portable or stationary they all have their advantages and disadvantages.

13-1 PORTABLE BODY– FRAME STRAIGHTENERS

Portable Pull and Anchor Unit

This type of portable equipment is designed to both anchor the vehicle and pull the damaged area (Figure 13-1). The vehicle is raised off the floor and placed on vehicle support stands. The mainbeam of the portable puller is anchored to the undamaged frame or lower body members (Figure 13-2), the vertical beam is connected to the damaged member by a chain. A hydraulic jack anchored to the main, or vertical beam of the puller is used to supply the corrective pulling force.

Pull-Only Units

The other type of portable equipment is designed to apply only the corrective forces (Figure 13-3). Both the puller and the vehi-

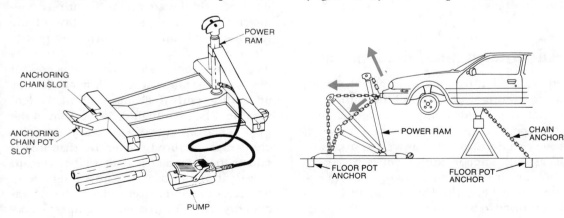

Figure 13-3   Portable pull units anchored to floor pots

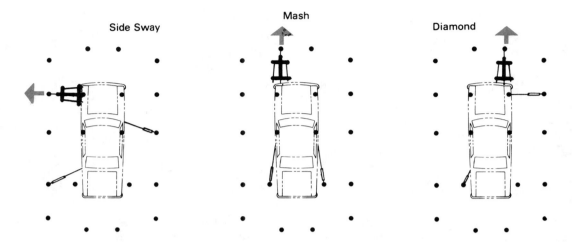

Figure 13-4   Pull set ups using floor pots   *Courtesy Blackhawk Mfg. Co.*

cle are anchored to specially designed floor anchor pots or rails embedded in the concrete floor.

A series of pots are installed in strategic layouts so the vehicle and puller can be anchored in any straightening position to make the necessary set-up (Figure 13-4).

Chains of high tensile strength are used to make both anchoring and pulling set-ups. They are designed to withstand far greater pulling forces, without breaking, than ordinary steel chains.

Advantages and Disadvantages

Figure 13-5 illustrates a variety of set-ups using a portable pull and hold puller and portable pull-only equipment connected to floor pots or rails. Each of these methods have certain advantages as well as disadvantages. Pull anchor equipment is very portable, but it is sometimes hard to anchor to the unitized vehicle. This equipment is usually limited to one pull at a time. Pull equipment anchored to the floor has worked well. However, it is not portable in that its use is limited to the location of the floor anchor system. The floor anchoring pot is often not in the right position to anchor the puller. A separate chain clamping system is needed to anchor the vehicle to the floor pots or rails.

The tram and self-centring gauges have been used with these pulling systems to check and measure the vehicle's straightness. One drawback, however, is that the centring gauges do not measure the upper body areas. This is a problem since some unitized vehicles are not built entirely symmetrical. For example, one section of the rear frame rail might be purposely placed off-centre compared to the other rail. As well, some front suspension towers are not positioned symmetrically. Either side may be set differently to change the wheel alignment to offset the high centre crown in the road. When one side of a section of the vehicle is manufactured off-centre, that area is said to be asymmetrical in shape. Due to these various measuring and straightening problems in the unitized vehicle, bench anchoring and fixture measuring systems evolved. Nevertheless, portable equipment is still used to pull light damage areas.

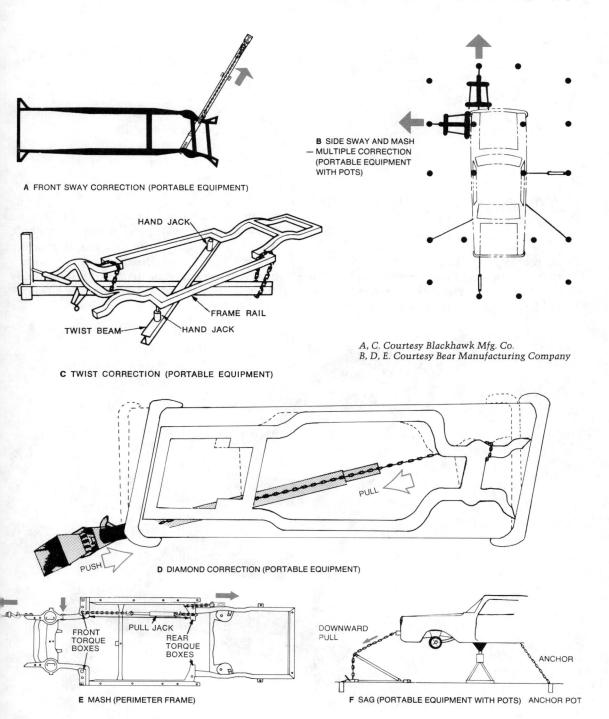

A FRONT SWAY CORRECTION (PORTABLE EQUIPMENT)

HAND JACK

FRAME RAIL

TWIST BEAM

HAND JACK

C TWIST CORRECTION (PORTABLE EQUIPMENT)

B SIDE SWAY AND MASH
— MULTIPLE CORRECTION
(PORTABLE EQUIPMENT
WITH POTS)

A, C. Courtesy Blackhawk Mfg. Co.
B, D, E. Courtesy Bear Manufacturing Company

PULL

PUSH

D DIAMOND CORRECTION (PORTABLE EQUIPMENT)

FRONT
TORQUE
BOXES

PULL JACK

REAR
TORQUE
BOXES

E MASH (PERIMETER FRAME)

DOWNWARD
PULL

ANCHOR

F SAG (PORTABLE EQUIPMENT WITH POTS)   ANCHOR POT

Figure 13-5   Typical basic correction hook-ups

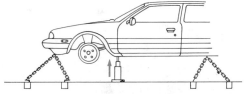

G HOLDING THE FRONT AND LIFTING UNDER THE COWL

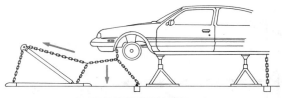

H USING A CHAIN BRIDGE TO MAKE A DOWN PULL

13-2 BENCH EQUIPMENT SYSTEMS

Bench equipment is used to repair medium and heavy structural-damaged unitized vehicles. The bench consists of a heavy solid steel framework. Most are mounted on large castors so they can be easily moved. Figure 13-6 illustrates a typical stripped bench. Note the row of bolt holes along the outer edge of each longitudinal bench rail. Some bench systems are designed to anchor and measure only, while others anchor, measure, and pull.

Figure 13-6   Stripped bench

Courtesy Blackhawk Automotive Division

Figure 13-7   Bench pinch weld clamps

Courtesy Chart Industries Limited

Anchoring System

Body holding clamps bolt directly to the bench and clamp to the lower pinchweld area of the rocker panels. The clamps are adjustable in that they can be moved in or out to fit the rocker pinchweld width, and up or down to adjust the height of the vehicle to the fixtures (Figure 13-7).

Bench and Dedicated Fixture System

The fixtures are variously sized and shaped steel members designed to bolt to transverse beams that are, in turn, bolted to the main bench rails. A reference chart for each vehicle is supplied by the bench manufacturer which indicates the location of each trans-

Figure 13-8   Bench and dedicated fixture system

Courtesy Blackhawk Automotive Division

verse beam to the bench and each fixture to the transverse beam. The height of the fixtures duplicates the height contour of the vehicle from the top surface of the bench (the datum plane).

The vehicle is actually lifted up and positioned on top of the fixtures. The clamps are then adjusted upwards and connected to the lower rocker panel pinchweld (Figure 13-8). The top of each fixture is designed to fit up to a specific reference point. If the vehicle fits all the fixtures, the lower area of the body has the correct width, length, and datum height. The top of the fixture is positioned in the body reference locations by a number of methods: some fixtures have a large pin that fits up into the body reference hole. Others actually bolt directly to the vehicle, usually where the bumpers or some other bolt-on parts are located (Figure 13-9). Note that the suspension tower fixture has a top plate that is bolted to the tower and that the vertical pin is in turn bolted to the top plate. The alignment pins can be

dropped by pulling a small cross pin and removing the bolt, when that particular section of the body has to be pulled into position. Once the fixture is in position, it is left connected to help prevent over-pulling of that area while the next section is pulled into position. These types of fixtures are referred to as a **dedicated** system because the fixtures are specifically designed for one type of vehicle. A different set of fixtures is required for each different manufacturer's vehicles. Because of this disadvantage, various universal measuring systems have also been developed.

Universal Systems

These systems are designed to sit on the top surface of the bench or a platform type rack; they are under the vehicle. Some can also be mounted on a light framework and used from the floor directly under a vehicle placed on four safety stands. Being **universal**, the gauge can be adjusted and set to fit any vehicle. The manufacturer supplies a reference chart book illustrating the correct settings for each vehicle.

The following describes a typical universal measuring system. Transverse crossbars are connected to one or two longitudinal main beams. Vertical-mounted adjustable pins are connected to the top of the transverse crossbars. A chart supplied by the equipment manufacturer illustrates the correct length settings of the cross beams to the main longitudinal beams, as well as their width settings and the pin heights. With the length, width, and height positions set, the unit is moved in under the vehicle, and the pointers are adjusted up to the lower reference points. All the pointers should touch and be in alignment to the lower body holes and other reference positions when the body is correctly aligned.

Many of these universal measuring systems

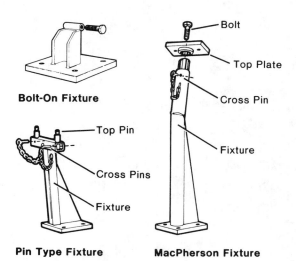

Bolt-On Fixture

Top Pin

Cross Pins

Fixture

Pin Type Fixture

Bolt

Top Plate

Cross Pin

Fixture

MacPherson Fixture

Courtesy Blackhawk Mfg. Co.

Figure 13-9   Fixture types

also have an additional front-mounted external gauge that is used to check the position of the front suspension towers. With some systems the gauge can actually be placed at any position along the length of the vehicle to check the upper body alignment of any one section. With other systems the gauge can only be used for the front towers. The two pointers can be moved along the upper bar and set to the towers' width as found in the vehicle's reference chart.

A Prototype Gauging System

A mechanical prototype gauging system designed by the author uses a gauge to surround each of the main control positions of the vehicle. Depending on the position and type of damage one to four gauges are used. Each gauge consists of an upper and lower fixed-length crossbar and two vertical hangers. The two crossbars and hangers connect

together to form a rectangular shape that surrounds a lateral cross-section of the vehicle at any of the control positions (Figure 13-10). This gauging system does not use the centre line of the vehicle. The control section of the vehicle being checked is centred in the gauge and all measurements are made from the gauge to the identical positions on the top, side, and bottom of the vehicle. Slidable castings in the crossbars are connected to a left- and right-hand threaded rod. Turning a crank at the end of the crossbars moves each casting in or out at the same speed and distance from the outer ends. The upper crossbar castings sit on or fasten to the top of the vehicle at any of the control positions. The top outer edges of the vehicle are automatically centred between the ends of the gauge.

Two vertical pointers are fastened into the lower crossbar slidable casting with their length set to datum from the top surface of

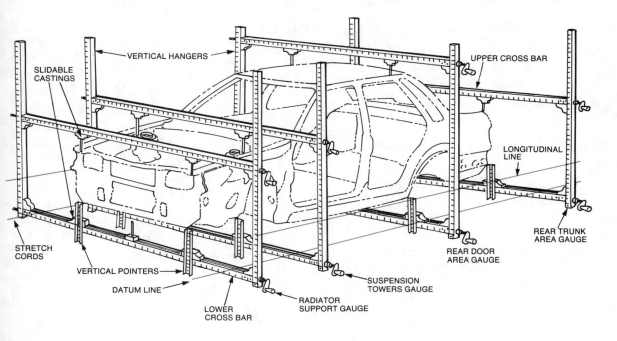

Figure 13-10   The gauge is used at four control positions

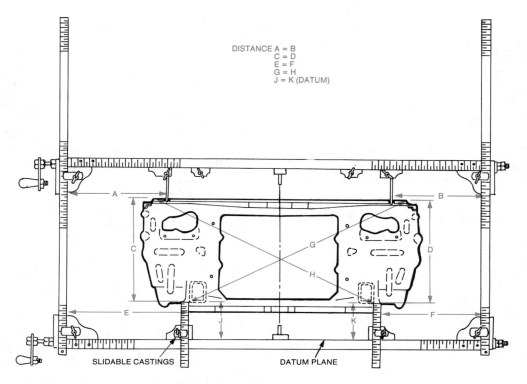

DISTANCE A = B
C = D
E = F
G = H
J = K (DATUM)

SLIDABLE CASTINGS   DATUM PLANE

Figure 13-11   Each gauge checks the height, width, and cross-section (diamond condition)

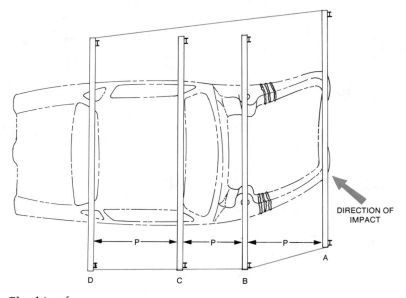

DIRECTION OF
IMPACT

Figure 13-12   Checking for sway

the crossbar according to the vehicle reference chart. The lower crossbar slidable castings are moved in by the outer crank and handle until the two vertical pointers just line up with the lower body reference hole.

If the two hanger measurements are the same, if the two lower pointers just touch, and if either edge is aligned equally to both reference holes, then that cross-section of the body has the correct lower and upper width, equal height on both sides, and it is **not** diamond shaped from corner to corner through its cross-section (Figure 13-11). When three or more gauges are spaced along the length of the vehicle, preferably at the control positions, any vehicle's longitudinal misalignment (sway) can be checked by either sighting the hangers or by placing a

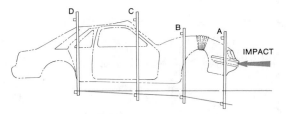

Figure 13-14   Sag

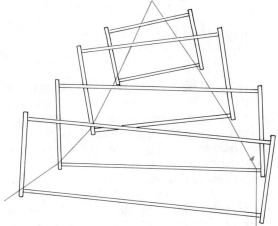

Figure 13-15   Twist

stretch cord along the vertical hangers (Figure 13-12). Similarly, by either sighting or by placing the stretch cord along the top of the lower crossbars front kick down (Figure 13-13), sag or twist misalignment can be checked (Figures 13-14, 13-15). With this system a tram gauge would have to be used to measure length. This type of mechanical measuring system, like some of the others, fastens directly to the vehicle and can therefore be used with or separately from the bench; other measuring systems can be used only with the same manufacturers' bench system.

The Laser Measuring System

This system uses a laser beam to intercept or hit targets positioned from reference holes

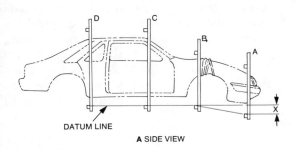

DATUM LINE

A SIDE VIEW

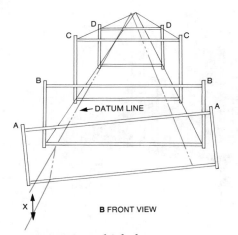

B FRONT VIEW

Figure 13-13   Front kick down

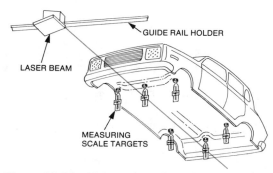

Figure 13-16   Using a laser beam through targets hanging from reference holes

and control positions on the vehicle. A **laser beam** is a very small, fine beam of light that does not spread or deviate off-course. The **targets** are made of clear and opaque plastics marked with a metric scale. They are hung from the lower reference holes or are magnetically attached to identical positions on each side of the vehicle. The point where the laser beam hits the targets is lit by a small round red dot (Figure 13-16). The beam will travel through the clear material, but not through the opaque material. The beam can

be shot directly at the targets from the laser unit or directed from the unit through deflectors or beam splitters to the target. The deflectors are small control boxes containing a series of mirrors to redirect (reflect) the beam at a 90° angle.

With some systems the complete laser unit is separate from the vehicle and is either connected to the bench or positioned on floor stands to the side of the vehicle. Others have the laser unit mounted under the vehicle.

13-3 FRAME STRAIGHTENING METHODS

Some **bench systems** were first designed only to anchor and measure the vehicle. For pulling, the bench itself is anchored to floor pots or rails. Portable pulling equipment is used to make the pull separate from the bench. This equipment is also anchored to pots or rails. This bench pulling system has

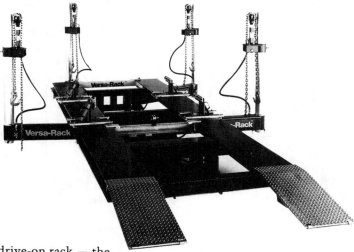

Figure 13-17   Stationary drive-on rack — the towers can be located anywhere around the rack

Courtesy Continental Collision Repair Systems

been limited to use only where there is a floor anchoring system. Other bench systems have been designed to use portable pulling equipment that connects directly to the bench. Some have multiple pulls; others are limited to only one pull at a time. The bench systems that have their anchoring, measuring, and pulling systems combined are truly portable in that they can be used anywhere in the shop.

Another type of system is a **stationary drive-on rack** with multiple pulling towers. The towers can be rotated to pull from any location around the rack (Figure 13-17). Any number of independent jacks connected with chains can also be used between the towers for additional "hook ups." One end of the rack lets down to allow the vehicle to be driven on and then quickly anchored to the sill pinchweld clamps. The rack-type equipment is versatile in that unlimited set-ups or pulls can be made at the same time. It can also be used for both unitized and conventional vehicles.

Set-Ups

The straightening theory is the same, whether the equipment is a portable, bench, or rack system. The undamaged section of the vehicle must be held in a fixed position while the straightening equipment supplies the corrective force to the damaged areas. The corrective force usually is applied in the opposite direction to that from which the damaging impact force was applied. The effectiveness of the corrective force depends entirely on the initiative of the repairperson in formulating the most effective **set-ups** to correct each specific type of damage.

To obtain a proper set-up, it is usually necessary to remove the interfering parts such as the bumpers, grille, and wheels. The suspension and engine must also be removed for some bench systems. Gas and brake lines

must sometimes be moved away from the rockers to allow the rocker anchor clamps to fit. The rocker pinchweld should be cleaned of any dirt and caulking or undercoat material where the rocker clamps are to fit. The clamp teeth should also be clean. Once the vehicle is clamped into position, it is very important that it stay put. With some measuring systems the complete measuring unit has to be reset if the vehicle moves once clamped.

When straightening the conventional frame, one pull was made at a time directly from the rail. The chains were fastened at the anchored and pulling end by wrapping them around the rail. Sometimes it was necessary to cut a small section out of the floor to make room for the chain to wrap around the frame. The same procedure can be used for unitized vehicles. It may be necessary at times to cut a small section from the floor to enable a clamp and chain to "get in" to clamp onto a rail or a rocker section.

Unitized Vehicle Damage and Repair

Collision damage on a unitized vehicle can be described as damage that moves through the vehicle in the shape of a cone (Figure 13-18). The point of impact is the point of the cone. This area absorbs the impact force by folding and crushing. As the impact force passes through the structure, the force spreads and is absorbed by a large area of the body (the body of the "cone"). The force continues to spread and be absorbed until it is used up (dissipated). The area at the point of the impact is **direct damage**. The damage created by the force spreading through the "cone area" is considered **indirect damage**. (See Chapter 12 for greater detail on types of damage.)

As a rule the "last damage in should be the first out." It is therefore important to care-

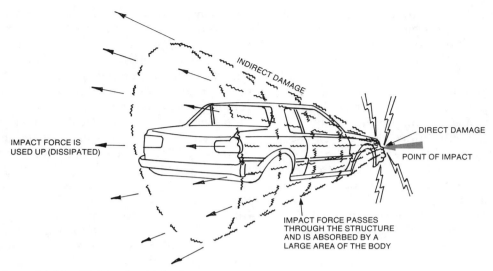

INDIRECT DAMAGE

DIRECT DAMAGE

POINT OF IMPACT

IMPACT FORCE IS
USED UP (DISSIPATED)

IMPACT FORCE PASSES
THROUGH THE STRUCTURE
AND IS ABSORBED BY A
LARGE AREA OF THE BODY

Figure 13-18   Unitized vehicle damage

fully check the vehicle for any indication of indirect damage. For example, it may be necessary to remove the rear seat cushion or check under the vehicle for marks in the floor rear wheelhousing area when the vehicle has had severe front end damage.

Pulling on the Unitized Vehicle. The first main pull should be made from the point of impact and in the exact opposite direction from the direction of the "hit." Since the conventional frame is much heavier than a unitized vehicle, it is easy to simply attach the chain to the end of the frame rail and pull. There is often no one place on the unitized vehicle that is heavy enough to "grab onto" for pulling. Its lighter layers of metal tend to only pull from one small area. On the conventional frame the entire area at the point of impact will come out, bringing the indirect damage with it. The metal on a unitized vehicle in the area of the pulling clamp will often stretch and tear. The best pull is when a multiple number of pulls are made from both the direct damage area and the other main rails and/or reinforcement panels in the damaged area of the point of impact. Multiple pulls more evenly distribute

the corrective forces throughout the vehicle (going in a reverse direction to that which the damage went in). Much less pressure is needed on any one pull.

1. Put a slight load on the pulling equipment and then check carefully to see how the damaged areas are reacting. Is the area pulling correctly? Are the anchoring clamps holding? If a bench and fixtures are being used, check the position of the holes in relation to the fixture pins.

2. Slowly increase the pulling pressure and try to relieve the strain on the indirect damage farthest away from the point of impact. Gradually increase the pulling pressure and continue to stress-relieve the damage areas, working toward the heaviest damage. Work with the "first in – last out" concept.

Stress Relieving

Conventional frame rails bend differently than unitized lower areas. Conventional rails are made of thicker, softer metal. They are shaped differently from unitized rails and they provide all vehicle support. The lower unitized rails are thinner and are made of high-strength steel. They are reinforced with the surrounding panels (that is, the rail is strengthened by the inner apron). Each rail or section tends to be lighter and more springy than the conventional frame rail which tends to bend "dead" with very noticeable kinks or wrinkles in specific areas.

The unitized rails bend in two ways. The bend can be in the form of noticeable kinks and wrinkles, either localized or spread along the rail, or the bend can be a matter of simply springing the rail out of position resulting in none or very few visible marks on the rail, apron, etc. One can easily see the kinks on the conventional frame and pull the rail until the kinks are out. It is not that simple for a unitized vehicle. It can be determined through the measuring process that the rail is out of alignment, but pulling it into position is no guarantee that it will not spring-back to some degree when the pull pressure is released. The tendency then is to over-pull the section past its correct length or alignment to compensate for spring-back and at the same time stress-relieve the area. However, over-pulling can be fatal. For example, if a rail is pulled too long, it is very hard to bring it back. The only alternative would be to replace it with a new rail.

Using Heat. Conventional rails, being thicker and softer, often will not straighten without the use of heat. While the rail is heated, the pull pressure is gradually increased. Heavy hammer blows are directed at the convex buckles as well as along the frame edges. The heat and the hammer blows relieve the tension. Usually all of the buckles come out. It is sometimes necessary to cut a small opening in the opposite side of the frame so a pry or blunt punch can be used to drive out the low areas. The buckles are then worked smooth and the small opening or "window" is welded shut.

Unitized rails must be handled differently. Because of their high strength and springiness, they need more stress-relieving, but not with heavy hammer blows directly on the rails. This practice will only mark and dent the metal. Instead, gradually increase the pull pressure; hold a hard wood block against the rail edges, inner apron, pressed ridges, flanges, etc., and drive it with a heavy bumping hammer. Considerable pounding is sometimes necessary to stress-relieve an area that is not actually kinked but is just sprung out of alignment over a given length. Do not over-pull the area.

Heat can be used, if necessary but certain rules must be followed. High-strength steels must not be heated over 340°C (650°F) for some types and up to 650°C (1200°F) temperatures for other types. Never heat over three minutes on any type or the high strength is lost in the heated area. Different manufacturers recommend various temperatures. Check their manuals when possible for their recommendations. Note the following colour/temperature chart.

Colour	Temperature (approx.)	
blue/grey – faint red	475°C	900°F
orange	650°C	1200°F
red/orange	825°C	1500°F
bright red	875°C	1600°F
dark cherry red	1000°C	1800°F
white	1200°C	2200°F up

Observing colour to determine the temperature is at best a guess. The colour one sees depends on the location of the area and the amount of natural light present. To make sure the temperature is correct use the **temperature indicating crayons**. Mark the area to be heated with a crayon rated according to the vehicle manufacturer's heat temperature recommendation.

Larger Areas of Metal. Heat can be used for removing stress over a large area by playing a soft, bushy neutral flame over the parts — especially along the rails, edges, pressed ridges, bends, etc. It is not necessary to burn the paint; just warm the areas, then use the wooden block and hammer with sharp blows to relieve the area while the pulling force is applied. On larger wrinkled areas, use a large, soft neutral flame. Slowly apply the pressure, check the measurements, and don't over-pull or overheat (or exceed the three minute limit). Take the heat away, tap the wrinkles and buckles, and allow the metal to cool on its own. (Don't use water to cool the area.) Lightly hammering the buckles as the metal is cooling helps shrink them down somewhat. It may be impossible to remove all the wrinkles completely, but they should be as smooth as possible. Wrinkles that are not completely removed will weaken the area which may bend again from normal road shock as the vehicle is driven. It is possible to remove a back section of rail to get at and "dolly" the wrinkles. Remove the section by drilling the spot welds. Cut the ends of the section on an angle if possible. If this section is cut out before the rail is pulled be very careful of over-pull. When replacing the section, use GMAW (MIG) welds and space the weld so there is no build-up of heat. Continually check the alignment of the rail during and after the welding process.

Never attempt to apply any corrective pressure to a bent frame member before welding any rips or cracks in the metal. If the pressure is applied to a cracked frame, the metal will continue to crack or tear.

In repairing minor damage and misalignment, no heat should be required, provided the pull equipment is set up to pull in a reverse direction to the impact force. As the pull is applied, the damage area should be worked with a hammer and dolly.

Repair Sequence

Because each condition of misalignment has a pronounced effect on each of the other conditions, a definite pattern of repair and checking should be followed. Although the repairer may be correcting two conditions with one set-up, continuous gauging checks should be made with each pull. A final gauging should be taken to check each condition. The following order of repair and checking will apply to most repairs:

1. Length (mash)
2. Height (sag or kick down)
3. Width
4. Sidesway
5. Twist
6. Diamond
7. Tracking

Length and height misalignments (commonly referred to as mash, sag or kick down) are directly related and should be corrected in the same operation. These corrections are normally made before sidesway, twist, or diamond corrections are completed because any variations in the height or length can affect a centre section twist condition.

After the length and height corrections have been made, the width and height distance through the upper control positions should be checked. The next check and correction should be centre-line, or major sidesway. After sidesway has been removed, any twist remaining in the frame and body assembly should be removed.

To sum up, the following basic rules should be applied to the repairing of collision damage in both unitized and conventional frame vehicles.

1. Locate all the damaged areas. Make visual checks of the damaged areas to determine the buckled and wrinkled areas. Use gauging equipment to determine both the amount and the type of damage present.
2. Determine the direction of the impact force on the vehicle.
3. Plan the repair procedure (the type and location of the different set-ups). Pull in a reverse direction to that of the impact force.
4. Make frequent checks of the anchor connections, especially with unitized vehicles. Sometimes the straightening forces can cause damage to these anchor areas.
5. Use the proper straightening techniques, such as: using extra jacks to aid in restoring unitized assemblies; using limited heat on wrinkles and buckles; using hammer and dolly to dolly out sheet metal wrinkles in unitized construction; and roughing out the damaged panels to be replaced before they are cut out.
6. Continue to check the frame and body dimensions as the repair work progresses.

Quite often, when straightening unitized damage, it seems all too easy to take a big hammer and simply drive out the damaged area. This is extremely bad practice. Sheet metal is easily stretched, and misalignment and poor fitting problems can easily occur. The damaged area assumes a rather "pounded" look. The damage must be gradually brought back by pulling the area in a reverse direction to which it was damaged. Remember, the pulls should be made with slow, steady pressure, while the wrinkles, kinks, and buckles are gradually worked out with the hammer and dolly process. The complete panel or section is gradually brought back to its correct shape and position. In this manner the damaged area does not end up with that "beaten" look.

Never use ordinary steel chains for set-ups because they are not intended to withstand the excessive pressures of the straightening equipment. Never apply heat to the pulling chains. Do not bolt the links together. Hang an old tarpaulin or loose chain over the main pulling chain so that, if a link does break, the snap-back will be reduced. The repair-person could be seriously injured by the snap-back of a chain breaking under pressure.

13-4 SUSPENSION SYSTEMS

The suspension units control the roadability and handling of the vehicle. There are many variations in suspension designs used by different manufacturers. Regardless of the design each system must control the wheel alignment and the up-and-down movement of the vehicle. Up-and-down movement is controlled either by coil- or leaf-type springs or by torsion bars. Some types of suspension units have relatively few parts; others are more complicated.

Commercial Vehicles

The heavy commercial vehicle front suspension system is simply designed. It consists of a solid, I-beam front axle and heavy leaf springs. The wheels are mounted on a spindle which pivots from king pins at each end of the axle (Figure 13-19).

Leaf springs are made of layers of flat, spring-steel plates called **spring leaves**. Some leaf springs are made from fibreglass. The leaves are held together by a centre bolt and rebound clips. The rebound clips prevent the spring leaves from twisting out of alignment and also prevent the main leaf from pulling away from the other leaves as the spring rebounds.

The main leaf, which is the longest, has an eye at each end. One eye of the spring is connected to a bracket on the frame. The other eye is connected to the frame by spring shackles. The shackles allow the distance

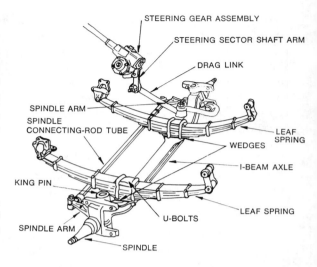

Figure 13-19   Heavy commercial vehicle front-axle assembly

between the eyes of the spring to increase and decrease as the spring flexes (Figure 13-20). Rubber bushings are used in the spring eyes to reduce the road shock and noise that transfer to the frame.

The axle is clamped to the spring at the centre bolt with U-bolts. When leaf springs are used in the rear suspension system of light trucks they are mounted under the axle. The vehicle's mass or weight is actually hung from the axle by the four U-bolts (Figure 13-21). This type of spring mounting

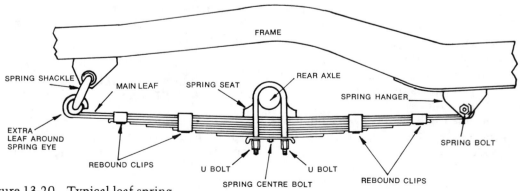

Figure 13-20   Typical leaf spring

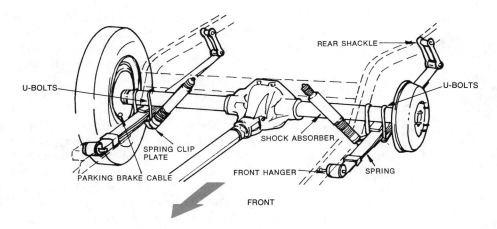

Figure 13-21   Leaf spring rear drive axle suspension system

allows the vehicle to sit closer to the ground than heavier commercial vehicles. Their springs are always mounted on top of the axle as illustrated in Figure 13-19. The mass or weight of the vehicle is carried through the spring to the axle.

Springs mounted under the axle are said to be **underslung**. Springs resting on the axle are **overslung**.

Many heavy commercial trucks and buses and some passenger vehicles use an **air bag** as the spring. The air bag, positioned between the frame and axle, is filled with compressed air. The air pressure in the bag is determined by the mass of the load. When the vehicle is empty the pressure is less, providing a smoother, softer suspension movement.

Passenger Vehicles

Coil Springs.   The majority of passenger vehicles use a **coil spring** and shock to control the up-and-down movement of the front and the rear suspension systems. The actual suspension design of each manufacturer will vary, but operating principles are all similar. Two very different types are the solid axle and the independent design. **Independent**

suspension means that each wheel can move up or down without influencing the movement of the other wheel (Figure 13-22). Independent suspension units use either a coil spring or a torsion bar to control vertical movement. All passenger vehicles have independent suspension systems in the front, and many also use a similar independent design in the rear.

Heavy trucks use a **solid rear axle** in both the front and rear. Rear-wheel drive passenger cars and light commercial vehicles also use a solid rear axle (Figure 13-21).

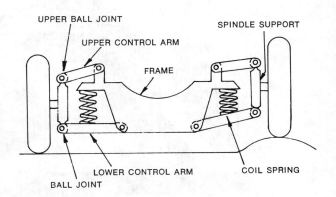

Figure 13-22   Independent suspension movement

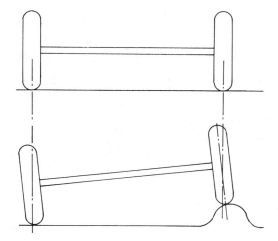

Figure 13-23   Solid axle — when one wheel moves the opposite must follow

Some front-wheel drive passenger cars use a non-driving lightweight trailing arm beam axle design in the rear. The solid axle design is strong and stable but may not have quite the smooth riding characteristics of the independent system. One wheel cannot move up or down without the wheel on the opposite end of the axle moving also (Figure 13-23).

When coil springs are used in the rear solid axle suspension system, the rear axle re-quires additional bracing (upper and lower suspension arms) to prevent forward, back-ward, and sideways movement. Figure 13-24 illustrates a rear drive axle with a coil spring suspension system.

Conventional frame vehicles use a rather heavy independent suspension in the front referred to as the **short, long arm (SLA)** arrangement (Figure 13-25). Note that the coil spring mounts between the lower con-trol arm and the frame crossmember. The upper control arm is shorter than the lower. The steering knuckle, or spindle support, is bolted to upper and lower ball joints. The ball joints are connected to the control arms. The inner ends of the control arms are mounted on forged steel shafts with rubber torsion bushings. The steel shafts are bolted to the front frame crossmember.

The wheels bolt to the hub. The wheel hub turns on inner and outer wheel bearings on the spindle (Figure 13-26). The inner bear-ing is much heavier than the outer bearing because it supports most of the vehicle's mass. The wheel turns from side to side at the ball joints.

The shock absorber fits through the centre of the coil spring. It slows down the **jounce**

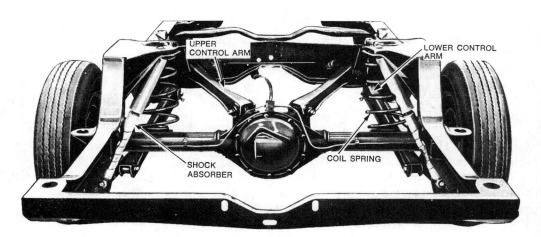

Figure 13-24   Coil suspension —solid rear drive axle   *Courtesy General Motors Products of Canada, Limited*

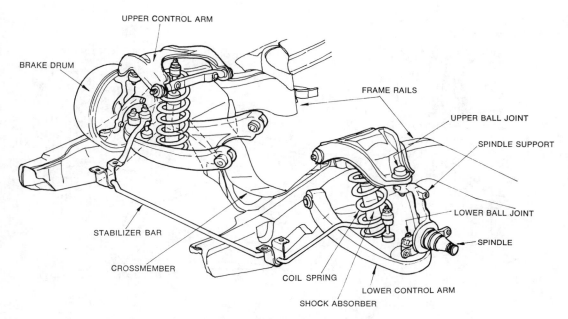

Figure 13-25   Independent, short-long arm (SLA) suspension

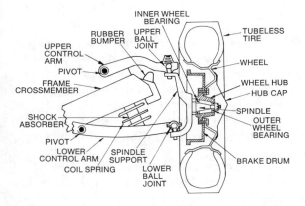

Figure 13-26   Ball-joint spindle support

and **rebound** movement of the wheel and control arms. Jounce and rebound are terms used to define up-and-down movement of the wheel. Jounce occurs when the coil spring is compressed such as when the wheel goes over a bump or if someone were to sit on the front of the car. Rebound occurs when the coil separates or when the front of the body only is lifted.

Independent Torsion-Bar Suspensions

With torsion-bar suspension systems, the up-and-down movement of the vehicle is controlled by the twisting action of the torsion bar. One end of the torsion bar is fitted into a socket at the inner pivot point of the lower control arm. The other end is connected to an adjustable anchor-and-cam assembly mounted to the frame. As the lower control arm moves up at the outer end, it causes a twisting action on the torsion bar. The springing effect is provided by the torsion bar's resisting this twisting force (Figure 13-27).

Adjusting the position of the anchor-and-cam assembly will change the tension on the torsion bar. More tension on the bar will raise the vehicle body; less tension will lower it. To prevent the outer end of the lower control arm from moving forward or backward, a strut is attached between the

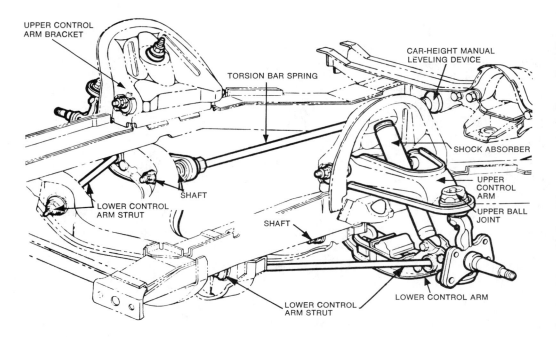

UPPER CONTROL
ARM BRACKET

TORSION BAR SPRING

CAR-HEIGHT MANUAL
LEVELING DEVICE

SHOCK ABSORBER

UPPER
CONTROL
ARM

UPPER BALL
JOINT

SHAFT

LOWER CONTROL
ARM STRUT

SHAFT

LOWER CONTROL
ARM STRUT

LOWER CONTROL ARM

Figure 13-27   Torsion-bar suspension system   *Courtesy Chrysler Canada Ltd.*

outer end of the lower control arm and the front frame crossmember.

Independent MacPherson Strut Suspensions

The MacPherson type is an independent suspension system of a rather unique design: it is lightweight and has few moving parts. The wheel spindle and steering arm are part of a vertical support housing. The lower end of the support housing is connected to the outer end of the lower control arm by a ball joint. The top of the strut is mounted into a strut tower or pocket built into the inner wheelhousing panel. The strut is similar to a standard shock absorber, only longer and heavier in design.

The coil spring at the top sits against an upper spring seat which fits against a bearing and upper strut mounting insulator and support.

The top of the strut (the piston shaft) goes through the centre of the spring seat and the bearing, and bolts to the upper mounting support. The upper mounting support bolts to the strut tower. The strut tower carries the vehicle weight and transfers the vertical road shock from the wheel to the coil spring and strut (shock absorber). The coil spring absorbs the wheel jounce and rebound impact forces. The MacPherson strut absorbs and smooths out the coil spring movement.

The side-to-side steering movement is controlled by the rotation of the complete support housing, including the coil spring, rotating between the lower ball joint and the upper bearing and strut shaft. The strut shaft itself, does not turn (Figure 13-28). By using this design no upper control arm, ball joint, or mounting brackets are necessary.

The MacPherson strut suspension system is the design used for the front of most rear-wheel and front-wheel drive vehicles. Some

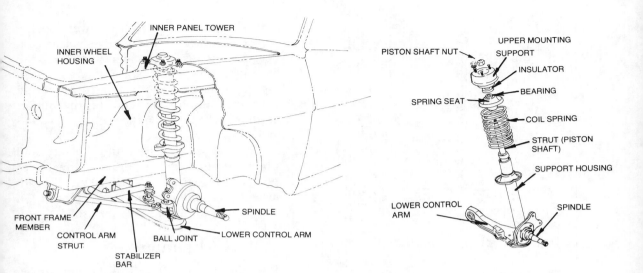

Figure 13-28   MacPherson strut suspension

front-wheel drive vehicles also use a similar design in the rear.

Stabilizer Shaft

A stabilizer shaft, or sway bar, is used with independent, front-wheel suspension systems. It is attached to the frame side rails and to both lower control arms (Figure 13-28). The sway bar stabilizes the spring action of the two front wheels to provide better steering ability and control of body roll. When one front wheel drops into a depression in the road, a twisting action is exerted on the shaft, which tends to prevent that corner of the body from dropping with the wheel.

Body roll is the tilting of the car body, caused by centrifugal force as the car rounds a turn. When a vehicle turns a corner, the spring of the outer front wheel is compressed, the spring of the inner front wheel is lengthened, and the stabilizing bar is twisted. The shaft's resistance to this twisting effect prevents excessive body roll by minimizing the difference in the spring lengths.

13-5 STEERING LINKAGE

The front wheels are controlled from the steering wheel by the combination of shafts, arms, rods, and a reduction gear unit. The reduction gear unit, at the lower end of the steering column, and the different leverage arms provide a mechanical advantage, enabling the driver to control the position of the front wheels with very little effort.

There are two very different steering systems: the centre link, idler arm steering gear design and the rack and pinion steering assembly.

Centre Link, Idler Arm, Steering Gear Design (Figure 13-29). This is usually used with the heavier short, long arm (SLA) suspension. The steering gear assembly is connected to the steering centre link by a steering or pitman arm. The tie rods connect from the relay rod to the steering arms. The tie rods are adjustable to set the wheel alignment.

Rack and Pinion Design (Figure 13-30). This is used with the MacPherson

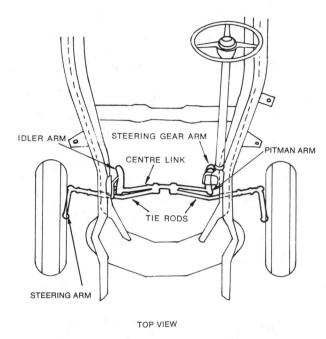

IDLER ARM
STEERING GEAR ARM
CENTRE LINK
PITMAN ARM
TIE RODS
STEERING ARM

TOP VIEW

Figure 13-29 Idler-arm steering-linkage assembly

strut suspension. There are fewer moving parts providing a more positive steering connection. The tie rods connect directly to the steering arms and the rack and pinion. Turning the steering wheel rotates the steering shaft and pinion. The teeth on the pinion mesh into the teeth on the rack to move the rack from side to side.

Both the steering gear and the rack and pinion design can be either manually or power operated. Each linkage system is adjusted at the ends of an adjustable tie rod. On some designs, two tie rods are used.

Wheel Alignment

Wheel alignment refers to the angular set of the front wheels that produces a true, free-rolling movement over the road. Steering ease and stability and tire wear all depend on the angular relationship between the front wheels and the frame.

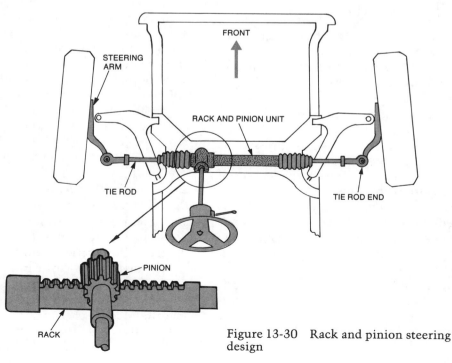

FRONT

STEERING ARM

RACK AND PINION UNIT

TIE ROD

TIE ROD END

PINION

RACK

Figure 13-30 Rack and pinion steering design

Settings. There are five different settings or angles, that are designed into the front suspension system by the manufacturer. These are, in their proper order of checking and adjusting:

- caster
- camber
- steering-axis inclination (formerly called "king-pin" inclination)
- toe-in, toe-out
- turning radius

With some suspension systems several of these settings can be adjusted. Others, such as the MacPherson systems, have many of the settings built-in with no adjustment provisions. In this case any misalignment conditions are caused by bent or worn parts.

Caster. Caster is the forward or backward tilt of the top of the king pin, or spindle support arm. Caster is measured in degrees from the centre line of the spindle support arm to the true vertical. Positive caster is the backward tilting of the spindle support from the true vertical. Negative caster is the forward tilting of the spindle support from the true vertical (Figure 13-31).

Positive caster projects the gravitational force acting on the mass of the vehicle ahead of the tire's road-contact point. The wheels follow the line of this force, which is transmitted through the centre of the spindle support.

Caster assists the front wheels to maintain a straight-ahead position. Unequal caster causes the vehicle to pull toward the side of less caster. The right front wheel is usually set with more caster than the left, to offset the road crown. Crowned roads make vehicles tend to pull toward the road shoulder. Recommended caster settings will vary slightly with locality, because some areas have higher crowned roads then others.

Camber. Camber is the outward or inward tilt of the top of the wheels. It is measured in

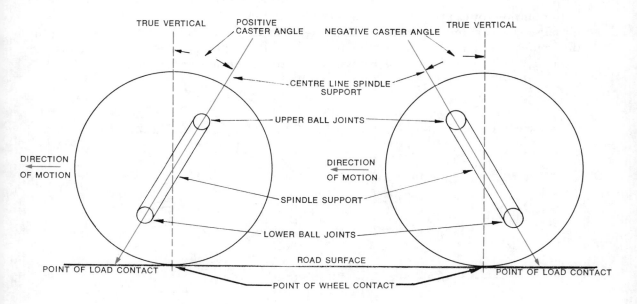

A POSITIVE CASTER — SIDE VIEW   B NEGATIVE CASTER—SIDE VIEW

Figure 13-31 Caster

A POSITIVE CAMBER — FRONT VIEW

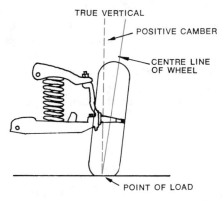

B NEGATIVE CAMBER — FRONT VIEW

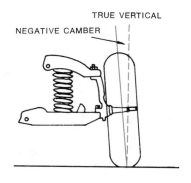

Figure 13-32   Camber

degrees from the top of the centre line of the wheel to the true vertical. Positive camber is the outward tilting of the wheel from the true vertical and negative camber is the inward tilting from the true vertical (Figure 13-32).

The purpose of camber is to compensate for passenger or cargo mass that is added to the vehicle, bringing the front wheels as close as possible to true vertical position

when the vehicle is moving. Position camber also ensures even load distribution on the large, inner, front-wheel bearings. The camber angle, combined with steering-axis inclination, serves to reduce the **scrub radius** as the wheels are turned (Figure 13-33A).

Steering-Axis Inclination. This is the inward tilt of the spindle support's centre line from the true vertical (Figure 13-33B). It is

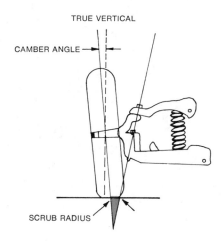

Figure 13-33A   Camber angle reduces the scrub radius

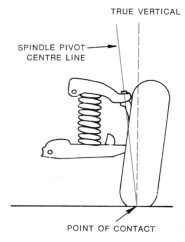

Figure 13-33B   Steering Axis inclination (ball joint)

built into the suspension system and is non-adjustable. Steering-axis inclination is used to accomplish three things: to improve vehicle stability (its ability to run straight); to reduce turning effort in parking or at very low speeds; and to reduce the tendency of the front wheels to "toe-in" or "toe-out."

Toe-In and Toe-Out. When the front wheels are closer together at the front than at the back, they are said to toe-in (Figure 13-34). Toe-out occurs when the distance between the fronts of the front wheels is greater than the distance between the backs of the front wheels.

The amount of toe-in or toe-out present on a vehicle is determined by measuring between the fronts and backs of the front wheels. These measurements are taken parallel to the road surface, at centre-axle height.

Most rear-wheel drive vehicles have a small amount of toe-in. A small amount of toe-in is necessary to offset camber and to compensate for the wheel's tendency to curve outward as the car moves forward. Front-wheel drive vehicles are likely to be set with a small amount of toe-out; the torque on the front wheels has a tendency to actually bring the wheels together at the front into a toe-in position.

Toe-in and toe-out are controlled by lengthening or shortening the tie rods.

Turning Radius. When the front wheels are turned from the straight-ahead position, the inner front wheel must turn a shorter distance than the outer wheel. This causes the front wheels to assume a toe-out position (Figure 13-35). When the front wheels are moved to make the turn illustrated, the inner wheels turn to an angle of approximately 23° with the car frame, but the outer wheel turns only to an angle of 20° with the frame.

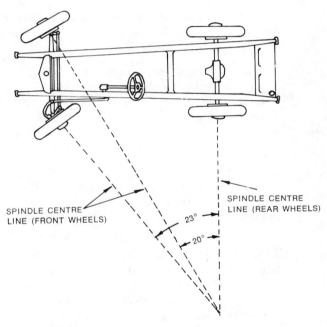

Figure 13-35   Toe-out on turns

Toe-out on turns is accomplished by mounting the steering arms at an angle greater than 90° to the spindles (Figure 13-36). When the tie rod is moved to the left during a right turn, it pushes against the left steering arm at almost a right angle. The right end of the tie rod not only moves to the left, but also swings forward (as shown by the upper dotted line) so that the right wheel is turned more than the left wheel. The directly

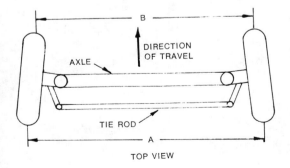

Figure 13-34   Toe-in (A-B at axle height)

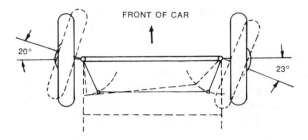

FRONT OF CAR

20°

23°

Figure 13-36   How toe-out on turns is obtained

opposite situation occurs when a left turn is made.

> It is extremely important that all the alignment angles of a motor vehicle be maintained properly, to secure greater tire mileage, easy steering, and passenger safety.

A vehicle damaged in a collision, especially in the front section, should have the front-wheel alignment checked and corrected, if necessary, before it is put back into service.

Tracking. Tracking refers to the correct alignment of the rear wheels for following the front-wheel tracks when the vehicle is moving in a straight-ahead position. When the wheel tread width is the same for both the front and rear wheels the rear-wheel tracks should follow directly over the front-wheel tracks. If the rear-wheel tread is different from the front (either narrower or wider), and if the rear wheels are correctly aligned to the front, both rear treads should overlap the front tracks, either inboard or outboard by the same mount.

When a solid rear axle is not mounted at a right angle to the longitudinal centre line of the vehicle, the rear wheels will cause the vehicle to "dog track" as it is driven straight ahead. The front wheels must be turned out

of their straight-ahead position to line up with the rear wheels. The rear-wheel track would be offset to the front tracks (Figure 13-37). Note that both rear wheel tracks are offset on the same side of each of the front tracks.

When the rear suspension design is the independent type, both wheels could be out of their correct alignment either in the same or in opposite directions. Should they both be angled in the same direction, the vehicle will dog track. In most cases, one or both wheels are more likely to be out of alignment in different directions and in differing amounts. When one or both are out of alignment in different directions, their tires will quickly wear and the vehicle will be rather hard to steer.

Incorrect tracking can be caused by broken or bent axles or their mountings, misaligned body sections, broken springs, or a broken centre bolt in a rear leaf spring. In some cases the suspension may simply be out of adjustment. A very basic tracking check can be made by slowly driving the vehicle straight through a wet spot on the floor or parking lot. The accurate method is to have the vehicle's four wheels aligned with a four-wheel alignment machine.

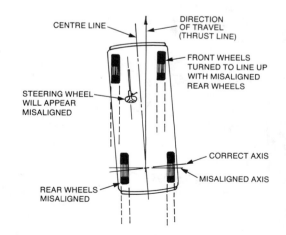

Figure 13-37   Dog tracking

REVIEW QUESTIONS

1. Briefly explain the two types of portable frame- and unitized body-straightening equipment.
2. What is the purpose of the typical bench?
3. How is the vehicle connected or held to the bench?
4. Explain the difference between a dedicated and a universal bench measuring system.
5. In your opinion, is there any need to use a tram gauge together with a dedicated or universal measuring system? If so, where?
6. Using the gauging system that surrounds the control positions, draw a diagram of one gauge surrounding a control section. Explain how the height of each side is compared, and how the squareness of each control section is checked.
7. How would the front gauge appear if the vehicle had (i) a kick down on one front rail, (ii) a sway in the front section between the radiator support and the towers?
8. Briefly explain how a laser measuring system operates.
9. The general straightening rule is "the last damage in should be the first out." Explain.
10. a) Explain what is meant by the term "stress-relieving."
    b) What methods can be used to stress-relieve the rails, pillars, and panels?
11. Why should heat be used sparingly on high-strength metals?
12. a) Why should ordinary steel chains not be used to make frame-straightening pulls?
    b) What safety precautions should be taken to prevent a chain from snapping back if it should break while under pressure?
13. What is a vehicle's suspension system designed to control?
14. List three methods that are used to control the suspension up-and-down movement.
15. Explain the construction of a leaf spring.
16. What is the purpose of the spring shackles that are used with leaf springs?
17. What is meant by the terms "underslung springs" and "overslung springs"?
18. When coil springs are used on the rear suspension system, the rear axle requires additional bracing. Why?
19. Define the term SLA.
20. What is the purpose of the ball joints?
21. Explain how the body height of vehicles having torsion-bar suspension units can be raised or lowered.
22. a) List the two parts of the MacPherson system that cushion and absorb the road shock from the wheel.
    b) List the suspension parts the road shock must transfer through from the wheel to the point where the shock enters the body structure.
23. What is the purpose of a stabilizer shaft or sway bar?
24. Briefly compare the two different steering linkage systems.
25. Explain the operating principles of the rack and pinion steering unit.
26. Explain the terms "caster," "camber," "toe-in," and "toe-out," and give the purpose of each.
27. Briefly explain how toe-out on turns is accomplished.
28. What does the term "dog tracking" mean?

14 SURFACE PREPARATIONS

14-1 Sandpaper
14-2 Sanding Operations
14-3 Masking
14-4 Surface Preparation

Automotive topcoats are designed to protect and beautify the surfaces to which they are applied. They will not cover or hide any imperfections left in the metal or old paint. The smooth, shiny topcoat films tend to actually magnify any small marks, scratches or imperfections, making them "stand out" or appear much larger and deeper than they actually are. Before the final top coats can be applied, all stone chips, scratches, and marks in the old paint must be removed. Surface rust embedded into the metal must also be removed and/or neutralized. Simply grinding off the rust scale is not sufficient. Any rust left in the metal tends to continue to form. It will eventually blister through the new primers and top coat.

14-1 SANDPAPER

Abrasive paper, commonly referred to as sandpaper is used to sand smooth old paint finishes and any undercoat materials that have been sprayed over the bare metal. Abrasive papers are produced by bonding an abrasive mineral to a paper backing. Five different minerals can be used: flint, garnet, emery, aluminum oxide, and silicon carbide. Flint, garnet, and emery are natural minerals. Emery is used for polishing steel; flint and garnet are used for sanding wood.

Aluminum oxide and silicon carbide are synthetic materals that are produced at high temperatures in electric furnaces. They are extremely tough and durable and are the only two minerals suitable for automotive sanding. Aluminum oxide is a grey-brown mineral that is bonded to a standard paper backing with a natural non-waterproof adhesive. Silicon carbide is a shiny, black mineral, bonded with a synthetic-resin glue to a waterproof paper. This combination of minerals, backing, and glue produces a sandpaper resistant to heat and water or other liquids. It is called "wet" sanding paper. Aluminum oxide abrasives are "dry" papers, as both backing and glue will soften when these sandpapers are used with water, dislodging the grit particles from the paper backing.

Wet sanding papers are usually fine grades of paper that would plug up very quickly if used dry. Using water with wet paper prevents the residue from sticking to the abrasive particles and plugging the sandpaper. The water tends to float the residue off the surface.

The coarseness or fineness of an abrasive paper is determined by the size of the abrasive grit on the paper. The size of the particles is identified by a number on the back of the paper. The smaller the number, the larger the abrasive grit and the coarser or rougher the scratch pattern produced. The number refers to the size of the openings in the screens through which the abrasive particles are passed during manufacture of the sandpaper. Grit sizes 16, 24, 36, and 50 are used on grinding discs. Sizes 36, 40, and 80 are used to sand plastic fillers. Sizes 80 to 320 are used on dry sanding papers to sand paints. Sizes 320 to 1500 are used on wet sandpapers. The coarser papers are generally designed to be used to cut off or level down the surface. The finer papers also cut but their main purpose is to smooth the surface.

14-2 SANDING OPERATIONS

The number and type of abrasive paper used to prepare the painted surface for refinishing depends on the purpose of the sanding operation and the type of topcoat to be used over the prepared surface.

The basecoat/clearcoat system paints and acrylic lacquer topcoats are more prone to showing sand scratches because of their high shine and smooth surface.

The surface to which these materials are to be applied must be prepared with a finer sandpaper than a surface that is to be covered with acrylic enamel or enamel. The ultra-

fine water papers are used to scuff or lightly sand the newly painted clearcoat surface. This smooths and removes any very slight imperfections without actually scratching the surface. The surface can then be machine compounded and polished to a deep shine.

> The sanding preparation, regardless of the topcoat material to be applied, can be divided into three separate operations: 1. feather-edging, 2. surface sanding, 3. blocksanding.

Feather-Edging

Feather-edging refers to the smoothing or feathering back of the sharp paint edge around nicks, stone chips, and along the edge of scratches. The sharp edge of paint left around the outside of an area that has been repaired must also be tapered, or feathered back, to prevent a noticeable ridge from showing through the new topcoat (Figure 14-1). If the paint edge around the stone chip is not feathered completely, a ring will show through the new topcoat. Such rings are often called **bull's eyes** (Figure 14-2). Feather-edging is done with a Size 80 to 150 open-coat paper on an air-driven sander.

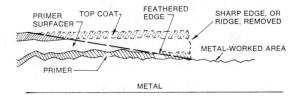

Figure 14-1   Tapering (feathering) back the edge

Air Sanders.   There are two different types of air sanders; the **orbital vibrator** and the **dual action** machine. The rectangular pad of the vibrator machine moves in an orbital

Photo by G.M. Haney

Figure 14-2 "Bull's-eye" ring resulting from insufficient feather-edging

oblong-shaped pattern (Figure 14-3). The dual action machine has a round pad (Figure 14-4). The disc movement is controlled by a shaft lock. When the lock is positioned to allow the main shaft to spin freely, the pad rotates in a circular motion similar to a grinder. This type of pad action is used to strip off paint or to level plastic fillers. When the lock is positioned to catch the shaft, the movement is changed to a combination of circular, orbital, and oscillating movements. The pad constantly changes direction. The dual action machines used in this way tend to feather-edge faster than the vibrator but the round pad is harder to fit into some places.

Both sanders are held flat on top of the paint and slowly moved back and forth along the paint edge. When either machine is moved from the bare metal into or over the paint edge the feather-edging process is not accomplished as effectively. The vibrator continues to remove all the paint, and the "step," or "edge," is merely moved out further.

Most vibrator pads are sized so that they are fitted from standard sheets of sandpaper folded into three equal parts (Figure 14-5). The dual action machines use a pre-cut round disc with an adhesive rear surface.

The coarse #80 paper is used when the paint build-up is thick from previous repaints. Number 120 or 150 paper is used to

feather-edge when there is very little paint build-up, i.e., on an original finish. The coarse paper cuts the heavy coats of paint down quickly but leaves deep scratches. The finer paper cuts slower, plugs faster, but makes a smoother feather-edge.

The feather-edge can be checked by feeling or looking at the edge. Each paint layer should be 4–7 mm wide. Feel across the

A VIBRATOR SANDER FEATHER-EDGING

B DISC SANDER FEATHER-EDGING

Photos by Minnesota Mining and Manufacturing of Canada Limited

Figure 14-3 (A) Feather-edging with a vibrator-sander, (B) Electric circular feather-edger and paint stripping sander

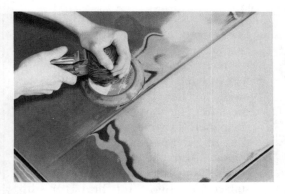

Figure 14-4   Feather-edging with a dual action sander

feathered edge with a flat hand, not just the fingers. If no edge can be felt, the taper is sufficient. Many painters will further feather the edge by using a medium paper (for example, 220) to reduce the coarse 80–150 abrasive scratches.

Because of the smallness of stone chips, they are extremely difficult to feather-edge to prevent bull's eyes. If there are a number of stone chips in one area, for example, the

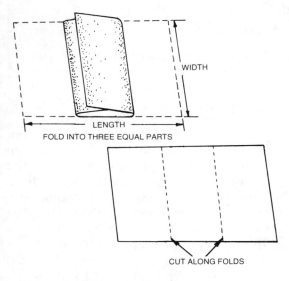

WIDTH

LENGTH

FOLD INTO THREE EQUAL PARTS

CUT ALONG FOLDS

Figure 14-5   Preparing vibrator pads from a sheet of abrasive paper

front of the hood, or a lower section of a panel that has been constantly peppered by sand or stones, it is better to completely strip all the paint off in that area. Isolated stone chips can be feathered by the normal method. They can also be repaired by using either machine to first sand into the chip area to clean it of any rust on the metal or any loose chips of paint. Surface sand the surrounding paint and prime the area. Then fill each stone chip with glazing putty. This is a fast, useful method particularly if the surface has had more than one coat of paint.

Always make sure the area of paint surrounding the feather edge is "back sanded" before priming the area. It is poor policy to apply primer over topcoats that have not been sanded.

"Back sanding" means to surface sand the paint, back or out from the feather-edge a few centimetres.

Surface Sanding

Surface sanding is usually done after the areas have been feather-edged and before any areas have been primed. All the painted surfaces that are to be repainted must be surface sanded with a fine paper. Only the very top shiny surface of the paint is sanded off "to the bottom of the orange peel." Most painted surfaces have a slight ripple effect said to be similar to that of the surface of the skin of an orange (Figure 14-6). The paint surface need only be sanded until these small "orange peel craters" have been removed. The smooth, sanded paint provides a clean surface to which the new paint can adhere. The fine, sanding scratches also provide an added "tooth" for the new paint to grip.

All paint surfaces must always be sanded before any new undercoat or topcoat mate-

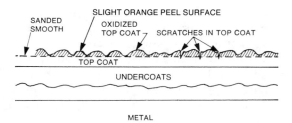

Figure 14-6 Surface sanding removes the shine, oxidized paint, and orange peel surface

rials can be applied. Undercoat materials must also have a final sanding to remove small "nibs" and "overspray" present on the surface before any topcoat material can be applied.

Numbers 220, 280, and 320 sandpapers are used for sanding enamels and acrylic enamels. Numbers 320 dry to 400 wet are necessary for sanding acrylic lacquers. Basecoat/clearcoat systems need numbers 320 dry to 320 to 1500 wet depending on the circumstances.

All surface sanding used to be done by hand. Most painters have now switched to sanding by using fine papers on either the dual action machine or the vibrator. The dual action machine produces a smooth mark-free surface. The vibrator machine is not as good as it tends to leave oval scratch marks in the paint surface. Only the small areas around the mouldings, window edges, corners, etc., are usually sanded by hand.

When the dual action machine is used to surface sand, a fine pre-cut self-sticking disc is used. If the vibrator is used, the standard sheet of fine paper is cut as for feather-edging. To prepare the abrasive paper for hand sanding, the paper is ripped in half crosswise, producing two pieces. Each new piece is then folded across its length into three equal parts, as shown in Figure 14-7. Folding the sheet of paper in this manner produces a sanding pad the size of an average hand.

For any method used, the sanding motion should be long straight back-and-forth strokes. The entire machine surface or hand should be held flat on the paint surface. Do not use excessive pressure. This traps the paint residue in the paper, forcing it to roll into a lump, plugging the paper and actually gouging deep scratches into the sanded surface. When the sanding residue has started to "lump" on the paper stop using it. When hand sanding, do not use the fingertips as they will cut grooves into the painted surface.

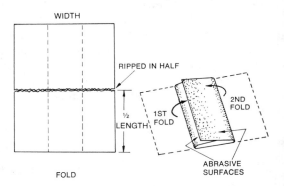

Figure 14-7 Preparing a sheet of sandpaper for hand sanding

Blocksanding

Whenever a damaged area of metal has been repaired, there are usually some rather deep scratches and very slight imperfections left in either the metal or in the body fillers. These marks are filled over with primer surfacer and, if necessary, glazing putty. The surfacer is sprayed on in two or more coats. The glaze is then applied over the surfacer with a rubber squeegie (Figure 14-8).

Blocksanding is the process of using a block type backing pad on top of the abrasive paper, to sand these built-up areas level.

Figure 14-8   Applying glazing putty

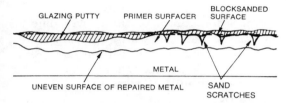

Figure 14-9   Blocksanding

The sanding block can be rubber, felt, or a stiff piece of cardboard. The block keeps the paper flat, to prevent it from curving in and out of the slight high and low spots in the primer surfacer and glaze. During sanding the "high" areas are cut down to the level of the lower areas (Figure 14-9). The abrasive paper should be a cutting paper, either sizes 120, 150, or 180. These papers are coarse enough that they cut and level the area. The surface is made level, but not smooth enough to be painted over without first being re-primed. Any small imperfections, slight low areas, deep scratches, and poor feather-edges are left filled with primer surfacer and glaze (Figure 14-10).

The sanding motion should be long, straight back-and-forth strokes. However, the sanding strokes should not come out past the primer onto the undamaged surrounding paint, as the coarse paper causes deep scratches that are hard to remove. The sanding procedure is continued until the com-

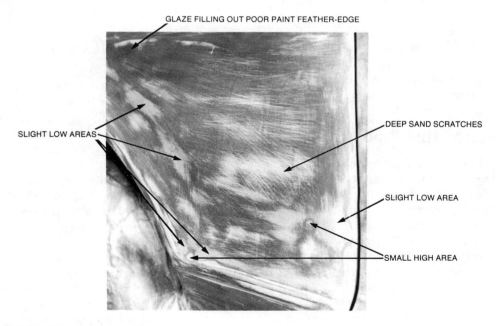

Figure 14-10   Glazing putty after blocksanding

plete area has been worked level and smooth. Should high spots of either metal or body filler start to show through, stop. Do not continue to sand over these high spots as it only defeats the purpose of the operation. Change the sanding stroke direction to work around the higher bare spots until the surrounding areas of surfacer and glaze are level. The area is then ready for re-priming.

Watersanding

Watersanding involves using a waterproof paper and water (or other liquid such as varsol) to smooth-sand the surface. Wet sanding is usually only done with the finer papers. A liquid soap is used with the water. The soap tends to lubricate the abrasive, improve the cutting action, and prevent the water from running off the surface being sanded so quickly. The watersanding process it not used for feather-edging since water should not be used on or around bare metal or body fillers. It is used mostly for a final surface sanding of both the paint and undercoats before the topcoat is applied. It is also used to lightly sand surface imperfections such as, dirt nibs, a light run, overspray, or orange peel from the surface of the clear coat materals. After sanding, the area is compounded and polished smooth.

Watersanding Procedure

The paper is cut and folded as for hand sanding. The paper can be used with or without a backing pad. A sponge is used to wet a small area of the paint surface. Dip the paper into the water and start sanding. Hold the sponge on the paint above the area being sanded. When the area being sanded starts to dry, lightly squeeze the sponge to add water to the paper and area. When the paper starts to become sticky to move, dip it into the water and quickly swish it about to clean off the

paint residue. Resoak the sponge and continue to sand.

The two problems associated with water sanding are that one cannot see through the sanding residue and water to tell how the sanding is progressing, and the dirty water runs down into the panel seams and gaps and dries, leaving the paint residue and a mess.

The first problem can be overcome by using a small glazing squeegie to wipe off the water and paint residue. It scrapes off the water and residue to clearly show the smallest of imperfections in the surface. If there are still marks showing, more sanding is needed.

The second problem can be overcome by taping the panel gaps to prevent the water and paint residue from getting into them. Once the main surface is sanded remove the tape and carefully watersand around the edges. Use clean water, a sponge, and a drying cloth. Wash and wipe dry each panel in order to remove all the sanding residue immediately after sanding.

14-3 MASKING

Masking tape and paper are used to cover any items that are not to be painted. In some cases, it is easier and quicker to remove small items such as emblems, ornaments, chrome letters, headlight rims, etc. All other items must be masked.

Masking tape is available in widths from 3 mm to 51 mm. The 18 mm width seems to be the most popular with painters. Some painters use newspaper to cover the larger areas such as windows and grilles, whereas other painters prefer to use regular masking paper. Special paper dispensers (Figure 14-11) designed to hold both masking tape and paper of varying widths are commonly used in paint shops. Half of the masking tape

Photo by Minnesota Mining and Manufacturing of Canada Limited

Figure 14-11   Paper and masking tape dispenser

is automatically attached to the edge of the paper by this dispenser.

> Masking is largely a matter of good judgement and practice. The most important thing to remember in masking is that the tape should be applied to clean, dry surfaces. The outside edge of the tape should be even with the edge of the item being covered. Failure to observe this basic rule will result either in unpainted areas along the edge of the trim, or in paint "overspray" on part of the masked object.

To apply the masking tape along the edge of a moulding, hold the roll of tape in one hand and apply pressure with a finger, to the tape as it comes off the roll. Carefully bring the tape down and line it up with the edge of the object to be masked. Slide the other hand over the tape to make sure the complete edge is stuck to the surface (Figure 14-12). This prevents any water or other liquid from seeping under the tape.

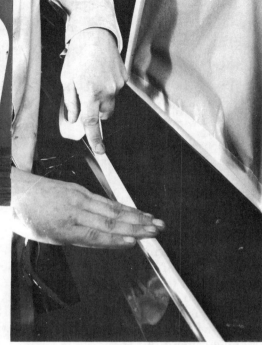

Photo by Minnesota Mining and Manufacturing of Canada Limited

Figure 14-12   Applying masking tape along the edge of moulding

Masking Windows

Some painters prefer to run a strip of masking tape around the edge of the window opening before applying the paper (Figure 14-13). Other painters apply the paper from the dispensing roller directly to the window opening. Either method is acceptable. The main point to remember is that the window opening must be completely covered to ensure that no paint is sprayed on the window and that no dirt is blown from around the edge of the glass onto the wet paint.

Always apply the taped edge to the longest part of the window when fitting masking

Photo by Minnesota Mining and Manufacturing of Canada Limited

Figure 14-13 Apply a strip of masking tape around the edge of a window opening

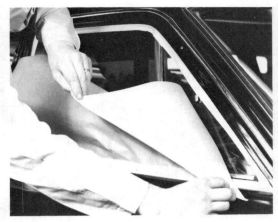

Photo by Minnesota Mining and Manufacturing of Canada Limited

Figure 14-14A Apply the taped edge of the paper to the longest part of the window opening and fold in the corners of the paper

paper to the window opening (Figure 14-14A). Cut off the excess corners of the paper or fold them behind the main covering. Outward folds provide an area in which sanding dust may collect. Tape down the edge of the paper around the whole window opening (Figure 14-14B).

When it is necessary to use two strips of paper to cover a window opening, tape down the centre seam also. If this is not done, dirt trapped between the two layers of paper will be blown onto the wet paint by the air pressure from the spray gun.

Never wind masking tape around an aerial or door handle. This is a waste of time and tape, and the tape is difficult to remove. Apply a long strip of tape up one side and down the other side of the aerial. Tape door handles lengthwise (Figure 14-15).

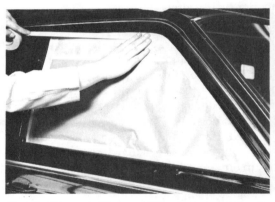

Photo by Minnesota Mining and Manufacturing of Canada Limited

Figure 14-14B Tape the whole edge of the paper around the window opening

Two-Tone Masking

When more than one colour is to be applied to an automobile, the colour of the smaller area is usually sprayed first. It is then neces-sary to mask off the first colour to protect it while the second colour is being applied.

The paint on a freshly painted area may peel as masking tape is removed. To prevent this, run the hand over the adhesive on the tape before applying it to the paint surface. This minimizes adhesive pull. To remove the

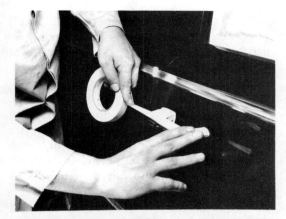

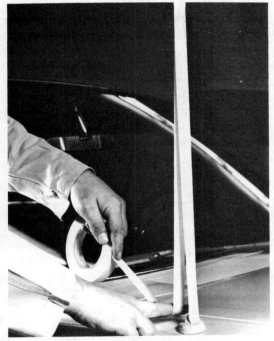

Photos by Minnesota Mining and Manufacturing of Canada Limited

Figure 14-15   Mask door handles and aeriels lengthwise

tape, hold and pull it at right angles to the strip of tape. Pull the tape away from the sharp edge of the second colour, as shown in Figure 14-16.

Always remove the masking tape as soon after the finish is tack-free as possible. The longer the tape is left on the surface, the stronger will be the adhesive's grip.

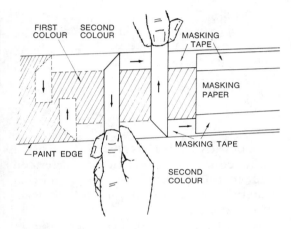

Figure 14-16   Roll the masking tape off the fresh paint at a right angle to the strip of tape

14-4 SURFACE PREPARATION

The first step in the refinishing procedure is to determine the type and colour of the original paint. A code number is given to each original paint colour by the automobile manufacturer. This code number is stamped on an identification plate which is mounted on various places on the vehicle depending on the manufacturer (Figure 14-17). Every paint manufacturer supplies a book of small colour chips showing the paint colours used by every vehicle manufacturer for each year. Compare the colour on the vehicle with the colour chip selected by code number and year of the vehicle.

Sometimes the type of topcoat material

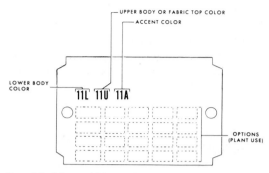

Figure 14-17   Typical vehicle identification plate

used on the vehicle is also listed as part of the paint code. However, the experienced painter usually knows the type of topcoat material used by the various vehicle manufacturers.

Identification can also be made by the appearance of the paint surface. An enamel surface, depending on its age, will have faded somewhat. It will have an oxidized film over its surface. Acrylic lacquers and enamels will have very little or no fade. They also tend to have a very smooth, glossy surface compared to standard enamels. Basecoat/clearcoat systems have a clear, deep-looking finish.

Another means for checking the type of finish is to rub a little lacquer thinner on the paint with the finger or the corner of a rag. If the finish softens and colour comes off the surface onto the finger or rag, the paint is an acrylic lacquer product. All enamel products are thermoset materials and are insoluble after they have dried. No paint or colour will rub off. The basecoat/clearcoat materials can be checked by lightly sanding an area. The sanding residue will be clear, with no colour in it.

It is advisable to refinish the vehicle with the same type of material that was used orig-

inally. However, by using special sealers it is possible to apply any type of material, regardless of the paint used first. The steps that must be followed in preparing the old surface for the new topcoat are the same regardless of the type of paint to be applied.

Some special preparations and precautions are recommended when either acrylic lacquers or other types of basecoat/clearcoat systems are used. The surface must be sanded with a finer paper than would be necessary if the topcoat were acrylic enamel. The paint manufacturers also recommend that a sealer be used before the top coat to prevent sand scratch swelling. Some of the base paints used with the basecoat/clearcoat systems, especially acrylic lacquers, use such strong solvents that they penetrate into the old finish and cause swelling of the sand scratches. When the solvent evaporates, the swelling goes down and the new finish shrinks into the scratch, leaving a similar scratch on the new paint (Figure 14-18).

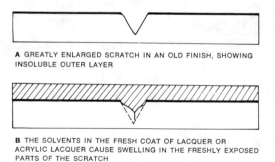

A GREATLY ENLARGED SCRATCH IN AN OLD FINISH, SHOWING INSOLUBLE OUTER LAYER

B THE SOLVENTS IN THE FRESH COAT OF LACQUER OR ACRYLIC LACQUER CAUSE SWELLING IN THE FRESHLY EXPOSED PARTS OF THE SCRATCH

C THE SWELLING RECEDES AFTER ALL OF THE SOLVENTS HAVE EVAPORATED AND THE NEW FINISH SHRINKS, LEAVING FURROWS SIMILAR TO THE OLD SCRATCHES

Figure 14-18   Sand scratches

Procedure to Prepare Vehicle for Paint

If the automobile is extremely dirty, wash it with water and a mild soap. Check the paint surface and seams for any indication of a recent "wax job." If it appears that the vehicle has been waxed, i.e., noticeable white traces of hardened wax in the seams, cowl vents, etc., the paint surface must be washed with a solvent-type cleaner specially formulated to remove wax, silicons, grease, and oil. Use plenty of clean cloths. Clean only a small area at a time and then wipe it dry thoroughly.

The next step of the procedure may vary, depending on the preference of the refinisher. Some painters prefer to sand the old finish and then blow and wipe the surface clean before masking the windows and chrome, particularly if the finish is to be wet sanded. This way the water used with the sandpaper does not soak into the masking paper. If following this procedure, take care when sanding around the chrome trim. Normally, however, the masking is completed first and then the surface is sanded.

All paint edges, stone chips, and scratches are feather-edged, using a size 80 to 150 paper on the vibrator or dual action feather-edging machine. The old paint is then either machine or hand sanded with a fine paper, size 220 to 280 for enamels, size 280 to 400 for acrylics and basecoat/clearcoat systems.

Any bare metal areas that have traces of rust formations or that are oily, i.e., a new unprimed replacement panel or soldered area, must be treated with phosphoric acid cleaner. The metal conditioner removes contaminants and slightly etches the metal surface to provide a better bond for the undercoat material. It must be wiped off the surface before it has dried or the surface washed with water and then wiped and blown dry. Failure to follow either of these procedures will result in a white phosphoric powder left on the surface which the primer will not bond to.

> Never wash body fillers with metal conditioners or water. They should be kept dry.

The undercoat materials are now applied to all bare metal areas, especially to any areas that have been cleaned with metal conditioner to prevent rust from reforming. If a coat of (corrosion inhibiting) primer is to be applied first, it should be sprayed on in one thin coat and then allowed to dry for 15 to 20 min before the primer surfacer is applied.

The primer surfacer should be sprayed on in thin, wet coats, allowing a short "flash-off period" between coats. (The time the solvent evaporates from the primer surfacer into the air.) The first coat should be sprayed to the edge of the old paint, with each additional coat covering more of the feather-edged paint area (Figure 14-19).

As many as 4 coats of primer surfacer are applied, depending on the depth of the feather-edge and old paint scratches in the repaired areas.

Some painters prefer to feather-edge the areas, then back sand only the feather-edge and immediate surrounding area before

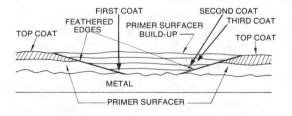

Figure 14-19   Primer surfacer is sprayed in thin, wet coats to build up the feather-edged area

spraying. Using this method, they can be building the feather-edge areas up with primer surfacer, allowing time for each coat to dry while they work on the remaining areas that are to be surface sanded.

Never apply undercoat materials over paints that have not been sanded, especially basecoat/clearcoats. The acrylic paints are so smooth that the undercoats cannot obtain a good bond. When the new topcoat is applied, its solvents sink into and soften the undercoats, creating a wrinkling or separating problem.

When the repaired areas have been built up with primer, they must be carefully checked for any visible scratches or marks. If the marks are minor, they can often be filled by simply spraying another coat of primer surfacer. Deeper imperfections must be glazed over. The glazing putty is applied with a rubber squeegie. If there are only small scratches, the glazing putty need only be applied to these areas, although it is often easier to glaze over the complete repaired area. If the decision to glaze the complete area is made early enough, it is not necessary to apply more than 1 or 2 coats of primer surfacer before adding the glaze. In either case, the glazed or primed areas are block sanded out with size 120 to 180 sandpaper. Do not blocksand out past the primed area, as the coarse sandpaper will make scratches in the surrounding undamaged paint. These areas are then recoated again with primer surfacer and another close check is made for any scratches or marks. If there are no visible marks, the surface is hand-sanded smooth with a fine paper, 280 to 400, depending on the type of top coat to be applied. Make sure the primer surfacer over-spray is well sanded. Blow and wipe off the surface with a clean rag. Make a careful check for scratches, sanding "cut throughs" or unsanded areas. Check particularly along mouldings, door handles, fender wheel openings, chips along door edges, etc. All the sanding dust and dirt must be blown from the vehicle. Open the hood, doors, and trunk lid and blow around the engine, door openings, trunk opening, especially if repair work has been done around these areas. After these areas have been given a good blowing close the doors, hood and trunk and continue to blow along all cracks, crevices, door openings, mouldings, gas filler doors, etc. Pay special attention to the cowl air vent grills.

With a clean rag in one hand and the air gun in the other, blow and wipe the complete areas to be painted, including all the masked areas. Wiping the surface with a rag tends to loosen any sanding dust from the surface while the air pressure blows it away. The blowing operation cannot be overstressed. It is most important if a clean paint job is to be accomplished. After a final check of the masking tape for correct alignment and adhesion, the vehicle is ready for the paint preparation steps.

REVIEW QUESTIONS

1. Why must any marks and scratches be removed from the original paint before the new topcoat is applied?
2. a) List the five different materials used in the manufacture of sandpaper.
   b) Which of the five are used for sanding automotive paint?
3. Why can't a dry-type sandpaper be used with water?
4. What is the purpose of using water or another liquid with wet sandpaper?
5. How is the size of the abrasive grit particles established and identified?

6. a) Explain the difference between open- and closed-coat sandpaper.
   b) What is the purpose of each?

7. "The coarser papers cut or level, finer papers smooth." Explain this statement.

8. Why must acrylic paints be sanded with a finer sandpaper than that used for enamels?

9. Use the terms "how," "why," "when," and "where," to explain the feather-edging process.

10. There are three methods that can be used to repair "stone chips" in paint. Briefly list and explain the difference in procedure.

11. Why, when feather-edging, should the machine not be moved from the metal into the paint edge?

12. List two methods of checking for the correct amount of feather-edge.

13. Define the term "back sanded."

14. How far or how much of the painted surface should be removed when surface sanding?

15. a) Why should heavy pressure not be applied to the machine while surface sanding or on the sandpaper when hand sanding?
    b) Why should the fingertips not be used when hand sanding?

16. Explain the purpose and procedure for blocksanding.

17. Why is it important not to blocksand out into the undamaged surrounding paint.

18. When high spots start to show through the blocked area, what procedure should be followed and why?

19. Define (i) back sanding, and (ii) orange peel surface.

20. Why is a liquid soap used in the water when watersanding?

21. Explain the watersanding procedure.

22. Explain the procedure for masking a door window.

23. Why should masking tape not be wound around an aerial?

24. When two-tone painting a vehicle, which colour should be applied first? Why?

25. a) What precaution should be taken before applying masking tape over fresh paint?
    b) Explain how masking tape should be removed from a newly painted surface.

26. How can the paint colour of a vehicle be identified?

27. What methods can be used to identify the type of paint on a vehicle?

28. When lacquer or acrylic lacquer top-coats are to be applied over old paint, the original surface should be sealed first. Why?

29. If the vehicle is to be sanded before it is masked, what precautions must be taken around the chrome mouldings?

30. In preparing a vehicle for repainting, all bare metal areas should be treated with metal conditioner. Why?

31. Explain how the primer surfacer should be applied to a repaired area. Use the following headings: number of coats; overlap of each coat.

32. Why should the primer surfacer be sprayed in thin wet coats with a short flash-off period between coats?

33. Undercoats should not be applied over unsanded surfaces. Why?

15 REFINISHING MATERIALS

15-1   Paints
15-2   Paint Ingredients
15-3   Topcoats
15-4   Undercoats
15-5   Wax and Grease Removers
15-6   Compounds
15-7   Metal Conditioner

The automobile industry uses several different types of paint: enamels, lacquers, acrylic lacquers, acrylic enamels, polyesters, urethanes, and polyurethanes. Each has different purposes as well as different application, drying, and final surface characteristics. Most of these paints are at least partially made from the same materials used in making plastics, and therefore have the same or similar characteristics. These materials are synthetic, i.e., chemically produced.

15-1 PAINTS

Paints can be defined as films employed to cover a surface, offering protective and/or decorative coatings. Paints are also used to control light and heat reflectance. Bright colours reflect more light and heat than do darker colours.

Drying Processes

Paints are applied to the surface as a liquid, changing as they dry to a solid continuous film. As paints dry, they go through different drying stages. The first stage is the **dust free** stage, meaning that any dust coming in contact with the surface only lays on top of the paint and does not embed itself in the surface. It can be wiped off after the film has hardened. As the drying process continues, the film next becomes **tack free,** meaning that the surface can be lightly wiped with the back of one finger without marring the surface. The third stage is reached when the film has completely changed from a liquid to a solid. The drying process (from a liquid to a solid) is accomplished by one or a combination of three different processes depending on the type of paint. The term **curing** is used to describe the gradual drying and hardening of the paint.

Evaporation. With some paints the drying process occurs through the evaporation of the solvents. These solvents evaporate from the wet paint film and are absorbed by the surrounding air masses. The change from liquid to solid occurs very quickly as the solvents evaporate into the air (Figure 15-1).

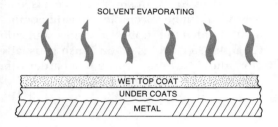

Figure 15-1   Solvent evaporation

Oxidation. This is a chemical union of the oxygen in the air with the wet paint film. As the solvent evaporates, oxygen is absorbed into the wet paint (Figure 15-2). A chemical reaction occurs between salts of metals in the paint and the oxygen in the air to oxidize and harden (cure) the film. The solvent

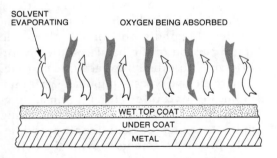

Figure 15-2   Evaporation oxidation

evaporation and oxidation process occurs on the paint surface rather quickly, drying the paint film to its tack free stage. The surface remains porous to allow the remaining solvent to escape and the oxygen to be absorbed. The complete solvent evaporation process could be completed in 24 h.

However, the oxidation or cure process can take up to 30 d before complete hardness throughout the film is obtained.

Polymerization. This is the process of uniting two or more different chemical substances. When mixed, the substances tend to chemically bond together quickly creating a chemical reaction that speeds up the hardening (curing) process (Figure 15-3). With some paints the hardening process is strictly by the polymerization method. With others, the polymerization method is used as an aid to speed up the drying process, along with the solvent evaporation and/or the later oxidation process.

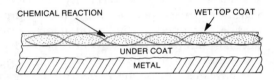

Figure 15-3   Polymerization

Many of the plastic type paints dry by the polymerization process. There are two different systems. One system is similar to adding the catalyst to the polyester resin used in body fillers. A very small percentage of hardener is used compared to the total amount of paint.

The other polymerization system is referred to as a **two component system.** The components are supplied in separate containers: one has the paint, the other the activator or catalyst and solvent. The two are mixed in varying proportions depending on the type and make. A common mixture is 1 part activator-solvent to 3 parts paint (Figure 15-4).

The rate of drying for the preceding three paint-drying processes can be further controlled by either air drying, forced drying, or baking the paint film.

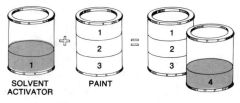

SOLVENT ACTIVATOR   PAINT

1 PART SOLVENT TO 3 PARTS PAINT

Figure 15-4   A typical solvent and paint mixture

When a paint film is allowed to **air dry** the rate of drying is totally dependent on the quality of the surrounding air. For example, cooler or moist damp air will not absorb the solvent as quickly as warm dry air. Good ventilation also speeds the air drying process. Air trapped in the paint booth soon becomes saturated with solvent. A faster drying time can be achieved by circulating warm fresh air through the booth. The fresh air speeds the solvent evaporation and oxidation or polymerization process.

Forced drying occurs when heat is applied, usually within a range of 30°C to 45°C (85°F to 110°F), to speed up the dry or cure. The heat can be applied to the vehicle by heating the complete room, often referred to as an oven, or by using moving banks of lights that surround the car. The heat makes the solvent "kick out" from the film very quickly where it is absorbed by the surrounding warm air. The heat spreads through the surrounding air into the paint and the complete vehicle. The heat tends to drive the solvent out of the paint film from the bottom up, as well as from the paint surface inward. Thus, the film is drying toward the middle. Portable or stationary banks of infra-red heat units are also used to force dry paints. They can be either electrically or gas fired. The infra-red equipment is generally designed to heat only the paint film and not the rest of the vehicle or the room. It is especially useful

for force drying "spots ins" and sections of the vehicle.

The **baking** method involves high temperature, usually over 130°C (265°F). The paint is cured very quickly; thus, a high rate of production can be maintained. This system is used exclusively in manufacturing rather than for refinishing, as the extreme heat would melt a vehicle's plastic components, harden the rubber materials, and ruin the upholstery. A baked-on finish is usually more durable, as it is cured to a harder film than an air dry or low heat finish.

15-2 PAINT INGREDIENTS

All paints, regardless of type, are made from three basic ingredients: pigment, binder, and solvent.

Pigments

Pigments are the solid portion of a paint. They are insoluble, finely ground particles similar to ordinary kitchen flour or talcum powder. Pigments do not dissolve. The binder portion of the paint completely encloses or is absorbed into each fine particle.

There are two types of pigments: **primary** (hiding) or **extender** (filler). Primary pigments are the coloured pigments, including whites. Extender pigments are always white.

The primary pigments provide the colour and hiding power. They provide an opaque finish, meaning that the paint film provides coverage to prevent light or sight from penetrating through the film. These hiding pigments also help to protect the binder portion of the film from the ultra violet rays of the sun and the oxygen in the air, which tend to oxidize and dull the paint film.

There is a tremendous difference in the mass and cost of primary pigments. For example, 1 L measure of a carbon black weighs 1.5 kg, compared to 1 L measure titanium dioxide white at 3.5 kg or zinc dust at 6.0 kg/L.

Primary pigments are often so colour-fast or strong that only small amounts need be added to the paint batch to obtain the correct colour. The rest of the pigments in the batch consist of extender or filler pigments. These are white, inert pigments. They are inert in that they do not have the power to chemically change or affect the characteristics of the paint. They are used only as a filler to add solid volume to the mixture. Extender pigments help to suspend the primary pigments in the binder, preventing them from settling into a hard lump at the bottom of the can. They also tend to prevent the wet film from sagging after spraying or brushing.

Pigments can be obtained from natural earth sources such as minerals. For example, some of the common colours obtained from minerals are the siennas, umbers, and some oxides. They are sometimes referred to as "earth" colours.

However, most of the pigments used in automotive paints are synthetic materials, meaning they are chemically produced from a combination of intermediate or secondary materials made as a result of processing natural materials. Most chemically produced pigments tend to be deeper or stronger in colour than natural materials. Their colour uniformity can also be more closely controlled, providing better colour matches from one batch to the next.

Some of the synthetic pigments are processed by using extreme heat to create the chemical change. Iron blue and ultra marine blue are two colours produced by this method. Black pigments are made by the fume process. Carbon black is produced by partly burning natural gas. Lamp black is made by burning oils in a limited supply of air. In each case, the oily black, sooty residue left after burning is collected, dried and ground into black paint pigment.

Binders

Binders are clear "resin" liquids, varying in appearance from colourless to a deep amber colour. They resemble sticky household glue or pancake syrup. The binder controls such things as the rate of drying and the method of drying, whether the paint dries by evaporation, oxidation, polymerization, or any combination of these three.

The binder also controls the paint's gloss and adhesion qualities as well as its resistance to abrasion, gasoline, moisture, sunlight, temperature, expansion, and contraction.

The binder is used to suspend and bond the many fine pigment particles together. It is also responsible for fastening the film to the surface and changing it from a liquid to a hard, glossy solid during the drying process.

The paint usually takes the name of the type of resin used. **Resins** can be either natural or synthetic materials. The original nitrocellulose lacquers, for example, used a natural resin made by treating small cotton or wood fibres with certain acids, thus the name cellulose lacquer. All of the other paints now use a synthetic resin.

The synthetic resins are also made from common natural materials such as natural gas, coal, petroleum, air, water, and salt. These materals are first processed to separate their molecules and atoms. The chemists then recombine them in many different ways through the use of heat, pressure and/or chemical reaction to form the various synthetic resins. Many of these resins are also used to make plastics.

Acrylics and **polyesters** are two resins that are used for plastics as well as for paint binders. These synthetic resins are far superior in gloss, colour retention, and drying time than any natural resins could be. They also produce a much tougher paint film. The characteristics of the paint are largely determined by the types of blends of resins used.

There are two very different types of plastic type paint resins: **thermoplastic** and **thermosetting.**

Thermoplastic resins soften or melt under heat or certain solvents. They then will set to a hard solid when cooled or when the solvent evaporates. Lacquers and acrylic lacquer paints have thermoplastic resins.

The thermosetting resins are, as the name implies, "set." Once they have become solid, they cannot be remelted. Enamel, acrylic enamel, polyester, urethane, and epoxy resins are all thermoset materials.

Solvents

The **solvents** are thin, clean liquids that evaporate from the paint as the film dries. Solvent is added to the paint to make the pigment-binder mixture workable and fluid during the paint manufacturing and spraying process.

The solvents used by the manufacturer to make the resin and pigment mixable and pourable are different solvents than those added by the painter to make the paint sprayable.

Solvent Sources

Petroleum Hydrocarbons. Common petroleum solvents are (reducers) gasoline, mineral spirits, naphtha or benzine, and kerosene.

Coal-Tar Hydrocarbons. These solvents are derived from condensed liquid made from the destructive distillation of coal. Solvents such as (thinners) benzol or benzene, toluol or toluene, and xylol or xylene are produced. This group of solvents has a stronger solvent power than petroleum solvents.

Ketones. Ketones are similar to alcohol. Acetone and methyl ethyl ketones are the two solvents of the group. They are colourless volatile liquids having a pleasant odour. They tend to feel cold on the skin, but are not usually harmful to it.

The solvent is the volatile part of the paint, whereas the pigment-binder is considered to be the non-volatile portion. Volatile materials are capable of evaporating easily. Some of these solvent gasses can also be toxic and extremely flammable. They should be treated with care to avoid dangerous conditions.

Thinners and Reducers. Thinners and reducers are solvents added to the paint by the refinisher to reduce the paint to a spraying consistency. They are also considered volatile materials similar to the solvent added by the manufacturer.

When the paint leaves the end of the gun, it is in the form of a fine spray. During this time, some of the solvent leaves the spray, evaporating into the air. The remaining solvent stays with the paint film to help it remelt into the previous coat and to allow the last coat applied to "flow out" into a smooth shiny surface. During this process the solvent continues to gradually evaporate into the air (Figure 15-5).

If the solvent remains in the paint too long, the paint film will start to run. A solvent which evaporates too quickly leaves the paint with a poor bond between coats and a rough dry surface.

Both thinners and reducers are made from a blend of the various strength solvents. A solvent compatible with one resin or a part of a binder mixture may have no effect on the rest of the particular paint binder. Paint solvents are therefore usually blends of different **active, latent,** and **diluent** solvents. Active solvents are strong. They act immediately to dissolve the resin-binder mixture. Latent solvents are slower working, and are therefore somewhat weaker if used alone. When they are correctly blended with an active solvent, the mixture controls the rate at which the solvent acts on the resin-binder. A diluent is a solvent that, as its name implies, actually dilutes the active-latent solution. A diluent extends the solution, rather than strengthening it.

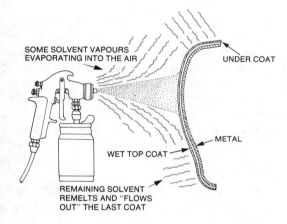

SOME SOLVENT VAPOURS EVAPORATING INTO THE AIR

UNDER COAT

METAL

WET TOP COAT

REMAINING SOLVENT REMELTS AND "FLOWS OUT" THE LAST COAT

Figure 15-5 Purposes of the solvents

The solvent must control the reduction for spraying, film flow, gloss, and drying rate. The main difference between different blends of the same solvent is their power to dissolve the paint binder and their rate of evaporation. Thinners are a much stronger and a faster-evaporating solvent than reducers.

Most paint manufacturers have at least three different blends of thinners and reducers. A fast evaporating material is recommended for use in cold weather, a slow evaporating solvent for use in hot weather. A medium slow solvent is a blend of the other two.

Thinners are used with all thermoplastic materials: topcoat and undercoat lacquers and acrylic lacquers. A special blend, high grade thinner, is used with acrylic lacquer topcoat materials.

Reducers are used with most synthetic thermoset topcoat and undercoat materials, — enamels, acrylic enamels, polyesters, urethanes, and epoxy paints. Some of these paints are supplied by the manufacturer in a ready-to-spray consistency and do not require any reduction other than the activator-solvent.

> Never intermix these two solvent materials or interchange their use with enamels or lacquers. When the wrong solvent is used, for example if a reducer is added to a lacquer, the mixture will immediately turn to a globular useless jelly. **Thinner** is used to **thin** lacquers (thermoplastic materials). **Reducers** are used to **reduce** enamels (thermoset materials).

Solvents are especially formulated by their manufacturers for use in their particular type of paint. They may not work as well with another manufacturer's paint.

Other Additives

Dryers. Small amounts of dryers must be added to paints that dry by the oxidation process. Dryers are the salts of certain materials, such as cobalt, manganese, zinc, or iron. They work as catalysts, speeding the oxidation process between the paint and oxygen in the air.

Plasticizers. These are small amounts of synthetic materials added to the paint to make the paint film less brittle and more flexible to allow the film to flex, expand, and contract with the metal without cracking.

15-3 TOPCOATS

The paints used in the automotive refinishing trade are divided into **topcoats** and **undercoats.** Topcoats are finish coats used to protect and beautify the surface.

Some manufacturers are clouding the standard paint types by giving their products combination names such as acrylic-urethane. Acrylic materials are thermoplastics, which are thinned with thinner. Urethanes are thermoset materials normally reduced with a reducer. The name acrylic-urethane would indicate a rather unusual mixture of two very different resins. Here is a good example of chemistry and synthetics. By modifying, combining, and processing, a new material with characteristics of both materials is developed.

All paint manufacturers do not have exactly the same products. Companies develop and formulate materials differently from their competitors. They also design their products to be used with their own solvents, following their recommended mixing and application procedures. The refinisher should therefore have a general knowledge of product materals, their uses, advantages, disadvantages, reduction, and application methods. However, each manufacturer's specific instructions must be followed when using their materials.

Enamel

Automotive enamels are synthetic or **alkyd** paints. The pigments are blends of natural and/or synthetically produced materials.

The binder is alkyd resin chemically produced from alcohols and acids. It is a thermosetting material and is reduced between 1 to 2 parts reducer to 4 parts paint. Once the paint has cured or hardened into a solid film, it cannot be remelted (Figure 15-6).

Enamels are applied in two coats, the first

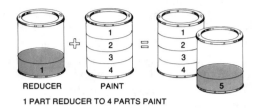

REDUCER   PAINT

1 PART REDUCER TO 4 PARTS PAINT

Figure 15-6   Enamel reduction

being a medium wet coat which provides a tack for the second full wet coat. A third coat is sometimes needed with poor covering colours. They dry to a medium gloss finish, and have excellent hiding power (that is, the ability to cover the surface and hide small imperfections).

Enamels are slow-drying paints, although the surface may be forced dry in less than an hour. When they are air dried, they usually take from 2 h to 6 h to surface dry.

Small amounts of hardener or catalyst can also be added to the paint, usually an amount up to 10% of the volume of paint before reduction. The catalyst reacts chemically with the binder to accelerate the drying or cure time of the film.

All synthetic enamels dry in two stages: the solvents (volatile materials) dry by evapora-

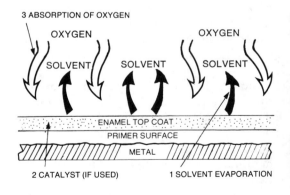

3 ABSORPTION OF OXYGEN

OXYGEN   OXYGEN

SOLVENT   SOLVENT   SOLVENT

ENAMEL TOP COAT
PRIMER SURFACE
METAL

2 CATALYST (IF USED)   1 SOLVENT EVAPORATION

Figure 15-7   Air-dry enamels require solvent evaporation plus absorption of oxygen to attain film hardness (catalyst can be used)

tion into the atmosphere and the non-volatile film hardens by the absorption of oxygen from the air (Figure 15-7). When heat is added, either by way of an oven or drying lights, both these actions are speeded.

The oxidation process of the binder is not complete for at least thirty days after application. Even though the surface may appear or feel hard, it remains somewhat porous to let the solvents out and the oxygen in.

This same oxidation process continues on the film surface long after the paint has completely dried. The sun, pollution, and other elements in the atmosphere continue to attack the enamel surface, tending to dull the shine or gloss and "weather" the film. Before enamel finishes can be recoated, this oxidized film must be sanded off to ensure a good bond for the new paint film.

Enamels have several major disadvantages:
1. They do not have a super shiny surface.
2. They soon start to oxidize and fade.
3. They dry slowly. This creates more dust problems, longer periods in the booth, and extra time before the surface can be re-taped for the second colour.

Standard enamels are quickly being replaced with acrylic enamels.

Lacquer Paints

Lacquer type paints dry very quickly by the evaporation process (Figure 15-8). The film forming binder does not have to absorb oxy-

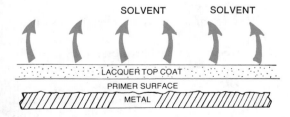

Figure 15-8   Lacquers require only solvent evaporation to attain film hardness

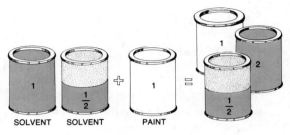

$1\frac{1}{2}$ – 2 PARTS SOLVENT TO 1 PART PAINT

Figure 15-9   Lacquer and acrylic lacquer solvent reduction

gen and oxidize as enamel type paints do. Lacquer paints are thermoplastic materials, i.e., they can be redissolved from a solid to a liquid and back to a solid. This characteristic makes them ideal for spot painting and blending purposes.

Lacquers have a lower solids content and therefore do not cover as well as do enamels. They must be applied in many thin, wet coats compared to two coats for enamel to obtain the same hiding power coverage.

Lacquer paints are always thinned with thinners for spraying. They are usually thinned to a ratio of 1.5 to 2 parts thinner to 1 part lacquer (Figure 15-9). All of the solvent and thinner is considered as the volatile part of the paint, most of it leaving very quickly after the paint has been applied. In 10–15 min the surface is tack free; within 2 to 4 h the solvent has completely evaporated and the film obtains complete hardness.

The surface to which lacquers are applied must be very smoothly sanded. Lacquers tend to have a smooth, shiny surface as the film is sprayed onto the surface. However, as the thinners evaporate and the paint dries, the film surface tends to shrink, becoming very dull and somewhat rough looking. After the film has completely hardened, the film must be compounded and polished to bring out its true colour and gloss. When lacquers are properly applied and polished, they produce a "deep-looking" finish having a very high gloss.

The one big disadvantage of nitrocellulose lacquers for topcoats was that the high gloss soon started to deteriorate or "weather." The film surface would develop a smoky dull haze which could only be removed by re-compounding and polishing.

Lacquer topcoat materials have been replaced with acrylic lacquer paints. Lacquer undercoat materials are still used in automotive refinishing although they are also gradually being replaced with acrylic and two component materials.

Acrylics

Because the original lacquer and enamel paints both had rather major disadvantages the manufacturers developed acrylic paint resins. Acrylic lacquers were developed first, to replace lacquer paints. The acrylic resins were eventually further modified for use in enamel products — thus acrylic enamels.

Acrylic Resins. These are thermoplastic materials. They were originally developed as a plastic for use in the manufacture of airplane windows. Acrylic resins are made by chemically processing gases collected from air, petroleum coal, and water into a clear water-like liquid. The main advantages of acrylics are:

1. They have a smooth, highly lustrous, scratch- and impact-resistant surface.
2. They do not fade. Prolonged exposure to the weather, sunlight, air, and pollution has a very slow effect on their clarity.
3. They have good resistance to heat and low temperature.
4. Being thermoplastic, they can be re-melted.

Acrylic Lacquers

Acrylic lacquers, although similar to nitrocellulose lacquers have many advantages over them. The acrylic resins are blended with other types of resins and plasticizers, or used alone as the complete paint binder, depending on the chemical design of the paint.

Stronger solvents are needed to thin acrylics; therefore, special blends of acrylic lacquer thinners are used to thin the acrylic paints at a ratio of 1.5 to 2 parts thinner to 1 part paint. These thinners are stronger and somewhat slower evaporating than those used with nitrocellulose lacquers.

Acrylic lacquers produce a hard, tough paint film affording excellent resistance to water, acid, alcohols, oils, solvents, detergents, and chemical fumes. The colour retention of the film is excellent.

Acrylic materials have a high solid content resulting in better covering power. However, three to five wet double coats are usually needed to obtain good coverage compared to two to three acrylic enamels.

Acrylics dry quickly by solvent evaporation only. They tend to shrink and dull as they dry and they must be compounded to bring out their true gloss. Because of their extremely hard plastic finish, it is almost impossible to compound the surface by hand. They must be machine compounded. Since they are thermoplastic they can be spot sprayed and "blended" without painting the complete panel.

Acrylic lacquers have certain disadvantages:

1. Due to their hardness, they tend to stone chip more readily than enamels.
2. They are hard to sand.
3. The surface to be painted must be well prepared, leaving only very fine sand scratches. Because of the high gloss of

the acrylics, every small imperfection is magnified. With enamels, these same imperfections would be covered.

4. The strong solvents used in the acrylics also play havoc with the base paints. These solvents are so strong, they penetrate into the base paint, causing them to soften and swell. The new topcoat film flows over the swelled basecoat and dries. The basecoat shrinks when the solvent evaporates, pulling the new film in with it. This, along with the topcoat shrinkage makes the surface rough and dull. Much of the solvent penetration and shrinkage problem can be overcome by not flooding the area with either heavy coats or many thin, wet coats. Apply the first two coats lightly to build a base and then allow sufficient time between the following coats for the solvents to evaporate.

Acrylic Enamels

The first acrylic enamels were originally designed with a high-bake thermoset resin. They could only be used by the vehicle manufacturer as the paint had to be baked at a very high temperature to polymerize(cure) the resin. Eventually air-dry acrylic resins were developed for use by the refinisher. These air-dry acrylic enamels use an additive hardener to polymerize and cure the resin in place of the high heat.

Acrylic enamels contain many of the best characteristics of both the acrylic lacquers and the alkyd enamels. The film dries quickly by the evaporation of the solvent and the polymerization of the resin. As soon as the solvent has evaporated from the surface, the film appears "non-tacky," dry to touch, similar to acrylic lacquers. The film is still soluble and melts when each additional coat is applied. Acrylic enamel finishes are dust free within 15 min and dry to handle within 1 h to 2 h, depending on colour and temperatures. Adding the hardener makes the acrylic paint film harder after 2 h than a regular enamel film which has dried overnight.

Two-tone colour tapings over the new film are safe after 2 or 3 h. A run or dirty spot can be water sanded, spot painted, and blended in, as the paint film is resoluble like lacquer.

Like enamels, acrylic enamels have a high solids content giving excellent coverage. The surface preparation need not be as well done as it must be for acrylics, but it should be slightly better than that necessary for enamels.

Two or more fully wet coats are needed to obtain complete coverage. The acrylic enamel materials are easily sprayed. There is less chance of runs occurring because of the rapid solvent evaporation. Each coat covers well and flows into a smooth glossy film. However, as the solvent evaporates the surface shrinks, losing some coverage and gloss. It is therefore better to consider more the amount of material used on the vehicle rather than the number of coats. Depending on the surface preparation and colour, two coats may be enough; with others, three or four coats may be necessary. The acrylic enamels dry to a durable finish and high gloss without the compounding and polishing necessary with lacquers.

Acrylic enamels are reduced with reducers, usually special reducers of a very slow drying blend. The ratio varies somewhat depending on the manufacturers recommendations, usually a 1 part solvent to 3 parts paint (or up to a 1 part solvent to 2 parts paint) reduction. The catalyst hardener must be used with acrylic enamels and in the correct amount (Figure 15-10). Too much hardener cures the film too quickly; too little

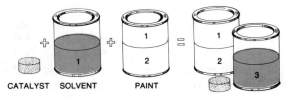

CATALYST   SOLVENT   PAINT

1 PART SOLVENT TO 2 PARTS PAINT

Figure 15-10   Acrylic enamel solvent reduction

does not allow the film to achieve complete hardness, so it would have a poor resistance to marks, solvents, chemicals, pollution, etc.

Acrylic enamels can also be forced dried to speed up the drying process without adding any additives other than the standard hardener. After most of the solvent has evaporated from the film, and it has started to polymerize, the film starts to oxidize as enamels do.

During the oxidizing process, a chemical change occurs in the binder changing the paint film into a fused, yet insoluble film. This oxidizing action toughens the film, creating greater resistance to water and gasoline spotting, scratching, yellowing, and fading. Once acrylic enamel film has completely cured it is not remeltable, since it is thermoset, but it is still much easier to spot paint and blend than ordinary enamels.

All paint manufacturers have not formulated their acrylic enamels the same. Each enamel has somewhat different characteristics. Some materials can only be recoated up to the time the oxidation cure begins (up to a 12 to 24 h period). During the time the film is oxidizing, the film is not resoluble. Should it be necessary to recoat the film, for example, if it is off-colour or to repair a run or dirty area, the solvents could attack the existing film creating a lifting or wrinkling problem. This curing period can last from eight hours up to eight days. Should

it be necessary to refinish over the previous film during this time, a special sealer must be applied first to prevent solvent seepage. Once the cure process is completed, the film binder returns to a compatible state and a sealer need not be used. Not all acrylic enamels are like this. Some have no critical recoat period. The paint film can be tested for solvent compatibility by rubbing acrylic enamel solvent on a small area of paint or especially on the edge of a featheredge. If there is no lifting reaction, a sealer is not necessary.

Precautions

1. At the present time the additives used in the acrylic enamel hardeners contain small amounts of isocyanates, chemicals that have been identified as causing allergic or asthmatic-type reactions in some people. Protective clothing — rubber gloves, safety glasses, and coveralls — should be worn when mixing these hardeners. An air-fed mask should be used while spraying the catalyzed enamel to prevent breathing in the harmful vapors. They may cause respiratory reactions. An ordinary filter type mask is not sufficient to filter out the harmful vapours.

2. Keep the paint away from extreme heat, sparks, or open flame.

3. Always check and follow the manufacturer's recommendations as to reductions, spray procedures, cure time, etc.

Urethanes and Polyurethanes

These are two materials that increasingly are being used as paint binders. Both types of resins can, by varying their formulations, be made into everything from paint resins and plastics to foams and fibres. Urethanes are often processed into foams used to make interior and exterior soft plastic crash panels, adhesives for bonding windshields, and impact absorbing plastics used for moulded bumper covers.

Both urethanes and polyurethanes are thermoset materials that can be formulated to either air dry or be force cured by adding a catalyst. (They can also be formulated into thermoplastic materials.)

As paint binders these materials have good adhesion and produce a fast-drying, exceptionally hard surface. The paint has a deep, "wet look" gloss and good resistance to abrasion and chemicals, as well as excellent resistance to dulling.

Urethanes can be formulated to air dry, like the urethane varnishes used on wood. Those used in the automotive field are of the two component system. A catalyst-solvent mixture is added to the pigment-binder mixture. Usually no other solvent is used. The two part polyurethanes cure quickly (in 2–3 h) because of the addition of the catalyst to polymerize the binder into a thermosetting film. The air-dry materials dry more slowly because they cure by oxidation.

Polyurethane films, after curing, remain flexible. This, combined with their extreme toughness makes the paints ideally suited for use where impact and vibrations, marking and scratching, chemical and weather resistance is important. Because of these characteristics, they are ideally suited for industry and fleet application.

Always follow the manufacturer's recommendations for reduction, number of coats, cure time, and spraying applications. Always wear suitable protective clothing, — especially an airfed mask — as the catalyst contains isocyanates which can be harmful to the respiratory system.

With the two component polyurethane, once the activator has been mixed with the paint the pot life is only 6 to 8 h. After this time, the material will harden in the can. Therefore, only mix as much as is necessary to do the job. The pot life can be extended somewhat by keeping the mixture in a cool place. The cold slows down the chemical cure.

Polyesters

Polyesters are used in paints, plastic fillers, and fibreglass. They can also be processed into thread fibres used to make clothes. Polyesters used in paints are fast-drying thermosetting resins that are cured by adding small amounts of a catalyst. The resin quickly cures into a tough, insoluble material with a hard surface that resists most solvents, acids, and salts. Most polyesters have a tendency to fade somewhat with exposure to sun and light.

Basecoat/Clearcoat System

The term basecoat/clearcoat refers to the system rather than a type of paint. A high solids (binder pigment) base material is sprayed onto the smoothly prepared surface. It provides the colour and covering part of the system. Some paint manufacturers are using acrylic lacquer base materials while others are using polyesters. Still others call theirs an acrylic-urethane base. Acrylic lacquers are thinned with thinners — usually 1 to 2 parts thinner to 1 part paint.

Polyester and urethane materials are reduced using from 1 to 3 parts reducer to 4 parts paint, depending on the manufacturer. Some types also require that a hardener be added.

Basecoat. Rather than recommending that the basecoat material be sprayed in one, two, or three coats, the manufacturers recommend that only enough material be used to provide the necessary coverage. Basecoats do not have a shine. They spray on and appear dull or flat looking. After a short drying period the surface is tacked off to remove any overspray dust, and one to three medium wet coats of clear material are sprayed over the base materials (Figure 15-11).

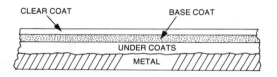

Figure 15-11   Basecoat/clearcoat system

Clearcoat. The clearcoat materials are urethane or acrylic-urethane blends of clear resin. All require a catalyst to make them cure chemically. Most do not require a solvent. Some manufacturers recommend that a small amount of a special slow-evaporation solvent be used in very hot weather.

The basecoat/clearcoat system provides a deep, glossy paint finish. The clear outer urethane film dries quickly and has good adhesion, producing a hard, abrasion-resistant surface. It also protects the pigments and metallics from attack by chemicals, especially acid rain, which fades or spots the surface of one-part paints.

Metallic Topcoats

Metallic finishes can be obtained in any of the topcoat paints by adding finely ground, powdered flakes to the paint. These powdered flakes can be made from aluminum, mica, or tin. Aluminum is the most common. The small flakes arrange themselves in various positions in the wet paint

film similar to falling leaves, creating a layered effect referred to as **leafing.** This leafing effect of the metallic flakes produces unusual brightness and hiding power. The metallic particles reflect the light, so that the colour and brightness appear to change when the paint is viewed from different angles. Therefore, metallic finishes may best be described as effects rather than colours. The effect will vary with the amount of thinning, the number of coats applied, and the method of spraying (wet or dry).

15-4 UNDERCOATS

The term **undercoats** refers to **primers, primer surfacers, putties,** and **sealers.** Undercoats are paints applied to create a bond between the substrate (i.e., metal, fibreglass, plastic, or original paint) and the new paint film. Some undercoats are also designed to fill small imperfections as well as providing the necessary bond and protection. Their general purpose is to prepare a surface for the final topcoat. Each material is specially formulated and prepared for a definite purpose

Originally, all undercoats were lacquer or enamel products. Lacquers were once used almost exclusively for automotive work because of their fast-drying qualities. They could be easily sanded and topcoated very soon after spraying. Their one disadvantage was somewhat poor adhesion and moisture resistance. Enamel undercoats had much better adhesion, moisture resistance, and filling qualities, but were very slow drying and hard to sand. Acrylic, polyester, epoxy, and urethane-base materials are replacing them.

The acrylic undercoats are thermoplastic air-dry materials. They dry quickly by solvent evaporation only. All the others are in the enamel thermoset family. They require either a small amount of catalyst (for example, with the polyester materials), or they have a two component system (for example, epoxy and polyurethane materials).

These new primers have superior adhesion, filling, and moisture resistance compared to the original lacquers and enamels. They dry by polymerization and their cure and hardness is complete in 1 to 6 h, depending on the type of material. They can also be forced dry to further speed the curing process. After curing, they are easily sanded for final topcoating.

Primers

A primer is an undercoat designed to grip the original surface tightly and establish a secure bonding base for later paint films. Primers are generally used over unpainted materials, i.e., metals, fibreglass, plastics, vinyls, etc., although they may also be used over old finishes.

Primers are a first coat material. They are applied in one thin, wet coat. They are not intended to be sanded. Their primary purpose is to promote adhesion and provide moisture and corrosion protection between the substrate and the next type of undercoat. They have no filling or levelling power. A primer contains very little pigment; it consists mostly of binder, ensuring good adhesion.

Primers can be of the lacquer, enamel air-dry or enamel-epoxy, or urethane polymerizing families. Standard enamels dry slowly by solvent evaporation and oxidation and require longer periods of drying time before recoating. Lacquer primer dries quickly by solvent evaporation only. It can be recoated almost immediately. Polymerizing primers are either catalyzed or of the two component system. Both types flash-off quickly but may take up to 6 h to dry completely.

There are special primers designed for use over unusual surfaces, such as aluminum, galvanized metal, and zinc.

Special Primers. **Zinc chromate** primer is a greenish yellow synthetic primer used on aluminum and aluminum alloys to promote adhesion and corrosion prevention coverage. It is reduced with reducers.

Vinyl wash primers are two component primers. One part contains the binder, containing a percentage of vinyl resins and zinc flakes to which is added the second part, the catalyst and solvent. Once these two materials are mixed and applied, a chemical reaction creates the cure (polymerization). This type of primer yields an excellent, strong, durable bond to the metals, especially to galvanized metal as well as uncoated steel and fibreglass. No additional solvent reduction is necessary. It is sprayed in one very thin wet coat and allowed to dry approximately 30 min to 1 h before recoating. It should not be sanded and thick coats should never be applied.

Wash primers are self-etching. They actually become part of the substrate to which they are applied. They should be recoated with a further primer or primer surfacer within a 4 h period. Once they cure without being recoated, their surface becomes hard and glazed. If they are not recoated before the end of the 4 h period they should either be recoated with another light coat of the same wash primer or lightly sanded before recoating with another undercoat. Wash primers are not designed to be used as the only primer between the substrate and the topcoat for exterior use.

The wash primer additive is a mildly corrosive acid. It should always be stored in a glass container. Avoid contact with the eyes and skin. Splashes should be washed off immediately with cold water.

Epoxy-type primer is a very tough durable primer containing epoxy resins as binder. Some are air drying materials. Most are two component materials. This material is excellent for both adhesion and corrosion protection. It also has good filling qualities.

Some epoxy-type primers are diluted with reducers, others use thinners. The two component materials are mixed first and then the solvent is added, usually from 10% to 25%. Epoxies dry quickly. They can be taped and lightly scuffed in 4 to 6 h. For heavier sanding some need 1 to 4 d.

> Always check the manufacturer's recommendations before using these special primers. They are not all formulated the same way.

Polypropylene and polyethylene primers are designed for use over plastic parts. They are available in aerosol cans or as a packaged material to be diluted and sprayed from the standard spray gun. Ordinarily paints do not stick well to plastics. Their surface is too smooth and slick. Standard primer and paint are also too inflexible for use with the soft or flexible plastics. These plastic primers create an intermediate bond between the surface of the plastic and the topcoat.

Primer Surfacers

Primer surfacers have a combination of binders similar to those used for primers and pigments. The pigments are a blend of primary (oxide) and extender-filler type pigments. Primer surfacers are formulated to be approximately one-half binder and one-half pigment. They are designed to provide good adhesion to the surface to which they are applied, to fill small imperfections in the

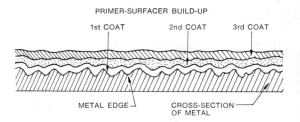

Figure 15-12   Primer surfacer fills small imperfections and bonds to the surface

surface (Figure 15-12), and provide topcoat holdout. Primers surfacers can be lacquer or acrylic (thermoplastic) or synthetic (thermoset) materials.

The thermoplastic (lacquer and acrylic) materials are used more extensively for automotive work, as they are fast drying and easily sanded. Lacquer and acrylic primer surfacers are thinned using 1 to 2 parts lacquer thinner to 1 part primer surfacer. They are sprayed in thin wet coats with a short flash-off period between coats to allow the solvent to evaporate. Sometimes as many as four or five coats are applied to build up the area and "fill out" imperfections. A lapse of 15 to 20 min should be allowed before attempting to sand lacquer primer surfacers, although thinner coats can be sanded sooner.

The thermoset primer surfacers have a higher solids content and a synthetic binder. They therefore fill faster with fewer coats and have better adhesion qualities than lacquer materials.

Air-dry enamel primer surfacers are reduced using 1 to 2 parts reducer to 4 parts primer, and sprayed in full wet coats. They dry by solvent evaporation and film oxidization. They also possess more corrosion and moisture resistance and flexibility after overnight drying than lacquers.

Their drawback is that they require a long

drying time (at least 4 h) before they can be sanded or topcoated. Lacquer primer surfacers can be applied over enamel type primer surfacers after 24 h drying time.

Enamel materials are used more on commercial vehicles where rough service and heavy use are common and therefore greater protection is needed.

Polyester, urethane, and acrylic urethane primer surfacers are all catalyzed materials. Some use only small amounts of hardener, while others are formulated as two component systems. Some are further reduced with a reducer and others are not.

The big advantage of these catalyzed materials is their high solids film build. Because of the nature of the binder, less solvent is needed to reduce the material to a spraying viscosity. Since a greater amount of pigment and binder is used in the paint, and since there is little solvent evaporation, the film thickness is quickly gained. One or two coats is equal to six or seven of the lacquer products. They are easy to sand and can be sanded after 1 to 3 h. Always reduce the primer surfacer first and then add the hardener. Clean the spray gun immediately after use with good quality thinner.

> Do not apply any type of primer surfacer in thick, heavy coats or attempt to load or flood the area with many, thin coats without a flash-off period. The solvent will be trapped in the film, resulting in longer drying, poor sanding, and topcoat shrinkage problems.

Putties

Putty is an undercoat much like primer surfacer but heavier in pigment content. It is applied with a rubber squeegie over deep

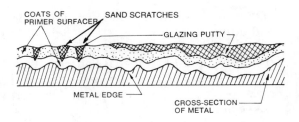

Figure 15-13   Putty applied over deep scratches and imperfections in the metal or old paint

scratches and imperfections in the surface (Figure 15-13).

Putties are usually lacquer materials. New polyester-type putties are catalyzed materials that dry quickly through the complete film build without shrinking as they dry. Lacquer materials dry by solvent evaporation from the outside in. The surface may appear dry, but when the top layer is sanded off, the rest is still soft. Lacquer putties tend to shrink as they dry. Should they be sanded smooth and the topcoat applied before the putty has thoroughly dried, the putty will continue to shrink and draw the topcoat in with it, leaving a flat or dull spot in the topcoat.

Lacquer putties are designed to be applied over primer or primer surfacer and are not recommended for application over bare metal or body fillers. Polyester putties can be used over fillers.

Sealers

Sealers are specially formulated blends of resins that dry quickly into a thermosetting film. They are used to protect the basecoats (primer, primer surfacer, old topcoats) from the solvents in the topcoat materials. These solvents, if allowed to enter the base materials, can cause problems such as uneven colour holdout, poor adhesion, shrinkage, and scratch swelling, and even wrinkling and lifting conditions.

A sealer is especially recommended when the new paint to be applied is a different type than the original. The sealer "seals" or separates the two, yet provides good adhesion between them.

The sealers are sprayed in one medium wet coat, then allowed to dry 15 to 25 min before the topcoat is applied. The sealer bonds to the base materials and helps to fill the sand scratches (Figure 15-14). It provides an excellent uniform insoluble film for the new topcoat to adhere to, resulting in the topcoat having a higher gloss and better colour uniformity with fewer coats. Sealers are especially necessary for use with acrylic lacquers, as they contain exceptionally strong solvents.

Always check the manufacturer's recommendations as to the type of sealer to use for a specific job and the procedure to follow. Some sealers must have the topcoat applied within an hour from the time the sealer was sprayed; if not, they cannot be topcoated for 25 h as the sealer enters a critical cure time. Sealers are generally not designed for use over bare metals, nor are they thinned before spraying.

15-5 WAX AND GREASE REMOVERS

Wax and grease removers are cleaning solvents that will dissolve wax and grease embedded in old paint (Figure 15-15). They are used to wash original painted surfaces that are to be repainted.

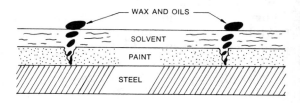

Figure 15-15 Solvent "floating action" loosens and dissolves wax, grease, or oil on the surface

Many polishes and waxes contain small amounts of silicon resin to which new paint will not adhere. The silicon resins present in the small pores of the original paint will cause the new film to "crawl" and leave craters or **fish-eyes** in the surface (Figure 15-16). Most paint manufacturers make special products that can be added to the paint

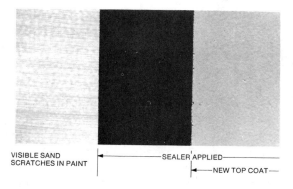

VISIBLE SAND SCRATCHES IN PAINT — SEALER APPLIED —
— NEW TOP COAT —

Courtesy Coatings and Resins Division, Ditzler Automotive Refinishes

Figure 15-14 Sealers minimize sand scratches

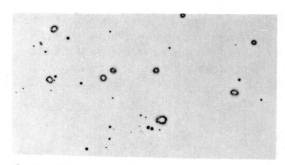

Courtesy CIL Automotive Finishes

Figure 15-16 Fish-eyes caused by painting over silicon resins

before it is sprayed to prevent fish-eyes from occurring. However, they recommend that it not be used unless absolutely necessary. It does not remove the silicon; it only prevents the effects of the resin from showing up in the finish coat.

Removing Wax

To remove wax, soak a rag with the solvent and then wash a small area with the wet cloth. Using a clean cloth, wipe the area dry. Change cloths frequently to avoid spreading the silicon over the surface.

Always clean the old paint before sanding it down. Sanding the surface before removing the wax will work the silicon particles deeper into the old paint.

15-6 COMPOUNDS

Rubbing compounds are mixtures of fine, abrasive particles suspended in a solution of water solvents and oils. There are different grades of compound varying in the size of the abrasive particles. Usually the finer grades are a white colour and the coarse compounds are brown.

Compounds are used on lacquer, acrylic enamel and lacquer, and outer clearcoats to rub out dullness, small dirt nibs, slight scratches, and orange peel. Orange peel is a painted surface that resembles the skin of an orange (Figure 15-17). Lacquer and acrylic lacquer finishes would dull after the solvent had evaporated. The compound is used to remove the orange peel and bring out the gloss. Lacquers are rubbed by hand. Acrylics and urethane clearcoats are so hard that they are first watersanded smooth with a very fine abrasive paper. The finish is then machine compounded to bring up the gloss. Compounds are also used to remove road film and dead pigment from oxidized paint before it

Courtesy CIL Automotive Finishes

Figure 15-17   Orange peel

is polished or waxed. Compounds are also used to clean bumpers and other chrome finished parts.

Compounds can be applied by hand or with an electric or air-operated polisher.

Hand Application

Apply the compound sparingly to a rubbing ball made of a clean, damp cloth. Rub the finish in one direction, with back-and-forth motions, until the desired smoothness is obtained. Wipe off the residue and polish the area to a high lustre with a clean, dry cloth.

> Always apply the compound to the ball, never to the surface itself.

Polisher Application

When using a power polisher, mix the compound with water to a creamy consistency. Apply the compound to the surface with a fine bristle brush. Polish the area so the compound spreads evenly and a bright, dry finish is produced. Use the same techniques as those used with the portable grinder. Apply only enough force to equal that created by the weight of the polisher. Use either a cross-cutting or buffing motion. Use the side of the polishing pad only when necessary.

A grinder is not suitable for use as a polisher. Grinder speeds are 5000 r/min and up; polisher speeds are about 1500 r/min.

Keep the polisher moving. If the polisher is stopped on the surface momentarily, the paint may overheat and a burn mark may be left on the paint.

15-7 METAL CONDITIONER

Metal conditioner is a blend of solvents and phosphoric acid. It is used to wash all grease, rust, and oxides from bare metal and soldered areas before they are primed. The phosphoric acid also etches the surface of the metal slightly. **Etching** is the process of roughening a metal surface to permit a better bond between the metal and the first primer coat.

Metal conditioner is reduced for use by mixing one part of conditioner with two parts water. This solution is applied to a surface with a rag, scotch pad, or a fine wire brush.

The wet surface is scrubbed until the rust and oxides dissolve. Then the conditioner is wiped dry with a clean cloth. If the solution dries before the surface is wiped, the area is wet again and then wiped dry. Some manufacturers suggest that the solution be washed off with water and then wiped and blown dry.

The treated area should be primed immediately after drying because of the treated metal will begin to rust in a matter of minutes. If the conditioner is not wiped or washed off, a white, powdered film will be left on the metal, preventing the primer from adhering to the metal.

Protect the hands and eyes when handling this material. If conditioner should get in the eyes, wash them out with clean water.

Tack Rag. A tack rag is a piece of cheesecloth that has been soaked in a non-drying varnish. It remains sticky or tacky. The rag is used to wipe a prepared surface clean of dust and lint particles before the area is sprayed.

Most paints and their additives are combustible, or explosive. Every precaution should be exercised while using them.

REVIEW QUESTIONS

1. List the purposes of a paint.
2. Explain the difference between the terms dust free and tack free.
3. a) List and briefly explain the three possible drying processes paints can go through.
   b) Which of three processes is slowest? Why?
   c) List two methods of speeding up the drying process.
4. Briefly explain the purpose of each of the three ingredients of paint.
5. What are the purposes of the extender pigments in the paint batch?
6. Define the terms thermoplastic and thermosetting.
7. What materials are the non-volatile part of the paint?
8. List two raw materials solvents are obtained from.
9. List and explain the two main purposes of a thinner or reducer.
10. Define the term "active," "latent," and "diluent" as they would be used to describe solvent characteristics.

11. What type of solvent should the refinisher use in hot weather? Why?

12. Why should an enamel paint not be waxed for at least 30 d?

13. List three disadvantages of a standard enamel paint.

14. What solvent is used to reduce enamel and by what ratio?

15. In what way does the drying of lacquers differ from that of enamels?

16. List the material and the ratio with which lacquer materials are thinned for spraying.

17. Why must lacquers be applied in many coats?

18. a) What type of material is used to thin acrylic lacquers and at what ratio?
    b) What problems do these strong acrylic solvents present?

19. List the characteristics of acrylic lacquer resin.

20. Using two columns, list the characteristics of acrylic enamel that are similar to acrylic lacquers in one column, and all those similar to enamel in the other.

21. Briefly explain the drying process of acrylic enamel.

22. Explain the drying differences between the urethanes used for wood and the polyurethanes used for automotive work.

23. List the main advantages of polyurethane materials.

24. Explain the basecoat/clearcoat system.

25. What types of materials are used for the basecoats and clearcoats?

26. What advantage does the clearcoat offer?

27. Explain the metallic paint leafing effect.

28. Explain the difference between a primer and a primer surfacer.

29. a) Explain how primers and primer surfacers should be applied.
    b) Why should a short "flash-off" period be allowed between coats of primer surfacer?
    c) Why must primer surfacers not be applied in thick heavy coats?

30. Make a chart to compare the advantages and disadvantages of a lacquer and an enamel primer surface.

31. List the advantages of the two component undercoat materials.

32. Explain the difference between a two component paint, compared to a catalyzed paint.

33. a) What is the purpose of a putty?
    b) What two types are there?

34. List and explain the purposes of a sealer.

35. Explain sand scratch swelling.

36. Why should old paint be washed with a wax and grease remover before the paint is sanded?

37. a) What is the purpose of rubbing compounds?
    b) Define "orange peel" as the term applies to paint.
    c) List two precautions that should be observed when using the power polisher.

38. a) What is the purpose of metal conditioner?
    b) How should it be used?

39. Why should metal conditioned areas be primed as soon as the area dries?

16

SPRAY EQUIPMENT

16-1   Spray Guns
16-2   Types of Spray Guns
16-3   Spray Gun Maintenance
16-4   Air and Fluid Refinishing Hoses
16-5   Air Transformers
16-6   Air Compressors
16-7   Respirators

The spray equipment consists of spray guns, an air transformer, and air compressors.

16-1 SPRAY GUNS

The spray gun is a precision instrument and should be treated as such. Neglect, carelessness, and improper cleaning are responsible for the majority of spray gun difficulties.

The purpose of a spray gun is to combine paint with compressed air to atomize (break up) the paint into a fine spray and then direct the mixture onto the surface in a controlled spray pattern (Figure 16-1).

All spray guns do not operate in the same way. There are different types of guns. The type is determined by the method in which the paint is moved through the gun, how the air is controlled going through the gun, and

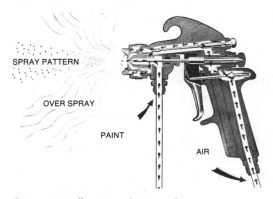

Courtesy DeVilbiss (Canada) Limited

Figure 16-1   Cross-section of a spray gun

where and how the paint and air are mixed together.

Before studying the actual spray gun operaton, it is better to first know the name and location of the principal parts. There are different spray gun manufacturers.

However, most use similar parts and the same operating principles.

Air Cap

The air cap is located at the front of the gun (Figure 16-2). There are two very different types: either an **external** or **internal** mix design. The air cap design determines where the paint and air are mixed.

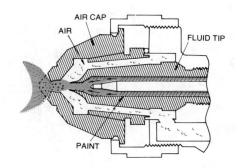

Figure 16-3A Internal-mix air cap

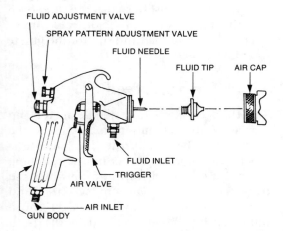

Figure 16-2 Principal parts of a spray gun

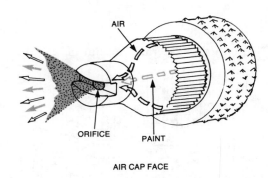

Figure 16-3B Internal-mix air cap face

Internal Mix. When the internal-mix cap is used, the paint and air meet and mix inside the front of the gun just behind the face of the air cap. The internal-mix cap has a single orifice in the centre of a slot machined into the face (Figure 16-3). The use of this type of cap is limited to slow-drying materials that will not quickly dry and build-up behind the cap and in the orifice. The internal-mix spray break up is rather coarse, resulting in a somewhat rough paint finish. This type of air cap is not suitable for automotive quality finishes. Its one advantage is that it produces very little overspray.

External Mix. When the external-mix cap is used, the paint and air actually meet approximately 15 mm out from the face of the

air cap. The external-mix air cap is easily identified by two ears (horns) that protrude out from the front of the air cap. There are a number of orifices in the air cap. These orifices must be accurately machined and correctly aligned to direct the air into the right location in the paint stream.

The air is ejected through two or more horn orifices, a centre ring-shaped orifice, and auxiliary orifices. The horn orifices direct the air that determines the size and shape of the spray pattern and supplies 20% to 25% of the air needed to atomize the paint stream. The centre orifice and auxiliary orifices supply the other 75% to 80% of air needed to completely atomize the paint (Figure 16-4). There can be one or more auxil-

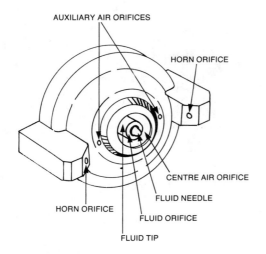

Figure 16-4A   External-mix air cap

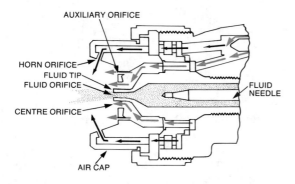

Figure 16-4B   External-mix air cap face

iary orifices on each side of the centre orifice. Multiple orifices are used when high viscosity (thick) materials are being sprayed. The additional air is needed to help atomize the thicker paint. The centre orifice is much larger than the others. When the cap is on the gun, the end of the fluid tip protrudes through the orifice. A ring or donut-shaped orifice is created between the outer edge of the cap orifice and the fluid tip (Figure 16-5). The cap must fit so that the fluid tip is exactly in the middle of the orifice, with an even gap around the fluid tip, for the gun to operate correctly.

Fluid Tip and Needle

The fluid tip and fluid needle meter and direct the correct amount of paint into the air stream. The end of the fluid needle is tapered to a point. It fits into a matching tapered seat in the tip orifice from which the paint is ejected. The movement of the fluid needle is controlled by the trigger and a return spring. When the end of the fluid needle is in the tip orifice, no paint can get out. When the needle is pulled back by the trigger, the tip orifice is opened and the paint can flow. When the trigger is released, the return spring forces the needle back into the tip seat. The tip and needle must be made and used as a matched set.

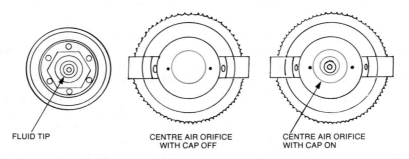

Figure 16-5   Centre ring-shaped orifice

When a heavy, coarse material is being sprayed, a fluid tip with a large opening must be used. A smaller opening is used for a thinner material.

Spray Pattern Adjustment Valve

The spreader adjustment valve controls the amount of air supplied to the air cap horns, which determine the size and shape of the spray pattern.

Fluid Adjustment

This adjustment screw controls the movement of the fluid needle, which controls the fluid flow.

Air Valve

The air valve controls the amount of air allowed into the gun. It is operated by the trigger. The end of the air valve stem is positioned against the trigger. When the trigger is pulled, the air valve is opened (Figure 16-6). Not all spray guns have an air valve. Those that do are said to be **non-bleeder guns.** These are the more expensive guns that are used with controlled air systems, i.e., when the compressor unit is equipped with an automatic pressure-control switch

to stop and start the compressor. All guns used for automotive refinishing are non-bleeder guns.

Spray guns that do not have an air valve are said to be **bleeder-type guns.** This type of gun is used when the air compressor has no control switch to start and stop the spray equipment automatically. Some air is allowed to escape through the gun at all times to keep the air pressure at a safe operating level. This type of gun/compressor arrangement is limited to small utility-type systems that are not suitable for automotive refinishing.

Spray Gun Adjustments

Air Cap. When the air-cap horn orifices are in a horizontal position, a vertical spray pattern is produced. By twisting the air cap a quarter turn so the orifices are in a vertical position, the spray pattern becomes horizontal (Figure 16-7).

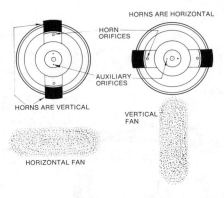

Figure 16-7   Air cap — spray pattern position

Spray Pattern Adjustment Valve. The spray pattern size and shape is controlled by the top or side adjustment valve. Turning the valve inward reduces the amount of air through the air horns, creating a small round "O" spray pattern. As the valve is opened the spray pattern gradually becomes more

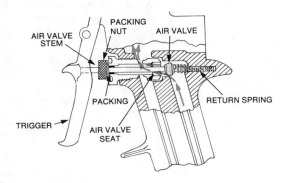

Figure 16-6   Air valve

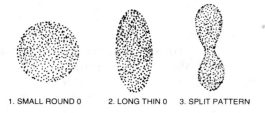

1. SMALL ROUND 0   2. LONG THIN 0   3. SPLIT PATTERN

Figure 16-8   Spray pattern shapes

oblong. When the valve is in the turned out position, the pattern resembles a long thin "O." Turning the valve fully open sometimes results in an undesirable split pattern resembling an hour glass or figure eight shape (Figure 16-8).

Fluid Adjustment Valve. The fluid adjustment valve controls the amount of fluid allowed out through the fluid tip into the air stream. It acts as a stop to control the backward movement of the trigger and fluid needle (Figure 16-9). It is turned out until the

first thread is showing when a full spray pattern is desired. Turning the control valve inward decreases the fluid tip movement and therefore the amount of paint allowed out of the fluid tip. When a small, round spray pattern is used, the fluid flow should be decreased accordingly, to prevent excessive coverage of the small spray pattern area.

Trigger. The air valve and fluid needle are both controlled by the trigger. When the trigger is pulled, the air valve opens before the fluid needle to provide a sufficient supply of air at the air cap to atomize the first drop of paint. When the trigger is released, the fluid needle closes before the air valve to ensure complete atomization of the last drop of paint.

A partly pulled trigger restricts both air and paint flow so that less paint is applied to the surface. This spray-pattern control is often used to blend or feather-in a small area, for example, around a door handle, where an additional full coat could cause a run.

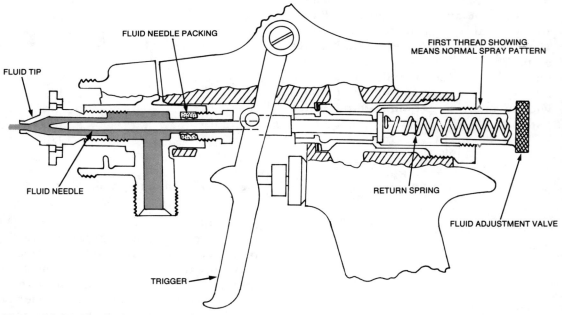

Figure 16-9   Fluid adjustment valve

16-2 TYPES OF SPRAY GUNS

Three different types of spray guns are used. They are siphon-feed, pressure-feed, and gravity-feed. The **feed** is the method by which the paint is supplied to the fluid nozzle.

Operating Principles of Siphon-Feed Spray Guns

This gun has an air valve and is therefore a non-bleeder gun. The air cap is an external-mix type. It is the typical gun used for automotive work.

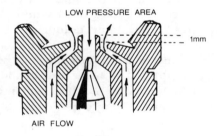

Figure 16-10   Fluid tip used on siphon-feed spray guns

The siphon-feed gun must use an external-mix air cap. The end of the fluid tip protrudes through the centre air cap orifice. The end has a slight outward flare and extends approximately 1 mm past the air cap face (Figure 16-10). When the trigger is pulled the air valve opens, allowing air through the gun and out the air cap orifices. Over half the total amount of air comes out through the centre ring-shaped orifice, completely surrounding or "ringing" the fluid tip.

A low pressure area is created in the centre of this fast moving "ring" of air, directly in front of the fluid tip (Figure 16-11). Air at the atmospheric pressure of the room enters the

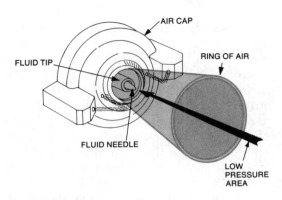

Figure 16-11   Ring of air creating a low pressure area

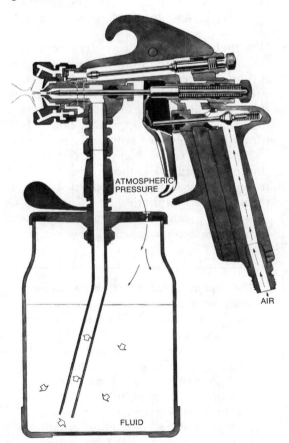

Courtesy DeVilbiss (Canada) Limited

Figure 16-12   Siphon gun — atmospheric pressure forces paint out of the gun

fluid container through a small vent opening in the cup. This atmospheric pressure is higher than the pressure of the air in the centre of the ring-shaped air stream directly in front of the fluid tip (Figure 16-12). The difference in pressure enables the atmosphere pressure, acting on the paint in the cup, to force the paint up the fluid tube and out through the fluid tip, into the low pressure area. The air from other air cap orifices (horn and auxilliary) join with the centre air ring and the paint approximately 15 mm past the face of the air cap. The paint is mixed with the air into a fine atomized spray and formed into the correct spray pattern.

With the siphon-type gun, an external-mix air cap must be used along with a protruding fluid tip to direct the air and create the low pressure area. The flare on the end of the fluid tip makes the ring of air funnel outward to create a larger low pressure area which in turn allows a greater volume of paint out.

The size of the siphon paint container is limited to about 1 L as the gun, when full of paint, is very heavy to hold out over the vehicle while painting.

Only very thin materials can be siphoned through the siphon gun into the low pressure area.

The vent hole and centre ring air orifice must be kept clean. Otherwise, very little or no paint will be emitted from the fluid tip.

If the centre ring orifice becomes clogged, no low pressure area is created, and therefore the paint cannot flow. When the vent hole in the top of the fluid container becomes clogged with paint, the air at atmospheric pressure cannot enter the fluid container and no paint will be emitted from the fluid tip.

Operating Principles of Pressure-Feed Spray Guns

In this system, the material is placed in a closed container which is pressurized by the air supply. The air hose is connected from the air transformer to a regulator on top of the fluid container. The regulator is adjustable and controls the pressure on the fluid in the container. The paint is forced up the fluid hose to the fluid nozzle. The amount of pressure acting on the fluid determines the rate at which the paint is supplied to the fluid nozzle.

The fluid container can be connected directly to the gun but, in most cases, it is a separate unit varying in size from 2.25 L to more than 270 L. The pressure-feed gun and separate container are used where large quantities of the same colour are to be sprayed.

The air needed to atomize the paint at the air cap is supplied by an air hose connected from the regulator on the fluid container to the air inlet on the spray gun (Figure 16-13).

Courtesy DeVilbiss (Canada) Limited

Figure 16-13   Pressure-feed spray gun and container

Siphon-Feed Guns vs. Pressure-Feed Guns

With the pressure-feed spray system, the atomizing pressure and the supply of paint at the spray-gun head can be controlled separately. With the siphon spray gun, the amount of paint used depends entirely on the amount of air pressure used to create the low pressure area. The siphon gun is capable of applying approximately 350 mL/min. With the pressure-feed system, up to three times as much paint can be applied per minute.

The pressure-feed spray gun can be used effectively in any position. When the siphon gun is tipped on too great an angle with a full cup of paint, the paint will run out the vent in the lid. If the paint suply is low, the siphon gun will be starved for paint.

Figure 16-14   Fluid tip used on pressure-feed spray guns

Both internal-mix and external-mix spray heads can be used with the pressure spray gun. However an external-mix spray head is always used for automotive work, as it produces a much finer spray. The external-mix head can be used only with a siphon spray gun. When the external-mix spray head is used with the pressure-feed gun, the fluid tip used has no flare and is shorter. The tip end sits flush with the air cap face. The fluid tip orifice is much smaller on the pressure gun than on the siphon gun. It is easier and faster to force paint through an opening when the pressure system is used (Figure 16-14).

Operating Principles of Gravity-Feed Spray Guns

With this type of spray gun, the fluid is held in the cup above the gun. It is forced down into the gun by the atmospheric air pressure acting on the fluid. The atmospheric pressure enters the cup through a small hole in the top of the cup lid, thus the term gravity feed (Figure 16-15). The complete fluid passage of the gun is always full of fluid. If the trigger is pulled without an air line connected to the gun, the paint simply runs out the fluid tip as soon as the fluid needle opened.

This type of gun is especially suited for spraying heavy-bodied, high-solids primers. There is a 100+ kPa (14+ psi) pressure advantage compared to a siphon-type gun, be-

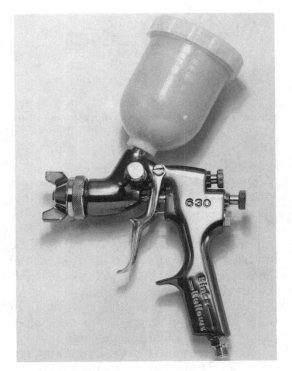

Courtesy Binks Manufacturing Company

Figure 16-15   Gravity feed gun

cause the fluid is above the gun and only has to run down into the fluid tip.

Materials can be sprayed through the gravity gun with from 70–105 kPa (10–15 psi) less pressure than with a siphon gun, producing fine paint break up with less overspray.

Note that the gun illustrated has three control valves. The side valve, common to most gravity guns, controls the size and shape of the spray pattern. The additional rear upper valve controls the air pressure through the gun, allowing the pressure to be changed from the gun for spot ins and blending. The rear lower fluid adjustment valve controls the fluid needle movement, which controls the amount of fluid allowed out of the fluid tip.

16-3 SPRAY GUN MAINTENANCE

Cleaning the Spray Gun

The spray gun should be cleaned immediately after the spraying operation is completed. If the paint is allowed to dry in the fluid passages and nozzle, the equipment is extremely difficult to clean.

Siphon-Feed Gun and Cup. Release the gun from the cup and, with the fluid tube still in the cup, unscrew the air cap two or three turns. Hold a cloth over the air cap and pull the trigger (Figure 16-16). The air will be diverted into the fluid passages, forcing the material back into the paint container. Empty the cup.

Wash the cup, the outside of the fluid tube, and the bottom of the fluid-container lid. Put a small quantity of cleaning solvent in the cup and spray it through the gun to flush out the internal passages. Spray the solvent into a rag which can then be used to clean the outside of the gun.

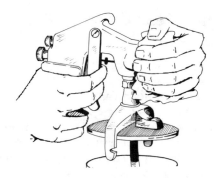

Figure 16-16   Cleaning the gun

Remove the air cap and check that all air orifices are clean. Dry the air cap and replace it on the gun.

Pressure-Feed System. Turn out the air-pressure regulating screw on the tank. Release the pressure in the tank through the relief, or safety, valve. Loosen the air cap.

Hold a rag over the air cap and pull the trigger. The material from the gun and fluid hose will be forced back into the pressure cup. Remove the paint and wash the pressure cup. Put cleaning solvent in the pressure cup and spray it through the hose and gun, flushing them out. Clean the air cap and fluid tip.

Wipe the gun and pressure cup dry. Reassemble the gun for future use.

Gravity-Feed Gun. Wash the cup and spray a small amount of cleaning solvent through the gun. Remove the air cap, wash and wipe clean the end of the fluid tip and the inside of the cap.

Cleaning Precautions

1. Never soak the gun body in cleaning solvent. The lubrication in the various packings will be washed away and small particles of paint will be carried into the air passages to either plug them or be blown out into the paint film as dried particles the next time the gun is used.

2. Never use a hard, sharp instrument, such as a pin or wire, to clean the air orifices in the air cap. A slight burr will cause an air turbulence, which will cause a paint build-up at that area on the cap or a distorted spray pattern. If the holes become clogged, soak the air cap in cleaning solvent and then clean the orifices with a match, a broom straw, or other soft material.

3. Never use an acid or alkaline solution to clean the gun. It will corrode the aluminum and die-cast parts.

Lubrication

The moving spray-gun parts should be lubricated occasionally. The parts that require lubrication are (refer to Figure 16-17):
(a) Fluid-needle packing
(b) Fluid-needle stem
(c) Air-valve stem
(d) Air-valve packing
(e) Trigger bearing screw
(f) Fluid-needle spring
The fluid-needle packing should be removed occasionally and softened with oil. The fluid-needle spring should be coated with a light grease.

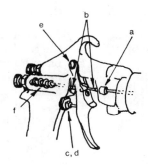

Figure 16-17   Parts requiring lubrication

Spray Gun Problems and Causes

Many spray gun problems are a direct result of improper or insufficient cleaning. Any paint build-up in or around the air cap or fluid tip orifices or the cup vent hole will prevent the gun from operating correctly. With the siphon gun the centre ring-shaped orifice is especially critical. If it is not clean, very little or no low pressure area is created and the paint will not flow. A partially or completely blocked fluid tip will also prevent fluid flow.

Air cap or fluid tip problems can be isolated by making a test pattern on a piece of

SPRAY GUN PROBLEMS AND CAUSES

Problems	Causes	Illustration
1. Jerky or spitting spray.	A. low on fluid B. gun tipped at excessive angle C. siphon leak at fluid tube, coupling nut, or at fluid tip thread (E) D. dry fluid needle packing or loose packing nut	Figure 16-18 Spitting

2. Fluid leaking from the front of the gun.	A. fluid needle not seating into the fluid tip seat B. paint build-up on fluid needle around trigger area C. fluid needle bent or worn D. paint build-up in fluid tip E. packing nut too tight F. broken fluid needle return spring	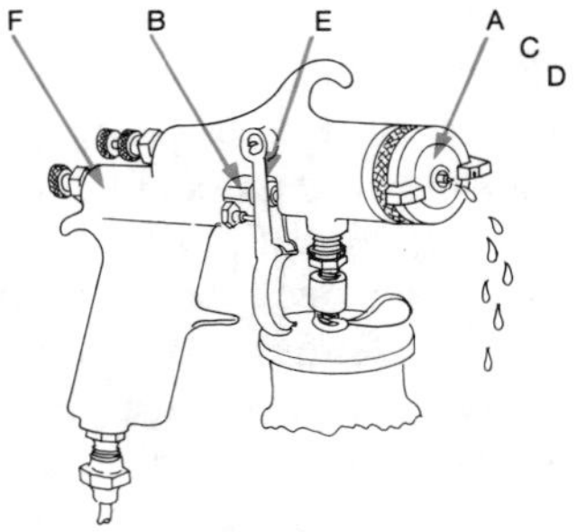 Figure 16-19 Fluid leaking from the front of the gun
3. Heavy top pattern.	A. horn holes partially plugged B. paint build-up on bottom of fluid tip nozzle C. bottom of air cap centre ring orifice plugged	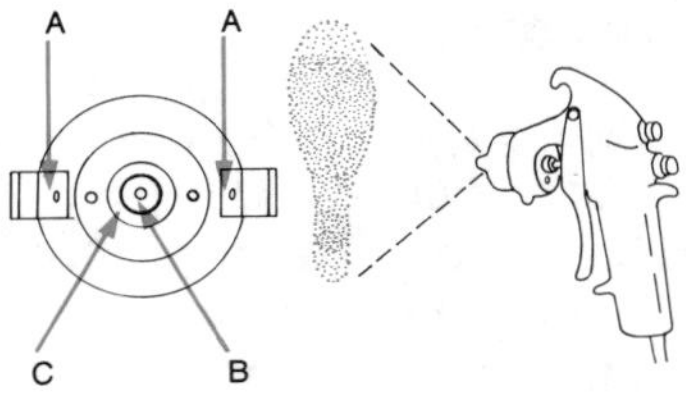 Figure 16-20 Top-heavy pattern
4. Heavy bottom pattern.	A. horn holes partially plugged B. paint build-up on top of fluid tip nozzle C. top of air cap centre ring orifice plugged	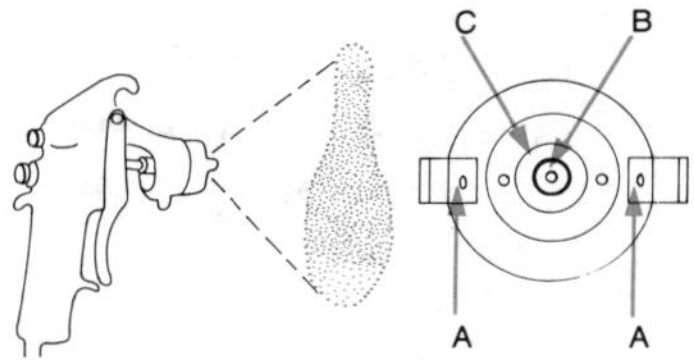 Figure 16-21 Heavy bottom pattern
5. Heavy right side pattern.	A. right side horn holes partially clogged B. dirt in left side of fluid tip nozzle C. left side of ring orifice plugged	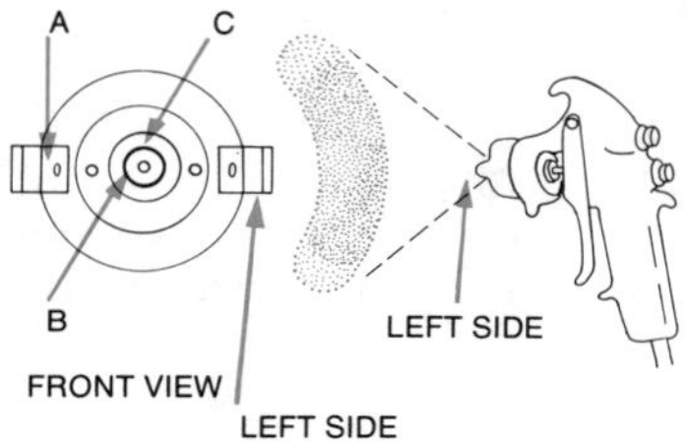 Figure 16-22 Heavy right side pattern

6. Heavy left side pattern.	A. left side horn holes partially clogged B. dirt on right side of fluid tip nozzle C. right side ring orifice plugged	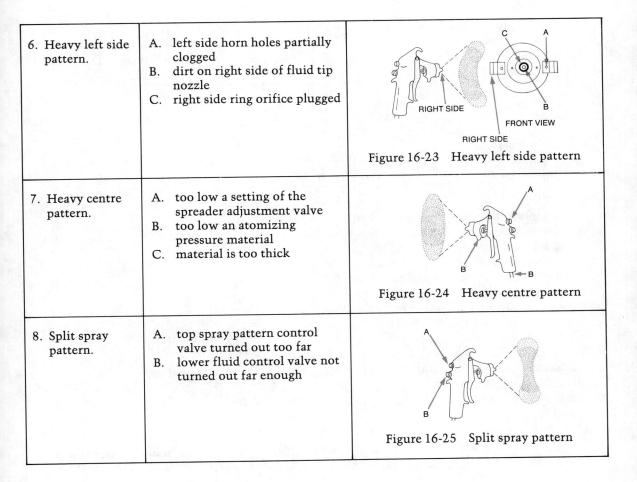 RIGHT SIDE FRONT VIEW RIGHT SIDE Figure 16-23 Heavy left side pattern
7. Heavy centre pattern.	A. too low a setting of the spreader adjustment valve B. too low an atomizing pressure material C. material is too thick	Figure 16-24 Heavy centre pattern
8. Split spray pattern.	A. top spray pattern control valve turned out too far B. lower fluid control valve not turned out far enough	Figure 16-25 Split spray pattern

cardboard or paper, rotating the air cap one-half turn, and then making another test pattern. If the faulty pattern is inverted on the second test, the problem is on or in the air cap. If the pattern remains the same, the problem is in or on the fluid tip. There could be some dried material stuck to the outside of the fluid tip, preventing a low pressure area, or stuck in the fluid tip orifice, preventing fluid flow.

16-4 AIR AND FLUID REFINISHING HOSES

The air hose usually has a red rubber covering. However, on some small, low-pressure outfits the air hose has an orange, braided covering. The inside of the air hose has a lining that is resistant to oil and water.

The fluid hose has a smooth, black covering. It has a special inner lining which resists

AIR PRESSURE DROP AT SPRAY GUN FOR 7.5 m (25 ft.) HOSE

Inside Diameter of Air Hose	Regulated Pressure kPa	psi	Pressure Drop kPa	psi
6 mm (¼ in.)	275	40	72	10.5
	415	60	90	13
8 mm (⁵⁄₁₆ in.)	275	40	17	2.5
	415	60	28	4

all common solvents — in paints, lacquers, and other refinishing materials — that readily attack ordinary air hose.

Follow the manufacturers' recommendations when selecting air and fluid hoses for use with spray equipment. There is a noticeable drop in air pressure because of the friction of the air or fluid rubbing on the hose walls as it moves through the hose. When an under-size hose is used, the spray gun is often starved for paint. The following table lists some air pressure drops for 6 mm (¼ in.) and 8 mm (⁵⁄₁₆ in.) diameter air hoses.

16-5 AIR TRANSFORMERS

An **air transformer** removes oil, dirt, and moisture from the compressed air, filters the air, and regulates the air flow. The air pressures, main line and regulated, are indicated on gauges on the transformer. Outlets to which the hoses are connected are provided on the side of the regulators.

Transformers usually are connected to the compressor by a take-off pipe connected off the top of the main-line air supply (Figure 16-26). Note also that the main-line pipe is installed with a down slope toward the compressor or a drain leg. These two methods are used to help prevent moisture or dirt particles from reaching the transformer.

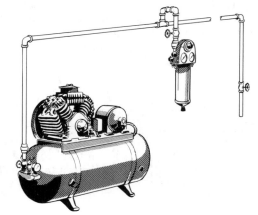

Courtesy DeVilbiss (Canada) Limited

Figure 16-26   Piping should slope toward compressor. Any moisture in the pipes will drain back to the tank.

The air enters the transformer at the main-line pressure inlet, and passes through a series of baffles, an expansion chamber, and a filter made of fibre, metal, or cotton wadding. Turning in the regulator knob opens a diaphragm that allows clean, dry air at the desired pressure to pass on to the spray gun (Figure 16-27). Regulators are explained in detail in Chapter 4.

A drain is provided at the bottom of the transformer tube to drain the impurities from the unit. The transformer should be drained regularly.

The volume of air a transformer can handle varies, depending upon its size. The volume

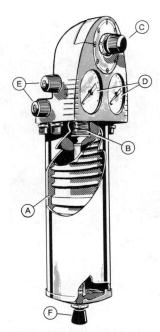

Courtesy DeVilbiss (Canada) Limited

Figure 16-27   Principal parts of an air transformer: (A) condenser (B) filtering device (C) air regulator (D) pressure gauge or gauges (E) outlet valves (F) drain

of filtered air required is the deciding factor in selecting a transformer.

16-6 AIR COMPRESSORS

The **air compressor** is a machine designed to pump air from the atmosphere and to compress it to a higher pressure. Gravity exerts a force on air, holding it to the earth. The air, in turn, exerts pressure on everything it touches. This pressure is called atmospheric pressure. At sea level, the air has an atmospheric pressure of 101.43 kPa, usually taken as 100 kPa for most applications. The higher one goes above sea level, the less the atmospheric pressure becomes. For ex-

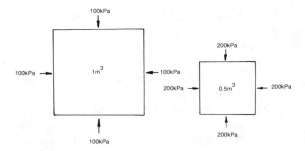

Figure 16-28   The effect of pressure on air volume

ample, about 1 km above the earth the atmospheric pressure is 80 kPa.

The amount of air a compressor can pump is referred to as the "volume" of free air, measured in cubic metres per minute removed from the atmosphere.

Forcing a volume of air into a container causes the pressure inside the container to increase above atmospheric pressure.

Figure 16-28 illustrates one cubic metre of air at 100 kPa and the volume of the same amount of air under pressure of 200 kPa. Doubling the pressure halves the volume of air. Compressed air is expressed as cubic volume (cfm) of air under pressure.

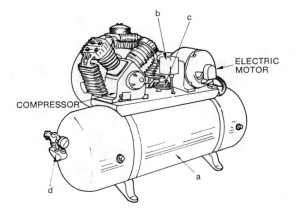

Figure 16-29   Air compressor unit

Compressors are driven by either an electric motor or gas engine. The larger compressors are usually equipped with (refer to Figure 16-29):

(a)   A heavy, steel storage tank to store the compressed air.

(b)   An automatic pressure switch for stopping and starting the motor at predetermined minimum and maximum pressures.

(c)   A check valve to prevent the air from leaking from the tank back through the compressor.

(d)   A safety release valve to relieve the pressure in the tank if the automatic pressure switch fails to shut off the motor.

Types of Compressors

Two very different types of compressors are produced. They are referred to as diaphragm-type and piston-type compressors.

The **diaphragm type** is a small compressor which develops low-volume air for use at low pressures.

It operates by the reciprocating action of a flexible disc, or diaphragm, that is operated by an eccentric (Figure 16-30). A com-

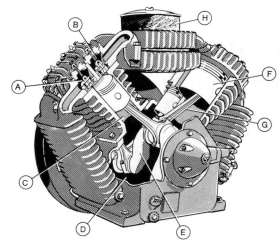

Courtesy DeVilbiss (Canada) Limited

Figure 16-31   Principal parts of a piston-type compressor

pressor of this type is not usually suitable for automotive work. It provides sufficient air for use only in the home or small workshop.

The **piston-type** is a larger air compressor which pumps through the reciprocating action of a piston in a cylinder. Air is drawn in through an intake valve as the piston moves down the cylinder. On the upward stroke, the piston compresses the air and an exhaust valve opens. The air is pushed out of the cylinder into the storage tank or air line as the piston reaches the top of the cylinder (Figure 16-31). The cycle is then repeated. A cycle is considered as one revolution of the compressor crankshaft.

Piston-type compressors can be further classified as single-stage or double-stage models.

Single-Stage Compressor. This style compressor has one or more cylinders of uniform size. The air is drawn in, compressed, and exhausted into the storage tank in one complete piston cycle (Figure 16-32).

Two-Stage Compressor. This type of compressor has two or more cylinders of unequal

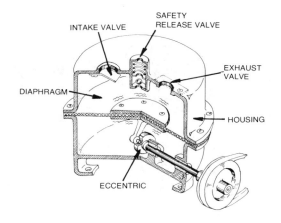

Figure 16-30   Diaphragm-type compressor

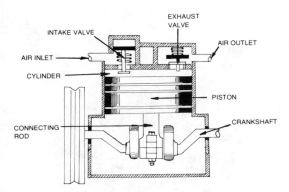

Courtesy DeVilbiss (Canada) Limited

Figure 16-32   Single-stage compressor

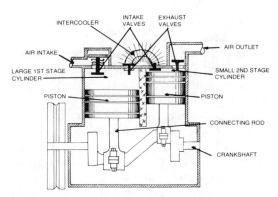

Courtesy DeVilbiss (Canada) Limited

Figure 16-33   Two-stage compressor

size. The air is compressed in two separate steps. The air is drawn in and compressed to an intermediate pressure in the first, or larger, low-pressure cylinder, and exhausted into a connecting tube called an **intercooler.** From the intercooler, the same compressed air enters a smaller cylinder where it is further compressed to a higher pressure and then exhausted into the storage tank (Figure 16-33).

Actual Delivery

No compressor is 100% efficient. There are always air losses due to friction, worn or slipping drive belts, worn compressor parts, or a clogged intake filter.

The higher the pressure needed, the longer it takes to compress the air and the less cubic metres per minute produced.

Single-stage compressors are not as efficient or economical when the air volume has to be pumped to high pressures. When pressures of 700 kPa or more are involved, the two-stage unit is more efficient, runs cooler, and delivers more air for the power consumed.

Most air equipment is designed to operate with relatively large volumes of air at medium pressure or less. For example, a siphon-feed spray gun uses about 0.25 m³ of air with a spraying pressure of 275 to 415 kPa. Effective operation of the air equipment is dependent more upon the capacity of the compressor as to how many cubic meters of air per minute it can pump, than on its ability to pump to a certain pressure rating. For example, a small compressor may take 0.10 m³ of air and compress it into 700 kPa. The pressure is high but the volume of air would not begin to operate a siphon-feed gun.

A suitable compressor for spray painting and auto body work should be capable of compressing large volumes of air to a medium pressure rather than small volumes of air to a high pressure.

A rule of thumb can be used to quickly estimate the delivery capacity of a compressor. The rule states that a 745 W electric motor will produce 0.115 m³/min and a 745 W gasoline engine will produce 0.057 m³/min. These valves are usually very close to the manufacturer's actual delivery specifications.

Compressor Maintenance

The oil in the compressor crankcase should be checked at least once every week and changed every two or three months. The manufacturers' recommendations should be followed with regard to the type of oil to be used. The bearings in the electric motor should be oiled periodically unless they are grease packed.

The belt tension should be checked and the air intake strainer cleaned at least once a week, the frequency depending on dust conditions in the shop. Accumulated dust should be blown from the cooling fans.

The drain on the bottom of the storage tank should be opened at least once a week to drain out oil and water that have condensed from the air. The safety-valve lever should be lifted periodically to make sure it is functioning properly.

Courtesy Binks Manufacturing Company

Figure 16-34   Cartridge-type face respirator

16-7 RESPIRATORS

Although the spray booth exhaust fan removes the "overspray" and fumes, the operator should always wear a respirator to avoid breathing in the paint fumes.

All hardeners used in paints contain isocyanates, materials that are the part of the hardener that act to toughen the paint surface. These isocyanates are highly reactive when they are inhaled as part of the vapour and mist overspray. They may cause nose and throat irritation, breathing difficulty, chest tightness, and lung injury through continuous exposure. Once a person has become sensitized to isocyanates any exposure makes the reaction more severe. Long term breathing or lung problems can occur.

There are four different types of respirators.

Dust Mask. This is a simple porous-type dust mask. It is designed to filter out solid particles such as paint dust while machine sanding.

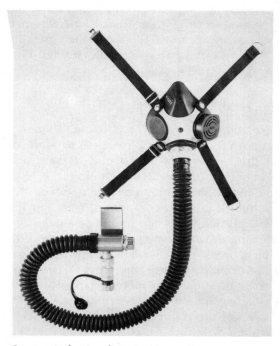

Courtesy Binks Manufacturing Company

Figure 16-35   Air supplied face-type respirator

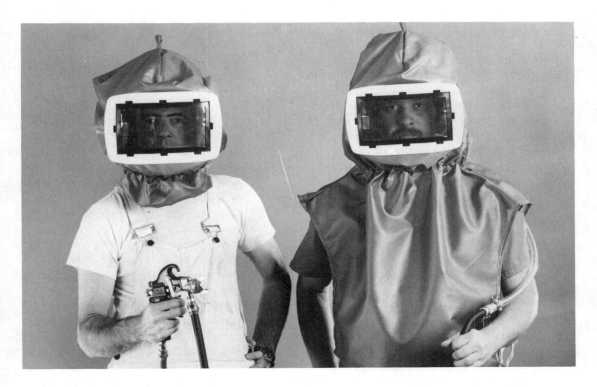

Figure 16-36   Air supplied hood respirator

Courtesy Binks Manufacturing Company

Cartridge Respirator. This is a more substantial respirator mask that covers the nose and mouth. One or more replaceable cartridge filters are used. The cartridge filters will filter dust and paint particles as well as organic solvent vapors. This type of respirator is suitable for use with paints that do not contain isocyanates (Figure 16-34).

Air Supplied Respirator Mask. This is a mask that fits tightly to the face. It is an air-feed type, with a short air line connected to a regulator worn or fastened to a belt (Figure 16-35).

Hood Respirator. These cover the entire head and neck area to offer a constant supply of breathing air, as well as protection to the eyes, ears, and skin from harmful vapours and fumes (Figure 16-36). They are connected by a short hose to a regulator, as is the air supplied mask. The air to the regulator can be taken from the compressed air line if the compressor air is suitable to breathe. It may have too high a concentration of carbon monoxide. The breathing air can also be supplied from a separate oilless air pump or supplied from bottled air.

The regulator allows control of the volume of air needed. The regulators are either designed as a **constant pressure** or **pressure-demand** type. A pressure-demand system only supplies air as one breathes inward. With constant-pressure systems there is a constant flow of air to the unit. Air-feed masks can be either type. Hood-type masks are usually the constant-pressure type.

REVIEW QUESTIONS

1. Define the purpose of a spray gun.
2. List the three factors that determine the spray gun type.
3. Draw a front view diagram of the external-mix air cap. Include and name all the air orifices.
4. Explain the shape of the air cap centre orifice when: (1) the cap is off the gun, and (ii) the cap is on the gun.
5. What is the purpose of the fluid tip and needle?
6. Define the terms non-bleeder and bleeder as they refer to spray guns.
7. List the adjustments that can be made on a siphon-type spray gun and explain the purpose of each.
8. Where should the fluid adjustment valve be set for "full spraying"?
9. The air valve and fluid needle do not open or close at the same time. What is the order of each operation, and why is this order important?
10. Explain the operating principles of a siphon-feed and a pressure-feed spray gun.
11. Which type of air cap can be used with: (i) a siphon spray gun, (ii) a pressure spray gun, and (iii) a gravity-feed gun?
12. When cleaning the spray gun, the cup is cleaned before the solvent is sprayed through the gun. Why?
13. When a spray gun is being cleaned, it should never be soaked in cleaning solvent. Why?
14. List the parts of the spray gun that need lubrication.
15. a) List two likely areas of paint build-up that cause poor spray gun operation.
    b) How can the probable cause of an improper spray pattern be quickly identified?
16. Draw a side view of an external-mix siphon air cap, fluid tip, and needle. Show and label all the air and paint orifices and their air and paint stream, including the start of the actual spray pattern.
17. Draw a side view of the pressure-feed external-mix air cap and fluid tip.
18. What are the purposes of the air transformer?
19. List and briefly explain the meaning of the two terms that are used to define compressed air.
20. a) What are the two types of piston air compressors?
    b) Explain how each one operates.
21. What type of compressor is better suited when pressures over 700 kPa are needed?
22. List the rule of thumb for an electric motor driven compressor.
23. How can a compressor of the correct power size be selected?
24. List the items on the compressor unit that should be checked and maintained periodically.
25. List and briefly describe the four different types of respirators.

17

PAINT PREPARATION AND SPRAYING PROCEDURES

17-1   Temperature of the Spray Booth and Vehicle
17-2   Viscosity
17-3   Stirring the Paint Material
17-4   Using the Spray Gun
17-5   Spray Gun Techniques
17-6   Spray Painting Control
17-7   Spraying Procedure
17-8   Refinishing the Complete Automobile
17-9   Common Paint Problems and Their Causes

Before discussing the actual painting procedure, the temperature of the room, vehicle, and, to a lesser degree, the type of paint must be considered. The type of paint being used and the temperature determine the reduction and mixing procedures. These must be done according to the manufacturer's recommendations.

The final surface preparation of the vehicle, the air and spray gun settings, and the spray gun techniques all contribute to the quality of the finished product.

17-1 TEMPERATURE OF THE SPRAY BOOTH AND VEHICLE

Paints are designed to be sprayed at a temperature close to 20°C (70°F). It is often impossible to control the temperature of either the paint room or vehicle being sprayed, so the solvent used, the mixing procedures, and the spraying techniques must be adjusted to compensate for either hot or cold conditions.

When the room temperature of the spray booth is above normal, too much of the solvent added to reduce the paint evaporates into the air during the spraying procedure. The paint will be sprayed on "dry" and not enough solvent will be left in the paint to make it flow into a smooth, shiny surface. The paint finish will be left with a dry, sandy surface. (Figure 17-1).

A cold room slows down solvent evaporation. Little of the solvent evaporates into the air during spraying, nor does it quickly evaporate from the paint surface. The solvent concentrates on the paint surface creating a very wet-looking finish, which is fine,

Courtesy Interchemical Corporation, Finishes Division

Figure 17-1   Dry, sandy paint resulting from poor "flow out"

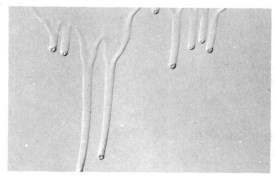

Courtesy CIL Automotive Finishes

Figure 17-2   Runs and sags

providing the paint does not continue to flow into runs or floods (Figure 17-2).

These same results are produced if an automobile is brought out of the sun into the booth and sprayed immediately. The hot metal "kicks out" the solvent, and the paint will not flow out properly. When a cold car is sprayed, the paint tends to flood the surface, often producing runs.

The first rule to be observed in spray painting, then, is to have the spray room, the automobile, and the paint at normal temperature — approximately 20°C (70°F). Then reduce the paint with the proper type and amount of solvent.

> The amount of solvent added to a quantity of paint should be measured and not just guessed at by dumping in "so much" solvent into the paint. Always follow the manufacturer's recommendations as to the type of solvent and amount of reduction necessary.

It is often not possible, due to extreme weather conditions, to maintain the paint

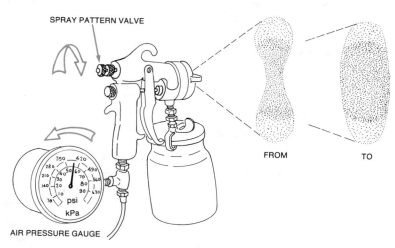

Figure 17-3   Lower the air pressure and close in the spray pattern valve slightly for over-reduced paint

SPRAYING PROCEDURES FOR VARYING TEMPERATURE CONDITIONS

Temperature Conditions		Resulting Cause	Paint Result	Possible Corrections
ROOM	HOT	• solvent evaporates quickly	• poor flow • dry, sandy appearance	• use a slower drying solvent • add more solvent * • hold the gun closer • move the gun slower
	COLD	• solvent slow to evaporate	• paint flows causing possible floods and runs	• use a faster drying solvent • thinner coats • hold gun back further • move the gun faster • allow longer drying period between coats
CAR	HOT	• fast solvent kick out	• poor flow • dry, sandy effect • possible orange peel effect	• use a slower drying solvent • add more solvent * • move slower • hold the gun closer • lower air pressure and possibly close spray pattern valve *
	COLD	• solvent slower evaporating	• possible flooding, runs	• use a faster drying solvent • use thinner coats • move gun faster • hold gun back further
PAINT	HOT	• by adding a measured amount of solvent paint is over-reduced	• possible flooding, runs	• cool the paint • thinner coats • move gun faster • hold gun further away • lower air pressure * • close spray pattern valve *
	COLD	• under-reduced by adding measured amount of solvent	• thick coat • rough, blobby appearance • orange peel effect or runs	• allow paint to warm up • higher air pressure • add more solvent

NOTE: * use less air pressure and possibly close the spray pattern valve slightly

room or vehicle at a normal temperature. Spraying often must be done under less than ideal temperature conditions.

Hot and cold temperatures can be compensated for by using either a slow- or fast-dry solvent. A slow-dry solvent is designed to evaporate slowly and is used for warm conditions. A fast-dry solvent is used for cold conditions. The medium-dry is the average solvent. It is used for room temperatures.

A limited amount of control can also be had by using more or less of the medium-dry solvent to over-reduce the paint during hot conditions and under-reduce it during cold conditions. The one major problem in over- or under-reducing is that the paint colour can be affected. Over-reduced paint is lighter, under-reduced paint is darker in colour. Extreme over- and under-reduction can also cause additional spraying and surface appearance problems. Thick coats can appear coarse or somewhat rough looking. Over-reduced surfaces can appear smooth but slightly fuzzy or hazy.

> Whenever more solvent is added to the paint, it is usually necessary to decrease the air pressure, as less air is needed to break up the thinner material. It is also sometimes necessary to decrease the pattern size slightly when spraying the thinner material to prevent a split spray pattern. (Figure 17-3).

The corrections in the preceding chart can be used to compensate for these temperature differences.

17-2 VISCOSITY

Different types of material are supplied by the manufacturer in varying "viscosities." The **viscosity** of a material is its "stickiness," or resistance to flow, determined by the length of time it takes for a known quantity of the material to flow through an orifice of a certain size. A thick material has a high viscosity, a thin material has a low viscosity. The viscosity of a material can be accurately checked with a viscosity cup. The cup is dipped into the paint, filled, and lifted out. The length of time (in seconds) the paint takes to drain through the orifice determines the viscosity of the material. The time is recorded until the stream first breaks into an intermittent flow or starts to drip. Most

paints are sprayed in the 16–24 s area. Enamels are highest at a 19–24 s range, lacquers and urethanes are in the 16–18 s range.

Since most paints are shipped at a higher viscosity (thicker) than they can be sprayed at, they must be thinned or reduced with a solvent. The reduction depends on the type of paint.

Thermoset materials (that is, enamels) are usually reduced with a reducer. Thermoplastic materials (that is, lacquers) are thinned with a thinner. The manufacturer always recommends the amount of solvent to be added, as either a percent of the total or as a ratio of so many parts of solvent to be added to so many parts of paint. The following chart illustrates some of the more common percent and mixing ratios used.

These percent/ratios indicate only the amount of solvent that is to be used. With some paints an additional small amount of catalyst must also be added, usually at a ratio of 8–10% of the paint volume (not including the solvent). The catalyst should always be added after the solvent. For some of the other paint materials, the ratio indicates the total solvent–catalyst mixture, and usually no other solvent is necessary.

The percent ratios can be further confused because the paint may be supplied in a litre, U.S. quart, or an imperial quart container. A litre has 1000 mL (35 oz.) and is a little smaller than an imperial quart (40 oz.) and a little larger than a U.S. quart at 32 oz. The litre will eventually be the industry standard and is also the easiest to break down. For example, with a ratio of 1 to 4 add 250 mL to each 1000 mL. Using a 50% (1 to 2 ratio), add 500 mL to 1000 mL.

Note that in each example, the solvent is added to an already full container of paint — an impossible task. One must therefore either use a container large enough to hold both the solvent and paint or split the paint into two equal lots, adding half the necessary

Product	Percent	Ratio Solvent Paint	
enamel	25%	1 to 4	
some urethanes	33%	1 to 3	
acrylic enamels and some epoxy primers	50%	1 to 2	
polyester base	80%	8 to 10	
acrylic basecoat	125%	1¼ to 1	
lacquer and acrylic lacquer	150% to 200%	1½–2 to 1	

solvent and hardener to each. With some paints, usually the type that uses only the solvent–catalyst mixture, the manufacturer only fills the container part way with paint allowing room for the solvent–catalyst to be added directly into that container. This mixing method is very simple if the complete container of materials is needed. However, if only a small amount of paint is going to be used some means of measuring the material is necessary.

Many painters prefer to catalyze the paint in small amounts, as it is needed. The hardeners are expensive and any unused catalyzed paint must be discarded. Never put it back into the unreduced paint, as the complete mixture would then have to be discarded.

A standard soft-drink can or an empty paint can makes an excellent measuring container. The soft-drink can top or paint can rim is easily removed by grinding through the top hemming flange. Four Canadian soft-drink cans equal one imperial quart. As a rough rule, four soft-drink cans, less one finger short of being full, equals one litre, and four soft-drink cans, two fingers short, equals one U.S. quart. For example, a 1 to 2 ratio would need two soft-drink cans of solvent to each one litre or quart of paint. After

the measured amount of solvent is added, use the viscosity cup to "fine tune" the mixture.

The standard paint cup will hold one litre of material. For those who prefer to mix the solvent and paint in the cup, the following chart lists the amount of solvent and paint to measure for the different ratios. Use a measuring cup to measure the materials.

17-3 STIRRING THE PAINT MATERIAL

Pigments vary greatly in mass. Some of the commonly used pigments are seven to eight times as heavy as the liquid part of the paint and tend to settle at the bottom of the can much faster than lighter pigments. The aluminum flakes in metallic colours are especially prone to fast settling. Two or three clean ball bearings are often added to the spray-gun cap to agitate metallic paints while spraying.

To mix the liquid and pigment together thoroughly, stir the paint with a clean, flat, steel stick at least 25 mm wide. Use a stirring as well as a lifting motion. Never use a sharp stick or screwdriver to stir the paint.

REDUCTION % AND RATIOS FOR USE IN A STANDARD PAINT CUP

%	Ratio	Solvent	Paint	Total
25%	1 to 4	200 mL 6^1/$_2$ oz.	800 mL 26 oz.	1 L 32 oz.
33^1/$_3$%	1 to 3	250 mL 8 oz.	750 mL 24 oz.	1 L 32 oz.
50%	1 to 2	333 mL 10^1/$_2$ oz.	666 mL 21 oz.	999 mL 31^1/$_2$ oz.
100%	1 to 1	500 mL 16 oz.	500 mL 16 oz.	1 L 32 oz.
125%	1^1/$_4$ to 1	555 mL 17^1/$_2$ oz.	444 mL 14 oz.	999 mL 31^1/$_2$ oz.
150%	1^1/$_2$ to 1	600 mL 19^1/$_2$ oz.	400 mL 13 oz.	1 L 32^1/$_2$ oz.
175%	1^3/$_4$ to 1	637 mL 20^1/$_4$ oz.	364 mL 11^1/$_2$ oz.	1001 mL 31^3/$_4$ oz
200%	2 to 1	666 mL 21 oz.	333 mL 10^1/$_2$ oz.	999 mL 31^1/$_2$ oz.

After the pigment and liquid have been mixed, slowly add the reducing solvent and continue stirring to mix the paint and solvent together. Add the catalyst last, after the solvent.

17-4 USING THE SPRAY GUN

Adjusting the Gun for Full Spraying

Set the fluid adjusting valve so the first thread is showing. Adjust the spray pattern adjusting valve to approximately three-quarters of the way out. The air cap horns should be horizontal for a vertical spray pattern.

Setting the Air Pressure

The air pressure at which the spray gun is operated depends a great deal on the type and viscosity of the material to be sprayed. A fairly low air pressure is usually used for acrylic lacquer products. The greater the viscosity (thickness) of the material the higher the air pressure must be to break up the material. The paint manufacturer recommends a certain pressure at the gun, not at the air regulator transformer. There could be considerable pressure drop between the regulator and gun depending on the hose size and length, and the quick disconnect couplings. The air pressure to the gun should be set with a gauge inserted in the line just before the spray gun.

The best way to determine the proper air pressure is to test the spray pattern on a

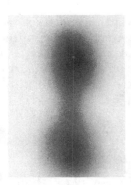

Figure 17-4   Correct spray pattern

Figure 17-5

Figure 17-6

discarded panel or a piece of masking paper. With the fluid adjustment valve turned so the first thread is showing, adjust the air pressure regulator to approximately 350–385 kPa (50–55 psi) at the gun. Hold the gun so that the air cap is 20–30 cm from the test panel. Give the trigger a quick pull and then release it. The spray pattern should be in the shape of a long, thin "O" and have a uniform distribution of material over the entire area (Figure 17-4).

If the paint in the spray pattern has a coarse, spattered effect, shaped as shown in Figure 17-5 or Figure 17-6 the air pressure is not sufficient to completely atomize the paint. Increase the air pressure at the regulator and test the spray pattern again. Too high an air pressure will produce either a dry, sandy spray in the shape of Figure 17-5 and excessive "overspray," or a split spray pattern in the shape of Figure 17-6. The air pressure should be adjusted so a smooth, even paint flow is obtained in the test pattern.

17-5 SPRAY GUN TECHNIQUES

Distance From the Work

The spray gun is held approximately 20 to 30 cm from the work. A recommended guide to the correct gun distance is the span of a hand (the distance from the end of the small finger to the end of the thumb) (Figure 17-7). Holding the gun too close to the surface being sprayed will cause the paint to flood, and runs will result. Holding the gun too far from the work will produce a dry, sandy spray and excessive "overspray."

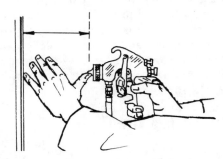

Figure 17-7   Distance from the work

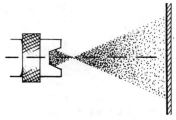

Figure 17-8   Hold the gun perpendicular to the surface

Hold the gun perpendicular to the surface (Figure 17-8). When the gun is held at an angle to the surface, a spray pattern that is wet on one end and dry on the other is produced (Figure 17-9).

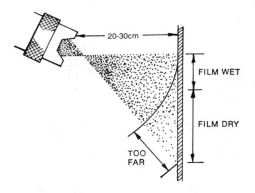

Figure 17-9   Spray gun held at an angle to the work surface

Move the gun in a straight, uniform stroke back and forth across the panel, keeping the gun parallel to the surface. Do not arc the spray stroke as this produces a spray that is dry on the ends and wet in the centre of the stroke (Figure 17-10). Each spray stroke should overlap the previous one by approximately 50%.

Triggering the Gun

The spray stroke is started before the trigger is pulled, and the trigger is released before the end of the stroke (Figure 17-11). If the trigger is held open while starting or stopping a stroke, a build-up of paint results, producing a run.

Speed

The speed of the spray-gun stroke depends entirely on the amount of paint to be deposited on the surface. When the surface becomes flooded, the speed is too slow. When a dry spray results, the speed is too fast. The

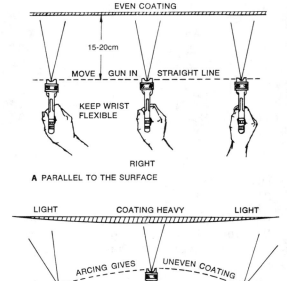

Figure 17-10   Spray stroke

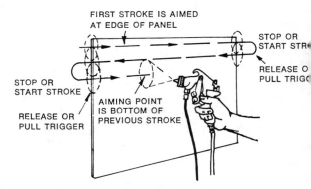

Figure 17-11   Triggering the gun — use alternate right and left strokes. Overlap the previous stroke by one-half.

proper spray-gun speed is chosen by observing the flow of the paint as it is deposited on the surface.

17-6 SPRAY PAINTING CONTROL

Type of Spray	Causes
1. Incorrect — thin coat; rough, dry surface; no lustre (Figure 17-12)	fluid control valve not open enough; gun too far away; paint too thin; air pressure too great; stroke too fast; overlap too small
2. Incorrect — heavy coat; sags, ripples, or orange peel (Figure 17-13)	air nozzle dirty; gun too close; paint too thick; air pressure low; stroke too slow; overlap too great
3. Controlled — medium coat; good flow; little orange peel and no sags (Figure 17-14)	gun clean and properly adjusted; gun distance good; paint reduction correct; air pressure correct; stroke good; overlap 50%; reducer or thinner correct; temperature correct

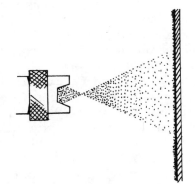

Figure 17-12   Thin coat

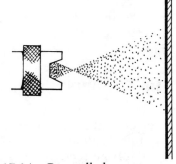

Figure 17-14   Controlled spray

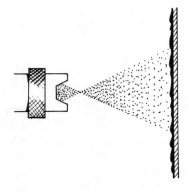

Figure 17-13   Heavy coat

Correcting an Improper Spray Pattern

A defective spray pattern can usually be traced to a partially plugged air-cap orifice or fluid tip. To check the possible causes, rotate the air cap one-half turn. If the position of the defective spray pattern changes, the trouble is being caused by the air cap. If the defective pattern does not change, the trouble is in the fluid tip or needle (Figure 17-15). Remove the defective part and clean its orifice thoroughly with thinners and a soft bristle brush. It may be necessary to use a

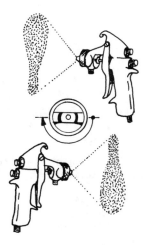

Figure 17-15   Rotating the air cap one-half turn to find the cause of a defective spray pattern

sharpened stick or toothpick to open the orifice. Never use a wire, as it may distort the orifice.

Matching Colours

The true colour of a newly sprayed paint is not apparent until the paint is completely dry. Wet colours cannot be expected to match dry colours perfectly since most colours darken after drying. The fact that the original finish will have "weathered" (oxidized and faded) also complicates colour matching. Road grime, industrial fallout, natural chemicals in the air, yellowed wax, and weather elements all contribute to paint oxidation.

Most faded paints can be compounded to remove the oxidized film, thus restoring the true colour and brightness of the paint next to areas newly painted. When the base paint of the basecoat/clearcoat system has faded, it cannot be compounded back to its original colour because of the outer clearcoat.

Most refinishing materials match the original colours quite closely. However, it is sometimes necessary to tint a colour to obtain the correct match. The ability to match colours well is usually a matter of trial and error, practice, and experience.

The new paint is often checked for colour match by comparing some paint on the end of the stir-stick to the original paint on door jambs or on some other area that has not been exposed to weathering. This method is not close enough for the basecoat/clearcoat system. The colour may appear to be a close match, but the colour will change considerably after the clearcoat is added. Most painters will spray a small area on a separate test panel with the basecoat when they spray the vehicle. They then clearcoat the test panel and compare it to the original. Should the basecoat need a slight adjustment it can be made and another light coat added before the clearcoat is applied.

When the colour match is not correct, the proper tint, or shade, is obtained by adding a small amount of a lighter or a darker colour, whichever is needed. A contrasting colour will change a shade much more quickly than a colour in the same tone. For example, a few drops of a dark mixing colour will produce a noticeable change in a light or medium colour. Much more mixing colour would have to be added to make a dark colour darker or to lighten a colour that is a bit too dark. When matching colours, it is advisable to check them in natural light, as they may appear off colour under different artificial lights.

Metallic Paints

Metallic paints are paints that have many small aluminum flakes added to the pigment-binder mixture. These colours or shades can appear different when viewed from various angles. The colour and shade of a metallic paint is determined by the way in which the aluminum flakes are suspended in

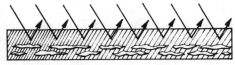

A UNIFORM REFLECTION (WET SPRAY)

IDEAL ALUMINUM ORIENTATION, WHERE FLAKES
INTERLEAF PARALLEL TO FINISH

B NON-UNIFORM REFLECTION (DRY SPRAY)

RANDOM ALUMINUM PARTICLES, WHERE FLAKES
SET AT VARIOUS ANGLES

Figure 17-16   The colour match of a metallic
paint depends on the way in which the
aluminum flakes are suspended in the paint

the paint. When the film is wet, the aluminum particles sink to the bottom of the paint
and lie flat, overlapping each other. The wetter the film, the lower the particles sink and
the darker the colour appears to be. When
the material is applied in a dry spray, the
aluminum flakes do not overlap properly,
and the particles sit at various angles, close
to the surface (Figure 17-16). This produces
a lighter, mottled finish. Light reflection off
the paint is not uniform.

Standard vs. Basecoat/Clearcoat Metallics. The aluminum particles close to the
surface in the standard metallics often
quickly "weather." They oxidize and fade
and the paint surface soon starts to lose its
brilliance and shine. At least three coats and
sometimes more, depending on the colour,
are needed to provide the necessary cover.
With the basecoat/clearcoat system only one
or two basecoats are needed. The base material is "high hiding" and quickly provides
the necessary surface covering. The base
colour has no shine — it is dull and flat

looking. It is not sanded, but a run or dirty
spot can be watersanded out. The area must
then be resprayed to cover the sanded area
and to obtain the same texture as that of the
surrounding surface. After allowing the basecoat the necessary drying time, the surface is
tacked off and two or three medium wet
clearcoats are applied. The clear outer topcoat provides a deeper shine and prevents
the aluminum particles and paint pigment
from oxidizing.

Matching Metallic Paints. Metallic colours, especially silvers, are hard to match
because of their large amount of aluminum
flakes. Standard metallic paints will not
match basecoat/clearcoat systems because
the aluminum in the standard paint cannot
be buried to the same extent as it is in the
basecoat/clearcoat system. The surface texture of each one is also different.

The colour, shade, and surface texture of
both types of metallic paints are greatly affected by various mixing and spraying techniques. Figure 17-17 illustrates three panels
which were sprayed with the same colour of
metallic paint in different degrees of wetness.

With either of the two types of metallics a

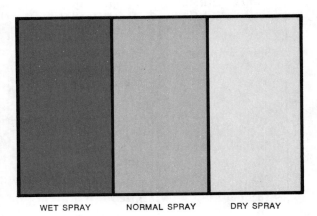

WET SPRAY   NORMAL SPRAY   DRY SPRAY

Figure 17-17   Application effect on the same
colour of a metallic paint

true colour match first depends upon the correct amount of reduction. Always follow the manufacturer's recommendations. Measure the solvent and use a viscosity cup to further check the paints if one is recommended. Make sure the paint is well stirred before each coat is applied (this applies to the basecoat only with the basecoat/clearcoat system), as the metallic particles soon settle. Set the pressures as recommended at the gun, not at the regulator, and adjust the spray gun adjustments fluid control valve to the first thread and the spray pattern valve to produce a correct long, thin "O" pattern. Other conditions that will affect the colour of a metallic material are listed in the following table.

When a metallic colour has to be matched to an existing colour, clean an area of the adjacent paint next to the area to be refinished. If this area is to be masked, do it so the paper can be easily removed to allow a colour comparison between the cleaned area and the refinished section. If the new colour is off, change one or more of the spraying procedures and recoat either the complete panel or enough of the edge next to the cleaned area to blend the two sections together.

With the basecoat/clearcoat system the basecoat will often appear to not match the original. The painter who suspects a mismatch should spray a small test panel at the same time and then clearcoat it and compare it to the original, before clearcoating the new base area on the vehicle. If any correction is needed, it can be done quickly before the clearcoat is applied.

FACTORS AFFECTING THE COLOUR OF METALLICS

	Variable	To Lighten the Colour	To Darken the Colour
Shop Conditions	Temperature	Warm	Cool
	Humidity	Low	High
	Ventilation	Increase	Decrease
Spray Equipment	Fluid Tip	Small Orifice	Large Orifice
	Fluid Flow Valve	Closed	Open
	Air Cap	High Air Consumption	Low Air Consumption
	Fan Width	Wide	Narrow
	Air Pressure at Gun	High Pressure	Low Pressure
Reducer Usage	Type of Reducer	Fast	Slow
	Amount	Over-reduce	Under-reduce
Spray Gun Technique	Distance from Work	Increase	Decrease
	Speed	Fast	Slow
	Flash-off Period	Increase	Decrease
	Final Coat (Panel Repair)	Misty Coat	Wet, Heavy Coat

17-7 SPRAYING PROCEDURE

The spraying procedure is determined by the type of material with which the area is to be refinished.

Enamels

Enamel products are sprayed in two coats, acrylic enamels in three. For enamel the first coat should be a medium wet coat. It is allowed to set from 10 to 12 min, until it becomes tacky. The drying speed is influenced by the temperature and humidity. When the first coat has become tacky, a final full-flow coat is applied over the first. It is difficult to rewet the surface to obtain an even wet flow on the second coat if the first coat becomes too dry.

With acrylic enamel the first coat should also be a medium wet coat with a second full-flow coat. A third thin wet levelling coat is then applied. A longer waiting time between the first and second coat is recommended. The reducing solvents are slower evaporating and the paint material is re-soluble, so the second coat is easily melted into the first coat. Should the second coat be applied too quickly, the concentration of reducing solvents could penetrate into the old finish or primed areas to cause swelling problems. Floods or runs on the surface of the new film can also occur. The third coat is applied immediately after finishing the second coat.

With both enamels and acrylic enamels the paint is then either force dried or allowed to sit in a temperature controlled room to air dry. Both enamels and acrylic enamels dry to a high gloss and need no polishing or rubbing although acrylic enamels can, after overnight drying, be lightly watersanded with ultra-fine paper and then machine compounded.

Acrylic Lacquers

Acrylic lacquer products are applied in two to six wet, single or double coats. A **double coat** is two coats applied one immediately after the other. The paint is then allowed to "flash-off" or "set-up" a few minutes, and the surface is recoated. It is especially necessary to let the solvent escape the first two or three coats before applying the next, as these coats act as a seal to prevent the solvent from entering the old finish. With each successive coat, the paint is thinned down a little more to obtain a better flow. The last coat usually is mostly thinner, with very little paint. Acrylic lacquer materials have to be buffed, or polished, with a fine rubbing compound to bring up the final finish.

Metallics

Metallics should be reduced as recommended, and a sufficient number of coats should be applied to obtain an adequate film thickness. Avoid thick, heavy, wet coats to prevent the metallic particles from flooding the surface. The metallic particles are much heavier than most paint pigments. Enamel and acrylic enamel metallic colours are sprayed in three coats. The first coat is applied in a light, wet film. When it becomes tacky, a full wet coat is applied, followed by a mist or fog coat to blend out any streaks or mottled blotches in the paint surface.

Streaking problems are usually caused by the spray pattern control valve being opened a bit too far, creating an hourglass spray pattern. Metallic blotches occur if one spot of the surface is sprayed wetter than the surrounding area. The metallic particles tend to flood, making the area appear darker.

Fogging is the term used to describe a very light, dry coat applied by cross-coating the previous coat. The gun is held as much as 60–90 cm from the surface and a quick "pass" is made over the area. The wet film tends to absorb the dry spray, blending out the darker area.

The fog coat must be applied at the right time. Should it be applied when the surface is too wet it would tend to help the surface flood more. If the fog coat is applied after the surface has become too dry, it would sit on the top, creating a very dry, sandy finish. The fog coat is usually applied panel after panel as the painter moves around the car. For example, the painter paints the rear quarter panel and the door, then goes back to the quarter panel, checks it and fogs it if necessary. The painter next does the front fender, checks the door, fogs it, and so on around the vehicle. Some painters prefer to paint the panel and then immediately fog it.

Metallics are usually sprayed with a somewhat higher air pressure than ordinary topcoat material to help avoid giving the surface a mottled effect.

The same procedures are used for the metallic basecoats of the basecoat/clearcoat system. The only differences are that the base does not have any shine and only enough material is applied to provide complete coverage. Slight streaks, flat or dull spots, and minor metallic sags will be hidden by the clearcoat. The clearcoats are applied in two or three coats following the same principles as those used for enamels.

Blending (Spot Spraying)

Blending is the gradual tapering of new paint into the original finish. This must be done when an area is spot sprayed or when a complete panel is refinished that has no natural divisions to separate it from the adjacent panels. The new paint in the undivided area must be blended into the original finish.

Acrylic lacquer materials blend easiest because they are thermoplastic (resoluble). The acrylics melt into the original finish (provided it is acrylic lacquer) to provide a uniform finish. Acrylic enamels can also be easily blended.

Enamel is not generally recommended as a blending material. An old enamel finish cannot be made soluble, and therefore cannot "melt" into the new paint. However, by following the blending procedure outlined below, a satisfactory blend usually can be obtained.

The complete area to be refinished should be sanded and prepared in the normal way. The area to be blended, beside the sanded area, is then compounded clean. The spot or the complete panel is then sprayed in the normal way to the edge of the sanded area.

All but a small amount of material is removed from the paint cup, and the material left in the cup is reduced by approximately 10%. The air pressure is decreased by 15% to 20% and the fluid adjustment valve is closed to one- and one-half turns. A medium wet coat is sprayed along the edge of the wet paint. The material and air pressure are further reduced, the fluid adjustment valve is turned in further, and another "pass" is made along the edge of the last spray. The procedure is continued, until the new paint has blended into the old.

Acrylic lacquer and acrylic enamel "spot ins" and blends can be machine compounded after they have dried. Never try to compound enamel "spot ins," as the compounding will dull fresh enamels.

Blending with the Basecoat/Clearcoat System

The basecoat/clearcoat system is half blendable. The base is easily blended. The outer clearcoat can be blended, but the complete panel is usually refinished.

The base materials are either acrylic lacquer (thermoplastic) or polyester (thermoset) materials. Both blend easily. The area to be "spotted in" is repaired using the nor-

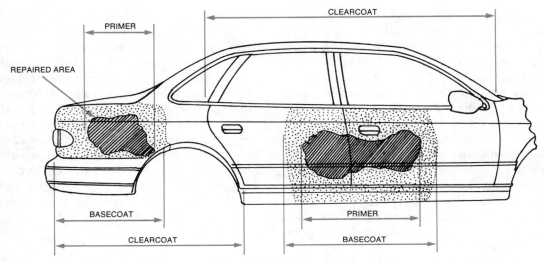

Figure 17-18   Panel blending: basecoat/ clearcoat system

mal sanding and priming procedures. The remaining clearcoat area of the complete panel is lightly sanded with ultra-fine water-type sandpaper. The repaired area is base-coated using the "spot in" procedures. Only enough material necessary to cover the repair area is used. The outer edges are blended by pulling the trigger a slight amount to feather the outer overspray into the original finish. After allowing the correct amount of drying time, the surface is tacked off and the complete panel is clearcoated (Figure 17-18). If a poor colour match is suspected, the complete panel and a portion of the next panel can be basecoated to blend in the colour. Both complete panels are then clearcoated.

17-8 REFINISHING THE COMPLETE AUTOMOBILE

When all the masking is completed and the surface is properly prepared, open the hood, doors, and trunk. Blow the dust, dirt, and plastic filling out from around the engine compartment, door opening, and trunk area. Close the hood, doors, and trunk and blow all the cracks, crevices, seams, cowl vent and along any exterior mouldings. Continue to blow these areas until no dust comes out. Now blow and wipe the sanding dust and dirt off the car, including the masking paper. Hold the blow gun in one hand and wipe the area with the rag held in the other hand. Bring the car into the spray booth, turn on the fan and blow out the seams, crevices, mouldings, etc., once more.

Using a low air pressure and small spray pattern, spray any door jambs, hood and fender edges, trunk opening, and wheels that are to be painted. If it is not a colour change, it is only necessary to "touch up" spray these areas. Wash off any overspray on the tires and cover the wheels with suitable covers to protect them from further overspray. Remove any paper used around the door trim panels, door pillars, etc., and close the doors, hood, and trunk. Carefully wash the entire areas to be refinished with a solvent suitable for this purpose.

If the vehicle is being sprayed with enamel, be particularly careful to wash off all overspray created from spraying the openings. Should the paint be acrylic lacquer, the overspray will be dry. It is not necessary to remove it unless there happens to be dirt in it. If so, it should be lightly sanded before the car is washed. In washing the surface, a small area should be washed with a cloth saturated with solvent, then wiped dry. Use clean cloths to wash and wipe the vehicle. A tack rag is then used to "tack off" the surface. The tack rag is lightly wiped over all the surfaces including the masking paper to pick up any lint or dust particles still present on the surface.

If the surface is to be sealed, the sealer is now applied in either one or two thin wet coats, then allowed to dry for 15 to 20 min before the final topcoats are applied. If a sealer is not used, the final topcoats are applied immediately after the prepared surface has been tacked clean.

The order in which each section is painted varies according to the preference of the spray painter.

With a cross-draft spray booth the section of the car closest to the exhaust fan is sprayed last (that is, the front). This prevents overspray from falling on a freshly painted surface as paint is drawn over the car by the fan. With a down-draft booth, the order is not so important. However, usually the front fenders and the hood are painted as one unit. Some painters prefer to paint the fender, the hood, and then the other fender (Figure 17-19). Others will start from the centre of the hood, moving out to the bottom of the fender. They then go to the other side of the vehicle and start again in the middle of the hood, and move out and over the other fender Figure 17-20. Using this method, the beginner may find it difficult to rewet the centre of the hood. It may be easier to obtain a smoother more uniform finish by using the first method.

Before beginning the actual spraying consider the following:
- the paint viscosity
- temperatures
- spray gun adjustments
- air pressures
- gun-handling techniques

The all must be balanced and regulated closely. If the first coat becomes too dry before the second coat is applied, it will be very difficult to get a good flow on the next coat.

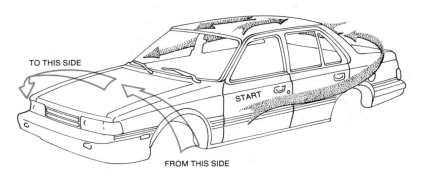

Figure 17-19   Painting across the hood

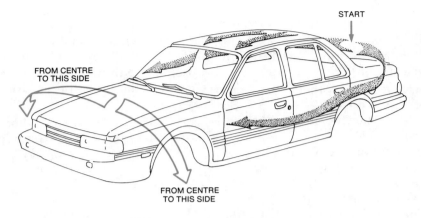

START

FROM CENTRE
TO THIS SIDE

FROM CENTRE
TO THIS SIDE

Figure 17-20   Painting outward from the middle of the hood

17-9 COMMON PAINT PROBLEMS AND THEIR SOLUTIONS

Checking, Crazing, and Cracking

Appearance (Figure 17-21).
(a)   Crow's feet (checks)
(b)   Irregular line separation (alligator checks)
(c)   "Dried mud" appearance (cracks)

Cause.
(a)   Insufficient drying of paint prior to recoating
(b)   Repeated extreme temperature changes
(c)   Excessively heavy coats of lacquer (cold checking)
(d)   Incomplete mixing of paint ingredients
(e)   Incompatibility of products (mixing in materials not designed for a product)
(f)   Recoating of a checked finish

A LINE CRACKS AND CROWFOOT CHECKS (ENLARGED)

Figure 17-21   Checking, crazing, and cracking

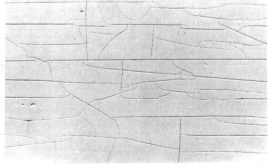

B LINE AND FIGURE CHECKS

Courtesy Coatings and Resins Division, Ditzler Automotive Refinishes

(g)   Thinner's softening acrylic lacquer (crazing)

Remedy. Remove the finish, right down through the checked paint, and refinish.

Prevention. In most cases, there is little one can do to prevent these conditions. They do not usually appear until some time after the painting is completed.

(a)   Wait a month or bake the first coat of paint, before applying the second.
(b)   Stir the paint thoroughly.
(c)   Seal a coat of one type of paint before covering it with another type of paint (e.g., painting acrylic lacquer over enamel).
(d)   Sand down and remove an old, crazed finish completely before repainting.

Blistering

Appearance (Figure 17-22).
(a)   Broken-edged craters.
(b)   Small, swelled areas like water blisters

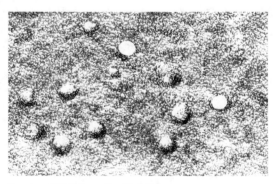

Courtesy CIL Automotive Finishes

Figure 17-22   Blisters

Cause.
(a)   Rust under surface
(b)   Oil or grease under surface
(c)   Moisture in spray-gun hoses
(d)   Trapped solvents

(e)   Exposure of paint to constant or repeated high humidity
(f)   Perforated rust holes in the metal

Remedy. Sand and refinish the damaged areas. Repair the rust perforations.

Prevention.
(a)   Clean and treat metal thoroughly.
(b)   Drain air lines of water frequently.
(c)   Thin products properly.
(d)   Allow proper drying times between coats of paint.

Peeling

Appearance (Figure 17-23). The top coat separates from the previous surface.

Courtesy Interchemical Corporation, Finishes Division

Figure 17-23   Peeling

Cause.
(a)   Improper surface cleaning
(b)   Use of incorrect undercoats
(c)   Poorly balanced thinning solvents.

Remedy. Sand and refinish the damaged areas.

Prevention.
(a)   Clean and treat the old surface thoroughly.
(b)   Use recommended primers for special metals.
(c)   Follow recommended refinishing practices.

Wrinkling

Appearance (Figure 17-24).

(a) Puckering of enamel

(b) "Prune skin" effect

(c) Loss of gloss as paint dries (minute wrinkling not visible to the naked eye)

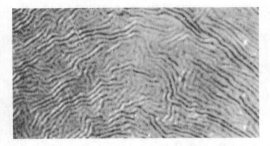

Courtesy Interchemical Corporation, Finishes Division

Figure 17-24   Wrinkling

Cause.

(a) Under-reduction or low air pressure, causing excessive film thickness

(b) Excessive coats of paint

(c) Fast reducers that create overloading

(d) Surface drying too quickly, trapping solvents

(e) Subjection of fresh paint to heat too soon

Remedy. Break open the top surface by sanding, and allow it to dry thoroughly. Then sand the area completely and refinish.

Prevention.

(a) Reduce enamels according to directions.

(b) Apply paints as recommended.

(c) Do not force dry until solvents have had time to "flash-off."

REVIEW QUESTIONS

1. Solvent is added to the paint to make it sprayable and to make its surface flow out smoothly. Explain what happens when (i) the room is extra hot, and (ii) the car is extra hot.

2. What type of solvent should be used for cold conditions?

3. List two spraying methods that might be used to compensate for:
    a) a cold room
    b) a damp or humid day
    c) a hot car

4. Explain what is meant by the "viscosity" of a material.

5. When extra solvent is added to the paint to compensate for a "too dry" condition, the air pressure must also be decreased. Why?

6. What ratio and type of solvent is recommended to reduce acrylic enamel and acrylic lacquer products?

7. a) How much solvent should be added to 3 L of paint using (i) a 1 to 3 ratio, and (ii) a 1 to 4 ratio?
    b) Explain how you would actually mix each, that is, the size or number of containers needed, procedure, etc.

8. Why should a thin stick or screwdriver never be used to stir the paint?

9. List the approximate gun adjustment settings for full spraying.

10. What shape should the spray pattern be for full spraying?

11. What adjustment can be made to correct a split spray pattern?

12. What noticeable paint surface characteristics are produced when (i) too much air pressure is used, and (ii) not enough air pressure is used?

13. Explain how the spray gun should be held and moved in relation to the surface being sprayed.

14. Why must the spray gun be held perpendicular to the surface while spraying?

15. Why must the spray gun be triggered at the start and end of each stroke?

16. When must the spray gun be triggered with relation to the start and end of each stroke?

17. What method can be used to locate the cause of a defective spray pattern?

18. How should a solidly plugged orifice be opened?

19. Why will wet colours not match dry colours?

20. Why are weathered enamel colours hard to match?

21. Define paint oxidation and list its causes.

22. Explain how the metallic flake is positioned to lighten and to darken a metallic colour.

23. Explain why standard metallic paint will not match basecoat/clearcoat systems metallics.

24. What spray-gun techniques can be used to lighten a metallic colour?

25. In spraying enamels, the first coat is allowed to become tacky (but not too dry) before the second coat is applied. Why?

26. When spraying acrylic enamels, a longer waiting period between coats is necessary. Why?

27. Explain the term "flash-off."

28. Why are lacquer products further reduced as each coat is applied?

29. Explain the cause of streaking and metallic blotches.

30. a) A third fog or mist coat is sometimes necessary with metallic colours. Why?
    b) How is it applied?

31. Give the procedure for blending paint into an area.

32. List the steps, in the correct order, for spraying a complete, prepared automobile. Include the preparation of the paint.

33. List three causes of paint wrinkling.

18

AUTOMOTIVE ELECTRICITY

18-1   The Storage Battery
18-2   Electricity
18-3   Circuits
18-4   Wires (Conductors)
18-5   Circuit Breakers, Fuses, and Fusible Links
18-6   Lamps (Bulbs)
18-7   Sealed-Beam Headlight Units
18-8   Testing Procedures

This chapter deals with the basics of electrical systems that may be encountered during various collision repair procedures.

The storage battery and alternator supply the electric current that operates the electrical components of the automobile. The battery supplies electrical energy to the starting motor and ignition system. Once the engine is running, the alternator supplies the electrical energy that operates the different phases of the electrical system and recharges the battery.

The alternator current output varies according to current demand. The demand depends on the number of electrical units being used and the state of "charge" in the battery. When many electrical units are being used and/or the battery is in a discharged state, the alternator output is much greater than when little electrical current is required.

18-1 THE STORAGE BATTERY

The storage battery contains a number of cells which are connected to each other by **lead links,** or **cell connectors.** Each cell is capable of producing about two volts of electrical pressure. Therefore, a six volt battery would have three cells and a twelve volt battery would have six cells.

Each cell consists of a number of positive and negative plates with thin layers of porous insulating material, called **separators,** between the plates (Figure 18-1). All the negative plates are connected together by a lead strap to form a negative group, and all the positive plates are joined together to form a positive group. The positive terminal post of the battery is the larger of the two and is usually marked with a + symbol. The nega-

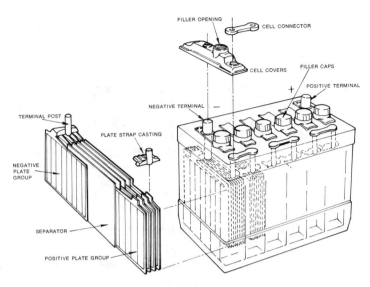

Figure 18-1   A 12 V battery

tive post is smaller and is marked with a − symbol. Some batteries are designed with side mount terminals rather than top type terminal posts (Figure 18-2).

The plates are submerged in a solution of sulphuric acid and distilled water. This solution is called the **electrolyte.** The elec-

Figure 18-2   12 V battery with side mount terminals

trolyte combines with the lead plates to create a chemical reaction which produces the electric current. When the battery is in use, the sulphuric acid in the electrolyte is used up by combining with both negative and positive plates to form a chemical compound called **lead sulphate.** When the sulphuric acid has been removed from the solution, the battery can no longer deliver a useful amount of electricity, and the battery is said to be **discharged.**

When an electric current is passed through the battery in the opposite direction to the discharge, the lead sulphate is broken up and expelled from the plates. The sulphuric acid returns to the electrolyte and the battery is gradually restored to its original strength, ready to deliver electricity again.

In operation, the battery gradually dissipates water from the electrolyte by vaporization. During charge, some battery water is decomposed to hydrogen and oxygen gas. If the solution level falls below the tops of the plates, water should be added. The only time it would be necessary to add sulphuric acid to a battery is when the battery has been spilled because of a vehicle collision or upset.

It is extremely dangerous to have a flame or to cause a spark around the battery both during the charging process and after the battery has been recharged. Ignition of the hydrogen gas that is emitted by the battery will blow up the battery.

Sulphuric acid is very harmful to skin, eyes, clothing, and the car finish. If some of the solution leaks out, it should be washed away as soon as possible with plenty of water. If the electrolyte comes in contact with the body or clothing, it should be washed off immediately with cold water and baking soda.

Charging the Battery

Before the battery is charged, the cells should be checked for the proper water level. When charger cables are connected to the battery, the positive cable must be connected to the positive terminal of the battery. The positive cable is identified by either a red clamp or a large + sign. The other cable must be connected to the negative terminal.

Always shut off the charger before disconnecting the cables; otherwise, a spark which could ignite the hydrogen gas and blow up the battery might occur. When removing a battery from a car, disengage the cable fastened to the ground first. This way it is unlikely that a spark will occur.

Using Jumper Cables. When an automobile is started with jumper cables, it is important that the two batteries be connected positive terminal to positive terminal and negative terminal to negative terminal. If this rule is not followed damage can result to the alternator or other electrical components.

18-2 ELECTRICITY

Electricity is a form of energy, and is created by the flow of electrons. Electrons are very small negatively charged particles. These negative particles concentrate at the negative terminal of any electrical source, such as a battery or alternator. Very few electrons are found at the positive terminal.

When the negative and positive terminals are connected together by means of a suitable electron path or circuit, the electrons tend to move away from each other toward the area where there are fewer electrons. The electrons therefore move from the negative terminal (the area of heaviest concentration) along the circuit to the positive terminal (the area of least electron concentration). Whenever electrons move through a circuit from the negative to the positive terminal, their movement is referred to as the electron flow or electrical current flow.

Electrical Terms

Voltage. A **volt** is the unit of measurement of electrical **potential** in a circuit. The electrical potential is responsible for the electron movement through the circuit. Potential (voltage) is determined by the amount of difference in the electron concentrations at the two terminals. The greater the difference, the higher the voltage or potential.

Voltage is measured by an instrument called a voltmeter. The SI unit symbol for voltage is V, as in a 12 V battery. For electrical formula work, a sloping V is used to indicate an unknown quantity of voltage. Most automotive electrical systems are of 12 V design.

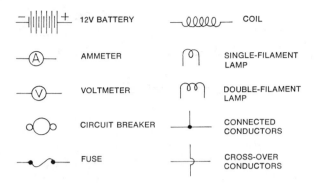

Figure 18-3   Schematic electrical symbols

Amperage. An **ampere** is the unit of measurement of the amount of electric current flowing past a given point. An **ammeter** is used to measure the amperage and to show the direction in which the current is flowing. The SI unit symbol for the ampere is A. Its quantity symbol is a sloping I.

Resistance. An **ohm** is the unit of measurement of the resistance in a circuit opposing a flow of one ampere moved by a potential of one volt. The SI unit symbol for the ohm is Ω. The quantity symbol is a sloping R.

Conductors

Conductors carry the electric current (electrons) from the source to the load and back to the source (Figure 18-3). They vary in size and material, depending on the distance the current has to travel and the amount of current to be carried. Copper, iron, tungsten, carbon, lead, aluminum, and silver are all used as conductors. (Tungsten, carbon, and lead are used more often in loads than as conductors.)

Insulators

Insulators prevent the electric current from leaking into another conductor. The type of material used is governed by the pressure in the circuit. Common insulators are rubber, plastic, cotton, fibre, Bakelite, porcelain, and glass.

Direct Current (dc)

An electrical current (electrons) which flows in only one direction through the circuit is referred to as dc. The current flows from the negative terminal through the circuit to the load and then returns to the positive terminal. Batteries produce the direct current used to operate the electrical equipment on the automobile.

All electrical systems have a certain **polarity**. This is determined by the battery post that is connected to the ground. If the positive post is connected to the ground, the car has a "positive-ground" system. If the negative post is connected to the ground, the system is "negative-ground." Most automotive electrical systems are now negative-ground.

Alternating Current (ac)

With ac current the electrons are made to flow first in one direction, then quickly reversed to flow back in the opposite direction. This ahead-back cycle is repeated every fraction of a second as the electrons move along the electrical circuit. If the cycle were to be repeated only once per second it would be said to have a frequency of one hertz (1 Hz). Most house electricity operates at 60 Hz. The electrons change direction 60 times a second as they move along the circuit. The automobile alternator produces ac current. Since all the electrical units on the automobile operate off direct current, the alternator output must be changed from alternating current to direct current. This is accomplished by **diodes** (one way electrical valves) in the alternator.

18-3 CIRCUITS

Electrical energy travels from the source, through the conductor to the work load, and back through another conductor to the source. The energy makes a complete "circuit." Electricity can flow only when a complete circuit is available. A control is added to every usable circuit in the form of a switch. The symbols used for this control are: •——• open; •——• closed.

In the automobile, the frame, body, and engine — good conductors — are used to form half the circuit, the **ground** (assuming negative ground). The current flows from the source to the work load by means of the body, frame, or engine and then returns to the source through the wire. Therefore, it is necessary to run one wire only to each work load to complete each circuit provided there is a continuous connection of metal parts. Many of the light housing and mounting parts are now being made of plastic material, non-electrical conductors. When plastic materials are used, a second wire must be used to complete the circuit from the load to the automobile ground.

Basic Circuits

The symbol for ground is

There are three basic types of circuits: series, parallel, and a combination of the two — series-parallel.

Series Circuit. This is a circuit in which the electric current has only one path through which to flow. The components or loads are connected end to end so the current that flows through one of them must flow through all of them. Current flows from the battery, through the ground, to the load or loads, then to the switch and back to the battery by way of the wire conductor. If any part of the electric circuit, even the bulb

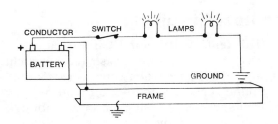

Figure 18-4   Series circuit

filament, were broken none of the electrical equipment would operate (Figure 18-4).

Parallel Circuit. In a parallel circuit, two or more pieces of equipment are connected to the circuit so that there are two or more paths for the current to follow. A break in any one of the parallel components will not affect the operation of the others (Figure 18-5).

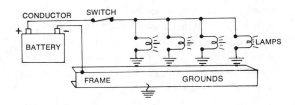

Figure 18-5   Parallel circuit

Series-Parallel Circuit. This circuit is a combination of the series and the parallel circuits (Figure 18-6).

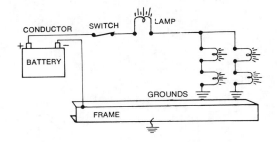

Figure 18-6   Series-parallel circuit

Other Circuits

Unintentional Ground Circuit. This is a circuit with little or no resistance to current flow. It is created when a conductor touches ground accidentally. Such a circuit usually occurs when the insulation of a conductor parts, allowing the bare wire to touch the ground (any metal part) (Figure 18-7).

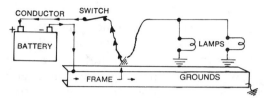

Figure 18-7   Unintentional ground circuit

The current flow by-passes the load to take the path of least resistance through the newly created shorter circuit. This low current flow resistance in the newly created circuit allows an excessive electron flow, which creates heat in the wire. The wire insulation overheats, melts, and possibly starts a fire, unless some means of control such as a fuse, circuit breaker, or fusible link has been built into the circuit.

Short Circuit. A short circuit occurs when two wires in a loom touch (Figure 18-8). The current then takes the path of least resistance, by-passing the load or loads of the normal circuit. An excessively large current flows under these conditions. Short circuits

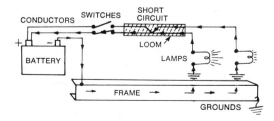

Figure 18-8   Short circuit

are sometimes caused while heating or welding during body repair operations; the wires in the wiring loom become cooked or melted together to cause short circuit problems.

18-4 WIRES (CONDUCTORS)

The circuits of an automobile electrical system are made up of wires of different sizes and lengths. There are two very different types of wires used: secondary wire and primary wire.

Secondary Wire

Secondary, or **high-tension,** wire is used for the high-voltage ignition circuits, as in spark plugs and coil wires. This type of wire has a rather small conductor but extremely heavy insulaton, to prevent the high-voltage surges from travelling through the insulation and going to ground before reaching the load (Figure 18-9).

RUBBER AND BRAID COVERING

NEOPRENE COVERING

Courtesy The Prestolite Company, Division of Eltra of Canada Limited

Figure 18-9   Secondary, or high-tension, wire

The centre conductor can be metal, i.e., copper, aluminum, but most high-tension wires have special carbon or graphite-impregnated cores.

Primary Wire

Primary wire is used for low-voltage ignition, lighting, and accessory circuits. Primary wire is also called **low-tension** wire. The conductor is made up of many copper strands of small diameter twisted together. The size and number of strands vary with the wire size (Figure 18-10).

The primary wire is made in a variety of different sizes. It is measured by the "gauge" numbering system: the smaller the wire, the higher the gauge number. A large wire can carry more amperage than a small wire. The size of wire needed for the different electric circuits is determined by the automobile manufacturer.

Courtesy The Prestolite Company, Division of Eltra of Canada Limited

Figure 18-10 Primary, or low-tension, wire

Wire Resistance

The resistance of a wire depends on the size of the conductor and the length of the circuit. The smaller the diameter, the greater the resistance; the longer the wire, the greater the resistance. When replacing a wire in the automobile electrical system, it is important that wire of the same gauge as the original be used. When a wire smaller than the original is used, its higher resistance will reduce the amount of current that can flow, and the loads (lamps, radio, etc.) will not operate properly. The smaller wire may overheat and cause a fire. Using a wire larger than the original will not cause any marked improvement in circuit performance and so is not economical.

Different-coloured wires are used for the automobile circuits to aid in tracing and checking electrical troubles.

Wire Connectors — Terminal and Snap-Together Type

Terminal connectors are generally designed to fasten to a terminal or post by means of a screw, bolt, or nut.

Many different shaped snap-type connectors are used, but all are similarly designed

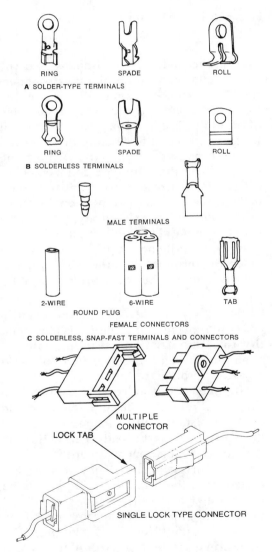

Figure 18-11 Terminals and connectors

Courtesy The Prestolite Company, Division of Eltra of Canada Limited

Figure 18-12   Crimping pliers

in that the male terminal snaps into the female end, making an electrical connection. The connectors can be designed either for single or multiple connections. On some of the multiple connectors there is a special lock that must be lifted before the two parts can be separated (Figure 18-11). Both the terminal and the snap-type connectors are designed to either solder or crimp to the end of the wires. A special pair of pliers is used to install the solderless crimp-type terminals onto the end of the wires. (Figure 18-12). It is important that enough pressure be used to pinch the terminal onto the wire so that a tight connection between the two may be made.

Replacing Connectors. Whenever it is necessary to replace a connector it is important that the same size be used to maintain the same electrical contact and therefore current flow through the circuit.

All joints and connections must be clean and tight throughout the entire circuit or the circuit resistance will increase, causing a low voltage across the loads. This will cause the electrical components to operate at less than their maximum efficiency. It is also important that the electrical components be well grounded, because a poor ground will cause a build-up of resistance to current flow so that the lights do not operate properly. These suggestions are particularly worth noting when the vehicle has been refinished.

Clean any paint, rust, or corrosion off all wire connectors and ground locations before reconnecting them.

With light housings made of non-conductive plastics, a separate ground wire must be used from the lamp to the body. Many manufacturers are now using printed circuit boards to provide the various internal circuits (including the ground circuit) in the plastic lamp housings (Figure 18-13).

Figure 18-13   Tail light housing printed circuit board

18-5 CIRCUIT BREAKERS, FUSES, AND FUSIBLE LINKS

These are safety devices which open the circuit automatically, preventing a further flow of current, when the amperage becomes too great. They are made with different amperage ratings for use with different types of circuits. The devices are installed in series with the components and circuits they protect. If one of the devices were not present in the circuit, an unintentional ground could cause the wire to overheat and start a fire. Circuit breakers, fuses, and fusible links are installed close to the current source so that as much of the circuit as possible is protected.

Circuit Breakers

The circuit breaker is a mechanical device that is activated by heat. When the amperage exceeds the device's safety rating, the heat created by the current causes a bimetal strip to bend, opening a set of contact points and stopping the flow of current through the circuit. When the mechanism cools, the contact points close, and the circuit is complete once more. This cycle is repeated until the fault has been corrected and the amperage is back to normal level (Figure 18-14).

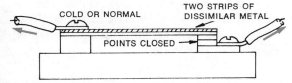

A BREAKER IS CARRYING A NORMAL LOAD. CONTACT POINTS ARE CLOSED AND THE CIRCUIT IS COMPLETE.

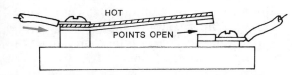

B BREAKER OVERLOADED, CAUSING THE BI-METALLIC STRIP TO HEAT UP. STRIP CURVES UPWARD SEPARATING THE POINTS, AND THE CIRCUIT IS BROKEN.

Figure 18-14   Circuit breaker

Fuses

There are different types of fuses. The older type is constructed of a glass tube with a thin strip of conductive metal passing through the centre. The metal strip is connected to steel end caps which seal the end of the glass tube and clip into the fuse panel clips. The newer, plug-in, style fuses have two bayonet terminals that plug into the fuse panel. This type is much easier to remove and replace.

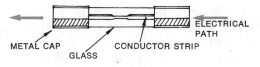

A GLASS TUBE TYPE

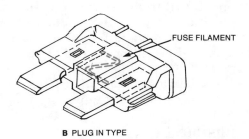

B PLUG IN TYPE

Figure 18-15A, B   Fuse types (A) glass tube type (B) plug-in type

The two types are not interchangeable (Figure 18-15). The size of their conductive centre strips determine the fuse amperage.

When two much current passes through the fuse, the strip of metal melts and the circuit is opened. When a fuse burns out, it must be replaced.

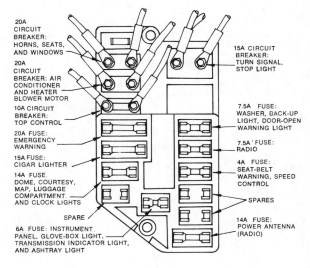

Figure 18-16   Fuse panel

Fuses (and circuit breakers) can be installed one to each circuit, or one fuse can be used to protect a number of single circuits.

Fuses are incorporated into a fuse block which serves the complete electrical system. A **fuse block** is a safety device which accommodates more than one circuit (Figure 18-16). In this system, one side of the fuse is connected to the conductor from the ignition switch and the other side is connected to circuit or circuits served by that fuse

The fuse connectors are labelled to identify the circuit and its amperage rating.

Fusible Links

Fusible links are short lengths of wire with rather heavy coverings. They are used in electrical circuits that are not generally protected by either fuses or circuit breakers, such as ignition and other engine compartment circuits. The fusible link wire size is four sizes smaller than the size of wire used in the circuit. (Figure 18-17).

Should any short-circuiting problems occur, the fusible link will melt and separate to open the circuit. Fusible links are similar to fuses in that once they have melted, they

must be replaced. Their wire gauge size is marked on the covering. The same size must be used to replace one that has short circuited.

18-6 LAMPS (BULBS)

Many different types and sizes of lamps, or **bulbs** as they are usually called, are used in the lighting system of the automobile. They are rated by the **candela** produced by a given voltage. All automotive bulbs are identified by a numbering system. The number is usually stamped on the base of the bulb. It classifies the lamp according to the candle power and amperage.

Some bulbs have two candela ratings. These bulbs have two filaments.

The bulbs used in automobile lights have either a single or a double filament (Figure 18-18). The filaments are made of fine, coiled tungsten wires which are vacuum-sealed in a glass chamber. This fine wire resists the current flow, producing heat which makes the filament glow. The length and size of the filament wire determines the resistance to current flow and therefore the

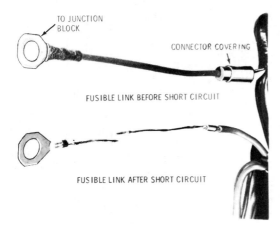

TO JUNCTION BLOCK

CONNECTOR COVERING

FUSIBLE LINK BEFORE SHORT CIRCUIT

FUSIBLE LINK AFTER SHORT CIRCUIT

Figure 18-17   Fusible link

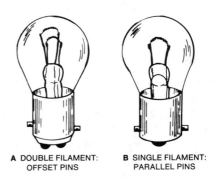

A DOUBLE FILAMENT: OFFSET PINS

B SINGLE FILAMENT: PARALLEL PINS

Figure 18-18   Double and single filament bulbs

bulb's candle power. If the glass enclosing the filament breaks, oxygen combines with the heat in the filament and the bulb burns out.

In most bulbs, one side of the filament is joined to the base of the bulb which is held in the light socket. The path of current therefore is from the negative terminal of the battery to ground, to the base of the bulb, through the filament, bulb contact, and switch to the positive terminal of the battery (Figure 18-19). When the filament breaks, the circuit is incomplete and the current will not flow. All of the lights on an automobile are connected in parallel. Should one burn out, the rest will continue to operate.

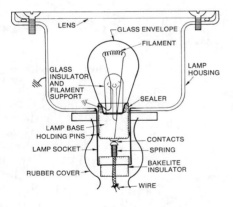

Figure 18-19   Lamp housing, bulb socket, and bulb

Double-contact bulbs which have two different-sized filaments are used in the parking lights and tail lights. The parking light bulbs, for example, produce two lights, one to be used as a parking light and the other, the brighter of the two, to be used as a directional signal. The same type of double-filament bulb is used in the rear lights. One filament produces the tail light. The other filament, the brighter of the two, produces the directional signal, the stop-light, or both. As previously explained, whether the larger filaments are used depends on the wiring circuits. When the stop-lights are wired through the signal-light switch, the same larger filament is used for both the stop- and signal-lights. When two separate circuits are used, separate bulbs are needed for both the stop and directional light.

Double-contact bulbs have two offset locking pins on the base, so that the bulb will fit into the socket only one way (Figure 18-18A). Twelve volt, double-contact bulbs are designated by the numbers 1034 or 1157. Bulb 1157 is a heavy-duty, double-contact bulb with heavier than normal filaments.

The two pins on the base of single-contact bulbs are the same height, as it makes no difference which way the bulb is installed in the socket. These bulbs are used in single-circuit lights like tail, stop, signal, and licence-plate lights (Figure 18-18B). Instrument panel and side marker bulbs are illustrated in Figure 18-20. They push in and lock into the socket. The other larger bulbs must be pushed in and turned to be locked into the socket.

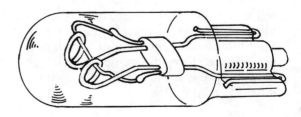

Figure 18-20   Side marker bulb

There are many different single-contact bulbs. The following chart lists some of the more common numbers and their applications.

Light Number	Application
67	licence-plate, parking lights
1156	back-up, turn signal, stop lights
194	instrument and side marker lights
57	instrument panel and indicator lights

Depending on the circuitry, some vehicle may have all double-contact bulbs, all single-contact bulbs, or a combination of both in their tail lights. When replacing a bulb, it is very important that the same type (i.e., single- or double-contact) and the same number be used. This is especially important in the signal-light circuits, as the flasher unit is usually designed to operate properly within certain candle power loads.

An inexperienced person jamming a single-contact bulb into a double-contact socket can cause very unusual light circuit problems. For example, the single contact of the bulb may be large enough to touch both contacts in the socket. Then, when the brake lights are operated, the current would be conducted to the socket contact, through the bulb contact, and into the tail light circuit where it would immediately "backfeed" into the front parking lights and all four side-marker lights.

18-7 SEALED-BEAM HEADLIGHT UNITS

The sealed-beam headlight units are round or rectangular in shape. Both types are also available in large or small sizes. In each case they consist of a sealed glass lens and reflec-

tor used with either a single or a double filament (Figure 18-21). Some automobiles are equipped with only a double-filament unit on each side. Others have both a double- and a single-filament unit on each side.

Some cars use **halogen** lights, which are brighter and longer focusing. They can be

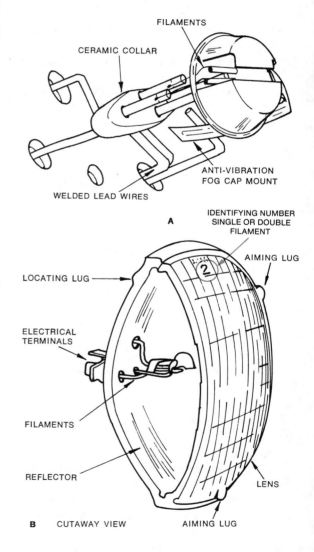

Figure 18-21 Sealed-beam headlight lamp

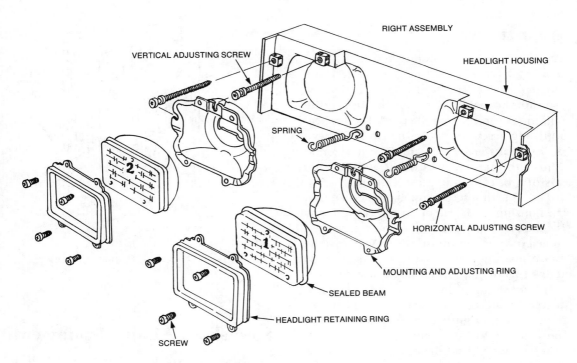

Figure 18-22   Typical headlight assembly

sealed units or have special single- or dou-ble-contact bulbs which mount in a steel or glass reflector. They must always be in-stalled as a set. Using only one with the con-ventional type would cause a spotlight effect on the oncoming driver.

The single-filament unit is designed for high-beam operation only, to provide a long, concentrated reach down the highway. A double-filament unit provides a high and low beam. In the double-filament, sealed beam, the filaments are positioned in the lamps so that the light produced by the up-per filament is spread over a large area close to the front of the car (low beam). The light produced by the lower filament is focused to project further down the road (high beam).

The sealed beams used in the dual-head-light system are identified by the numbers 1 and 2 moulded into the lamp lens at the 12-o'clock position. The #1 unit is the sin-gle-filament lamp while the #2 unit is the double-filament lamp. The number 2 unit is always positioned on the outside from the single beam #1 light. This ensures that the outer-most width of the vehicle is always indicated. There are moulded lugs posi-tioned differently on the backs of the two sealed beam units to prevent them from being installed other than in their correct mounting ring.

When high-beam lights are used, all four headlight units are operating. When low-beams are used instead, the single-filament unit goes out and the double-filament unit operates on low beam only, providing an "on-focus" light for city driving and for meeting other vehicles. Figure 18-22 illus-trates the construction of a typical dual-headlight assembly.

Adjustments

The mounting ring is connected to the light housing by two adjusting screws and one tension spring. The adjusting screws allow the units to be adjusted so the light beam will focus correctly on the road. The vertical adjusting screw controls the up and down position of the light beam. The horizontal adjusting screw controls the side-to-side position of the light beam (Figure 18-23).

The adjusting screw nut is connected into the housing. The head of the adjusting screw is connected into a slot in the mounting ring so that turning the adjusting screw in tips the mounting ring inward, while turning out the screw tips the mounting ring outward.

It is most important that the headlights be correctly adjusted (aimed) so that the driver has maximum lighting on the road ahead of the vehicle. Yet they must also not be adjusted so as to blind the oncoming driver as two vehicles meet.

It is not necessary to change the headlight adjustment screws when replacing a sealed-beam lamp. Only the retaining ring screws need be removed.

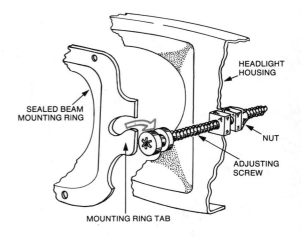

Figure 18-23   Headlight adjusting screw

Specialized Aiming Equipment

Headlight aimers mount onto the sealed beam against the three aiming lugs on the surface of each light. The aiming equipment is held against the aiming lugs by a suction cup. Figure 18-24 illustrates typical headlight aiming equipment. The procedure to adjust the lights varies according to the make of equipment.

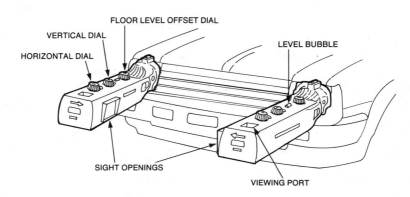

Figure 18-24   Headlight aiming equipment

18-8 TESTING PROCEDURES

The procedures to test various electrical components can be complicated, especially those that are controlled by computers. Using the wrong testing procedures can result in further damage to the computer, the wiring circuits, and the electrical components. Some computers are so sensitive that a charge of static electricity can be enough to damage them.

> Never MIG (GMAW) weld on a vehicle without first disconnecting the battery terminals. The electrical current from the welder can back-feed through the body ground half of the circuit, into the electrical component (including the computer) possibly damaging them.

Diagnosing the Problem

When there is a problem, do not immediately start tearing apart the wiring, lights, etc. Take a minute to analyse the problem, then check the possible causes in a logical order. The following are some common examples of light problems that can occur after a damaged vehicle has been repaired.

Example 1. No lights are working. This would indicate the battery is disconnected or fully discharged, the ignition switch is not on, a fuse is blown, or a wiring problem exists.

Example 2. Only half the lights are working. If all the lights are working on one side only, it would indicate fuse, wiring, poor ground problems, or blown bulbs on that circuit only.

Example 3. One or more lights are not working on each side of the vehicle. This would indicate localized problems such as a burned-out bulb or bad ground problems.

> The ground side of the circuit is as important as the actual wiring itself. The current must be able to make a complete circuit. A poor ground is often indicated by a very dim light. A poor ground can be caused by a badly rusted bulb socket, or by paint in the socket or on the socket mounting surfaces, or by a broken printed circuit in the tail-light housing.

Example 4. When one set of lights are turned on, for example, the left signal light, other unrelated lights such as the tail light also come on and flash. This type of condition would indicate a short circuit. A bare spot in the signal-light circuit wire is touching a similar bare wire in the tail-light circuit. Consider where the vehicle was repaired — might the wiring harness have been pinched in the accident? Was heat or welding used, and in what area? Could the wires in the harness have been melted together to create the short circuit? Could the wrong bulb — perhaps a single-contact bulb in a double contact socket — have been used by mistake? Consider that the lights were likely working before the accident: was something missed and not repaired during the repair procedure or was the problem actually created during the repairs?

Light and circuit tests can be easily made with a test light and/or an ohmmeter.

Testing a Bulb

To test a bulb remove it from the socket. Check it for a broken filament by turning it upside down and looking for a piece of the filament lying on the glass.

If there is no broken-off piece, check the

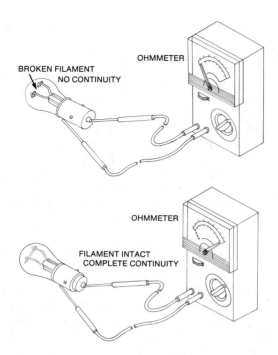

Figure 18-25   Testing the bulb using an ohmmeter

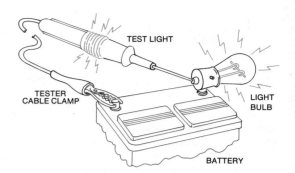

Figure 18-26   Testing a bulb with a test light

filament for a fine break. If none can be seen, use an ohmmeter to check for continuity. Place one probe on the base, the other on the bulb contact. If the filament is broken, the ohmmeter will not register (Figure 18-25).

The bulb can also be tested with a battery. Place the bulb contact on one terminal and touch a wire or the test light to the bulb base from the other battery terminal (Figure 18-26). A sealed-beam headlight can also be checked by using the ohmmeter to test for continuity or with a test light and battery.

Testing a Lamp Socket

Remove the bulb, turn on the lights, and connect the wire clip of the test light to a good ground on the vehicle. Carefully touch the test-light probe onto the socket bulb contact (Figure 18-27). Do not allow the side of the prod to touch the socket housing

(if it is metal) or an unintentional ground will occur which will likely blow the fuse. If the test light goes on, there is current at the contact. The problem is likely to be a poor ground between the bulb base and the socket housing or between the socket housing and the body.

The ground circuit will be directly through the socket to the housing and then to the body if all the parts are metal. Whenever any of the parts are plastic, a separate ground wire is needed to by-pass the plastic to ground the bulb socket to a metal part of the vehicle.

These ground wires from plastic light housings are often not connected separately to the body. They are usually all joined together through the wiring harness and connected to ground by one wire, often some distance away from the actual light. Check to see if this ground wire is connected and if the screw is tight. If there is no current to the light socket, separate the connector and use the test light to check the harness side of the connector (Figure 18-28).

Checking the Fuse and Holder

Check the fuse to see if it is burned out. If not, use the test light to jump across the two fuse clips. Make sure the ignition switch is on. If the test light goes on, then the current flow is to the load side of the fuse box.

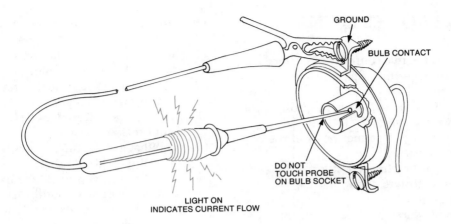

Figure 18-27   Testing the bulb socket contact

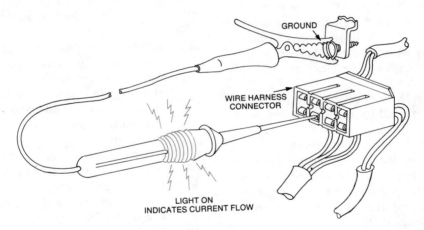

Figure 18-28   Testing the wiring harness connector

Checking for a Broken Wire

The outer insulating covering of the wire may appear perfect but the conductive inner strands of wire may be separated. Move out from the fuse box, ground the test light, and carefully poke the sharp prod of the test light into the wire. If the test light works, that section of the wire is conductive. Continue to check a further section of the wire until the break is found.

If there is not current flow in the wire immediately out from the fuse box, then the problem could be in the connector in the back of the fuse box. By using these basic checks, the cause can often be quickly isolated.

> When more serious electrical problems occur, check the vehicle's manual for the recommended testing procedures and the components wiring circuits.

REVIEW QUESTIONS

1. a) List the two sources of the electrical energy that operates the automobile.
   b) When is the energy from each source used?
2. How are the terminal posts of the battery identified?
3. Explain the change that takes place in the electrolyte as the battery is being discharged.
4. How is water gradually lost from the battery?
5. What procedure should be followed if the electrolyte should come in contact with a person's eyes, skin, or clothing?
6. Explain the procedure for charging a battery with a battery charger.
7. Briefly explain the electron flow theory.
8. What is the ampere? A volt?
9. Explain the differences between a conductor and an insulator.
10. Define the term "polarity."
11. Briefly explain the difference between alternating current and direct current.
12. State the purpose of the frame, body, and engine in the electrical circuits.
13. Explain the difference between a series and a parallel circuit. Draw a diagram of each.
14. Explain how an unintentional ground circuit is established.
15. How is the size of primary wire measured?
16. What determines the amount of amperage that a wire can carry?
17. Why must all electrical connectors be kept tight and clean?
18. Explain the differences between a circuit breaker and a fuse.
19. a) What are the differences between a single- and a double-contact bulb?
    b) Why are the pins on the base of the double-contact bulbs offset?
20. Draw a lamp and lamp housing, the battery, and the switch symbols. Complete the circuit and illustrate the current flow through each of the items.
21. How are the dual, sealed-beam headlight units identified?
22. Which of the dual headlights operates when the lights are on low beam?
23. What provision is made for adjusting or aligning the sealed-beam lamps?
24. Draw diagrams and explain how the mounting ring is fastened to the retaining screws.
25. List the parts that must be removed to replace a sealed beam unit.
26. Draw diagrams and explain two methods that can be used to check for broken bulb filaments.
27. The left rear tail light does not operate. List the testing procedure you would use to find the cause.

INDEX

Abrasive papers, 298–299
AC welders, 171
Acetylene, 146
Acetylene cylinders, 146–147
Acrylic enamels, 321
Acrylic lacquers, 320
  spraying, 363
Acrylic resins, 315, 320
Active gas, 178
Active solvents, 316
Adhesive tape, double-faced, 64
Adjustable body spoon attachments, 95
Adjusting
  deck lid, 222–226
  sealed beam headlight units, 384
  spray guns, 335
Aerials, masking, 307
Air bag spring, 287
Air cap, spray gun, 333–334
Air compressors, spray gun, 345–348
Air drying, 312–313
Air hammers, 44
Air pressure, spray gun, 356–357
Air refinishing hoses, 343–344
Air sanders, 299–300
Air supplied respirator mask, 349
Air transformers, spray gun, 344
Air valve, spray gun, 335
Alkyd paints, 318
Alternating current, 171, 374
Aluminum oxide, 298
Amperage, 171, 374
Amperage setting, arc welding, 175–176
Anchor nuts, 60
Applying plastic fillers, 112–113, 116–118
Arc welding, 168–188
Arc welding rods, 173
Arc welding speeds, 175
Automobile history, 1–4
Automotive enamel, 318–319
Aviation snips, 45

Backfire, 152
Baking, 314
Balanced flame, 151

Basecoat/clearcoat system, 323–324, 364–365
Battery, 371–373
Bench equipment, 274–276
Bending, 222
  deck-lid hinge, 225
  deck lid-to-hinge mounting panel, 224
  door, 238
  effects on steel, 66
  flange along the edge of a crowned panel, 210–212
  hood, 228
  right-angle flange, 207–209
  scrolled flange, 210
Bevel, reverse or mating, 139
Binders, 315–316
Bird nesting, 180
Bleeder-type spray guns, 335
Blending, 364–365
Blistering, 368
Blisters in filler, 118–119
Blocksanding, 302–303
Blowoff, 151
Blowpipe, 150
Board file, 51
Body clearance (twist drills), 45
Body construction, wooden, 1–2
Body files, 50–51
Body filing techniques, 74–75
Body fillers, 68, 107–119
Body mounts, shimming the, 242–243
Body jacks, 90–96
Body roll, 291
Body trimmer's pliers, 41
Bolts, 53–57
  cutting off heads of, 163
  sizes, 54
  strength, 56–57
  threads, 55–56
  types of, 53–54
Bourdon tube, 149
Box frame, 247
Box wrenches, 38
Braze welding, 163–166
Brazing, 163
Bronze welding, 163
Buckles, 87–88

Buffing, 81
Build-up, 156–157
Bulbs, 381, 385
Bull's eye, 300
Bumper bolts, 54
Bumpers, 15–16
  adjustments, 233–234
Bumping, 67
Bumping hammers, 46
  pick, 46
Butt joining a complete replacement panel, 139–140
Butt joint, 153

Cables
  charger, 373
  electric arc, 170
  jumper, 373
Camber, 293
Candela, 380
Cap screws, 53
Carburizing flame, 151
Carriage bolts, 53–54
Cartridge respirator, 349
Castellated nut, 58
Casters, 293
Catalyst, 108–109
Causes of misalignment, 220
Causes of spray painting troubles, 359
Cell connectors, 371
Centre-link, idler arm, steering-gear design, 291
Centre pillars, 11
  trim, 28
Centre punch, 44
Channel design, 247
Channels, 8, 67
  window run, 24
Charger cables, 373
Charging the battery, 373
Chassis, 4, 5
Checking, crazing, and cracking, 367
Checking electrical energy in the battery, 373
Chisels, 43–44
Circuit breakers, 379
Circuits, 170, 375
Clamps, 42

Cleaning precautions, spray guns, 340
Clips
  snap-in, 63
  snap-over, 64
  threaded, 63
  tubular speed, 59–60
Closed-box design, 247
Closed-coat discs, 78
Coal tar hydrocarbons, 316
Coarse thread, 55–56
Coil spring energy absorber, 15–16
Coil springs, 287
Cold chisels, 43–44
Collision damage, rules for repairing, 253–256
Combination-crowned panel, 98
  force exerted against the end of, 101–102
  force exerted on, 100–101
  repairing, 101
Combination pliers, 41
Combination wrench, 39
Commercial vehicle frames, 253
Commercial vehicle suspension systems, 286–287
Compound curve, shaping a flat sheet over a, 215–216
Compounds, 329
Compressor maintenance, 347–348
Compressors, spray gun air, 345
Conductors, 347, 375
Constant current machine, 175
Contact tips, 177
Contraction, 190–192
Control of spray painting, 359
Control positions, 257–262
Conventional vehicle design, 5–6, 247–248
Convex file, 75
Coolant, 19–20
Corner joint, 153
Correcting an improper spray pattern, 359
Cotter pin, 58
Coupling, quick change, 94
Crack, welding a, 199
Cracked parts, repairing, 138
Cracking, 367
Craters, 368
Crazing, 367

Creases
  forming in sheet metal, 213–214
  repairing, 104
Crimping pliers, 378
Cross filing, 76–77
Cross-peen hammers, 47
Crosscutting, 80–81
Crowned panels
  bending a flange along the edge of a, 210–211
  filing, 75
Crowns, 8, 98
Crow's feet, 367
Curing paint, 312
Current, 374
  alternating, 374
  direct, 374
Cutting attachments, oxy-acetylene equipment, 161
Cutting off heads of rivets or bolts, 163
Cutting plate, 161
Cutting sheet metal, 162
Cutting with welding tip, 161
Cylinders
  acetylene, 146–147
  care of, 147
  oxygen, 146

Damage
  direct, 88
  factors determing type, 97
  indirect, 89
  pivot point of, 87
  study of, 85–90
Datum reference plane, 259
DC welders, 171
Dead centre, 45
Deck lid, 13–14
  fitting adjustments, 222–223
Deck-lid hinge, bending the, 224
Deck-lid lock and striker catch, 14, 226–227
Deck-lid-to-hinge mounting panel, bending or straightening the, 224–226
Delaminates, repairing, 139
Dents, minor, 71–71
Diagonal-cutting pliers, 41
Diagonal measurements, 264
Diamond, 257

Diaphragm-type, air compressor, 346
Diluent solvents, 316
Dinging hammers, 46
  pick, 46
Diodes, 374
Direct current, 171, 374
Direct damage, 88–89
  repairing, 90
Disc cutter, 78
Disc sander, 299–300
Disc grinder, 80–81
Distance of spray gun from work, 357–358
Dog-tracking, 296
Dollies, 47–49
  methods, 70–71
  principle of action, 69–70
Door adjustments, 235–244
Door construction, 20-21
Door fitting, 234–244
  bending, 238–241
  checking and adjusting, 235–236, 244
  forward and back adjustment, 236
  in and out adjustment, 235–236
  raising or lowering, 235
Door handles, 26
Door hinges, 234–235, 238, 240, 241
Door lock cylinder assembly, 22
Door lock striker catch adjustments, 244
Door opening corrections, 242–244
  jacking, 242
Door panel, forming a partial, 216–218
Door seal, 244–245
Door trim, 21–22
Double-coat, 363
Double-contact bulbs, 381
Double-curve, shaping a flat sheet over a, 215–216
Double high-crowned panel, 98
  pushing force exerted on, 99
  repairing, 99–100
Drift punch, 44
Drill body, 45
Drill point, 45
Drill shank, 45

Drills, twist, 45
Drip mouldings, 12
Drives, 40
Dryers, 317
Drying processes, 312
Dual action sander, 99
Ductility, 65
Dust mask, 348

Edge joint, 153
Edges
  forming rolled, 212
  shrinking, 203
Elastic limit, 65
Elasticity, 65
Electric arc welders, 168–188
Electric welding, 168–188
Electrical symbols, 374
Electrical terms, 171, 373
Electrode classification, 173
Electrode holder, 170
Electrodes, 176
Electrolyte, 372
Enamels, 318–319
  drying process, 318
  reducing, 318
  spraying, 363
Epoxy adhesives, 122–123
Epoxy primer, 326
Etching, 330
Evaporation, 313
  of solvents, 316–317
Expansion, 190–192
Extender pigments, 314
Extensions
  hydraulic jack, 95
  slip-lock, 95
Exterior fasteners, 63
Exterior trim, 29
External-mix air cap, 333, 335

Fan, 19
Fasteners, special, 56–61
Feather edging, 299
Feed, 337
Feel method, 74
Fender washers, 62
Fenders, 16–17
Fibreglass reinforced plastic, 131
Fibreglass repairs, 131–138
  precautions, 134
Filaments, 381
File coarseness, 43

File handle, 50
Files, 43
  body, 50–51
  half-round, or convex, 75
Filing
  cross and X, 76
  crowned panels, 75
  flat panels, 75
  method, 74
  plastic fillers, 113–115
  reverse-crowned panels, 75
  techniques, 74–76
Filler panel, 18
Fillers, 68, 107–108
  applying, 111
  finishing, 113–116
  mixing, 110
  problems and remedies,
    118–119
  used over previous coats,
    116–118
Filler pigments, 314
Fillet weld, 153–154
Fine thread, 56
Finishing washers, 62
Fish-eyes, 328
Fish plates, 250
Fitting, 221
Flames, welding, 151–152
Flanged hex nut, 58
Flanges, 8
  bending along the edge of a
    crowned panel, 210–211
  bending a right-angle, 208
  forming rolled, 212
Flare nut wrench, 39
Flashback, 152
Flash-off period, 327
Flat chisels, 44
Flat lap joint, 140–142
Flat panels, filing, 75
Flat washers, 61
Flex heads, 96
Flexible disc, 346
Floor pan assembly, 9–10
Fluid adjustment, 335
  valve, 336
Fluid needle, 334
Fluid refinishing hoses, 343–344
Fluid tip, 334
Flush mounted, 24
Flux, 163
Fogging, 363

Folding sandpaper, 301
Forced drying, 314
Force flow, 87
Forces, type of, 97
Forming
  creases in sheet metal,
    213–214
  rolled edges, 212–213
  partial door panel, 216–218
  straight line curves, 213
  straight ridges in sheet metal,
    213–214
Forward-and-back door adjust-
  ment, 236
Frame construction, 247–253
Frame design, 247–253
Frame dimension chart, 260–261
Frame gauges, 262–263, 266
Frame metals, 250
Frame misalignment, 253
  checking for, 254
Frame repairing, 253
Frame straightening equipment,
  270–279
Frame straightening methods,
  280–285
Front cowl assembly, 10-11
Front end assembly, 16–18
Front fender assembly adjust-
  ment, 231–232
Front kick down, 255
Front of the hood, fitting,
  229–230
Fuse block, 380
Fuses, 379, 386
Fusible links, 380
Fusion welding, 154, 157

Galvanized metals, welding, 145
Garnish mouldings, 27
Gas metal arc welding, 169,
  176–183
Glass, door, 23
  safety, 29–30
Glass breakage, 30-31
Glass mats, 131–134
Glazing putty, 303
Gouges, 104
  repairing, 104
  shrinking, 203
Gravity-feed spray guns, 339–340
  operating principles, 339–340
  cleaning, 340

Grease removers, 328–329
Grille, 18
Grinders, 77–81
  disc, 80–81
Grinder safety rules, 79–80
Grinding discs, 78–79
Grit sizes, 78, 299
Ground, 375
Gun control, 181
Gun positions, 181

Hacksaws, 42–43
Hair-line cracks, repairing, 139
Half-round file, 75
Halogen light, 382
Hammer and dolly methods, 70-71
Hammers, 46–47, 69
  bumping, 46
  bumping pick, 46
  cross-peen, 47
  dinging, 46
  heavy, 69
  installing a new handle, 47–48
  light, 69
  long-pick, 46
  round-faced, 47
  square-faced, 47
Hand snips, 44–55
Handles, masking, 306
Handsanding, 302
Hardener
  cream, 108
  liquid, 108
Hatch back, 14
Header panel, 18
Headlight units, sealed beam, 382–383
Headlining, 28
Heat, effects on metal, 190–197
Heat control, 173
Heat distortion
  preventing, 197–198
  repairing, 198
Heating the frame, 283
Heavy-duty drive, 40
Heavy, hammer on-dolly method, 71
Hex key wrench, 41
Hex nuts, 58
High amperage setting, 175
High crowns, 98
High spots, methods of
  detecting, 74–76

High-strength steel, 83–85
  disadvantages, 84–85
  tensile strength, 85
  types, 83
  yield strength, 85
High tension wires, 376
Hinge buckle, 87
Holes, repairing, 135–137
Hollow rivets, 62–63
Hood, 14
  bending, 228
  fitting, 227–230
  fitting the front of, 229–230
Hood lock and safety catch, 15
Hood respirator, 349
Horizontal position, 153, 159
Hoses, welding cylinder, 150
"Hot spot," 201–202
Hydraulic body jacks, 91–92
  safety precautions, 96–97

I-beam shapes, 247
Ice pick, 44
Identification plate, 307
Impact absorbing bumpers, 15-16
Impact driver set, 37
Impact forces, 97–104
Improper spray patterns,
  correcting, 359–360
In-and-out door adjustments, 236–237
Independent suspension systems, 287, 289–290
Indirect damage, 89
  repairing, 90, 253
Inert gas, 177–178
Inner splash panels, 17
Insulators, 374
Intercooler, 347
Interior hardware, 24–27
Interior trim, 24–27
Internal-mix air cap, 333

Jack attachments, 91–92
Jack extensions, 91
Jacking, 221
  door opening, 235, 242
Jacks, mechanical, 90
  hydraulic, 91–92
Jig, 4
Jounce, 288
Jumper cables, 373

Ketones, 316
Kick panel, 28

Lacquer putty, 327
Lacquers, 319–320
  reducing, 354
  spraying, 363
Laminated safety glass, 29–30
Lamps, 381–382, 385
Lap joining a partial panel, 140–142
Lap joint, 153
Laser measuring system, 279–280
Latent solvents, 316
Lead links, 371
Leaf springs, 286
Leafing, 324
Light, hammer on-dolly method, 70–71
Lighting the welding torch, 151
Lip clearance, 45
Lips, drill, 45
Lock and striker catch, 226
Locks, 13, 14, 22
Lock striker plate, positioning, 242
Lock washers, 61
Long-pick hammers, 46
Low amperage setting, 175
Low-crowned panel, 100
  force exerted on, 100
  repairing, 100
Low spots, methods of
  detecting, 74–76
  picking up, 77
Low tension wire, 377
Lowering the door, 235

Machine screws, 57
MacPherson strut suspension
  system, 290
Mandrel, 62
Mash, 256–257
  checking for, 268
Masking, 305–307
Matching colours, 360
Mechanical body jacks, 91
Metal conditioner, 330
Metal finishing, 68
Metal screws, 64
  sheet, 57–58
Metal stamping, 3–4
Metal strength, 193–194

Metallic topcoats, 324
  matching, 361
  spraying, 363
Methods of detecting high and
  low spots, 74–76
Metric threads, 55
Midget drive, 40
Mig welding, 176
Minor dents, 71–73
Misalignment
  causes of, 220
  sequence in repairing, 257–258
Mix, 333
Mixing plastic fillers, 110–111
Molecular realignment, 82
Moulding fasteners, 63

Needle-nose pliers, 41
Neutral flame, 151
Nitrocellulose lacquers, 320
Non-bleeder spray guns, 335
Notches, 210–211
Nuts, 58–59
  castellated hex, 58
  flanged hex, 58
  hex, 58
  retainer, 58
  sizes, 59
  slotted hex, 58
  square, 58
Nut insert, 63

Off-centre loads, 96
Offset screwdrivers, 37
Ohm, 374
Open circuit, 375
Open-coat discs, 78
Open-end wrenches, 38
Optical ratings, 31
Orange peel, 329
Orbital sander, 299
Overhead position joints, 181
Over- reduction of paint, 354
Overslung springs, 287
Oxidation, 313, 319
Oxidizing flame, 151–152
Oxy-acetylene equipment,
  146–152
  acetylene cylinders, 146–147
  assembling, 150
  blowpipe, 150
  flame, 151–152
  hoses, 150
  oxygen cylinders, 146

precautions, 147
regulators, 147–148
tips, 150
Oxygen cutting, 161–162

Paint ingredients, 314–317
Paint problems and their
  solutions, 367–369
Paints, 312–324
  reducing, 354
  stirring, 355–356
Panels
  inner, 8–9
  outer, 8–9
  quarter, 11
  repairing, 85–87
  replacing, 139–140
  rocker, 9–10
  strength, 7–8, 82
Parallel circuit, 375
Parts of a spray gun, 332–334
Passenger vehicle suspension
  system, 287–289
Patches, welding, 198–199
Peeling, 368
Penetration, 156
Petroleum hydrocarbons, 316
Phillips screwdrivers, 36
Pick hammers, 46
Picking up low spots, 77
Pigment, 314–315
Pin holes in filler, 118
Pin punch, 44
Pipe thread, 56
Piston-type air compressor,
  346–347
Pitch, thread, 55
Pivot point of damage, 87
Plasma arc cutting, 186–188
Plastic drive rivets, 60–61
Plastic fillers, 107–119
Plastic parts, repairing, 123–127
Plastic welding
  how to use, 128–131
  tips, 129–130
  welders, 127–128
Plasticizers, 317
Plate, cutting, 161–162
Pliers, 41–42
  body trimmers, 41
  combination, 41
  diagonal cutting, 41
  needle nose, 42
  vise grips, 42

Plug welds, 154, 166, 185
Point of impact, 72
Polarity, 170, 172
Polisher application of rubbing
  compounds, 329–330
Polishing, 329
Polyester putty, 327
Polyester resin, 315
Polyesters, 323
Polyethylene primer, 326
Polymerization, 313
Polypropylene primer, 326
Polyurethane enamels, 322–323
Pop rivets, 62
Portable puller, 271
Pozidriver screwdriver, 36
Precautions when repairing
  fibreglass, 109
Preheat flames, 161
Preheat orifices, 161
Preparing the resin mix,
  134–135
Pressure, 97
Pressure-feed spray guns
  cleaning, 340
  operating principles, 338
  vs. siphon-feed guns, 339
Pressure in regulators, 148
Primary pigments, 314, 326
Primary wire, 377
Primers, 325
Primer surfacer, 326–327
Priming plastic fillers, 119
Principle of dolly action, 69–70
Pry bars, 50
Puddle, 155
Pulling force, 97
Punches, 44
Punctures, repairing, 135–137
Push and pull rams, 93–94
Push-in trim clips, 60
Pushing force, 97
Putties, 327

Quarter panels, 11
Quick-change coupling, 94

Rack and pinion steering, 291
Radiator, 19–20
Radiator coolant, 19–20
Radiator cradle adjustments,
  232–233
Radiator support, 17, 18, 19
Raising the door, 235

Rams, 93–96
  attachments, 95–96
  extensions, 94
  types, 93–94
Ratcheting box wrenches, 39
Rear kick down, 255
Rear window, 31–32
Rebound, 289
Reducers, 316
Reducing
  acrylic enamels, 321
  acrylic lacquers, 320
  enamels, 318
  enamel primers, 326
  lacquers, 318
  lacquer primers, 326
  paint, 354
Reduction gear unit, 291
Refinishing the complete auto-
  mobile, 365–366
Refinishing hoses, air and fluid,
  343–344
Regulator valve gauges, 149–150
Regulator pressure, 148, 149
Regulators, 147–149
Removing minor dent, 72–73
Removing the underseal, or
  sound deadener, 72
Removing warping, 219
Removing wax, 328--329
Replacing connectors, 378
Resin mix, preparing the,
  134–135
Resins, 107, 121, 315
  silicon, 328
  thermoplastic, 316
  thermosetting, 316
Resistance, 374
Respirators, 348–349
Retainer nut, 58
Retaining link clip, 61
Reveal mouldings, 32–33
Reverse bevel, 139
Reverse-crowned panels
  filing, 75–76
  force exerted on, 103
  repairing, 103
Reverse polarity, 172
Ridges, 8, 67
Right-angle flange, bending a,
  207–209
Rip, welding a, 199–200
Riveting pliers, 62

Rivets, 62
  cutting off heads of, 163
Rocker panels, 9–10
Roll buckle, 87–88
Rolled edges, forming, 212–213
Roof rails, 11-12
Round-faced hammers, 47
Rubber bumper attachments, 96
Rubbing compounds, 329–330
Rules for repairing collision
  damage, 253–256
Rules for straightening sheet
  metal, 86–87
Running beads, 154–157,
  173–174

Safety glass, 29–32
Safety rules
  hydraulic jack, 96–97
  grinder, 79–80
Sag, 254–255
  checking for, 267
Sander, disc, 299–300
Sanding block, 302–303
Sanding operations, 299–304
Sandpaper, 298–299
Sandpaper minerals, 298
Sash channel, 24
Scratch awl, 44
Scratch patterns, 68
Scratches, repairing, 104
Scratching to obtain an arc, 173
Screwdrivers, 35–36
  offset, 37
  Phillips, 36
  Pozidrive, 36
  torx, 36
Screws, 57–58
  machine, 57
  metal, 64
  sheet metal, 57–58
  sizes, 58
Scrolled flange, bending a, 210
Scrub radius, 294
Sealant-bound glass, 31–32
Sealed-beam headlight units,
  382–384
  adjusting, 384
Sealers, 327–328
Seat construction, 28
Seat track mechanisms, 28–29
Secondary wire, 377

Self-centring frame gauges, 262
Self-centring gauges, 266
Separators, 371
Sequence in repairing conditions
  of misalignment, 257–258
Series circuit, 375
Series-parallel circuit, 375
Set-up, 281
Shaping a flat sheet over a
  double or compound curve,
  215–216
Sheet metal, 65–67
  characteristics, 65
  cutting, 162
  damage to, 87–89
  effects of bending on, 66
  expansion and contraction in,
    194–196
  properties, 81–82
  repairing procedures, 90
  screws, 57–58
  strength, 82–83
  straightening, 86–87
  stretched, 103–104
  thickness, 82
  welding, 159
Shielded metal arc welding,168,
  172–176
Shimming, 221, 242
Shims, 221
Shock absorbers, 288
Short circuit, 376
  cycle, 179
Short, long arm suspension, 288
Shorty ram, 93–94
Shrinking, 200–204
  edge, 203–204
  gouge, 203
Side rails, 248
Side mounted hinge, 227
Sight method, 74
Silicon carbide, 298
Silicon resins, 328
Single-contact bulbs, 380–381
Single-crowned panel
  force exerted against the end
    of, 101
  force exerted along the length
    of, 102–103
  force exerted crosswise to,
    102
  repairing, 102
Single-stage air compressor, 346

Single-stage regulator, 148
Siphon-feed spray guns
  cleaning, 338, 340
  operating principles of, 337
  vs. pressure-feed guns, 339
Slotted hex nut, 58
Snap-type connectors, 377
Snips, 44–45
Socket wrench sets, 39–40
Solid rear axle suspension
  system, 287
Solutions to paint problems,
  367–369
Solvents, 316
  evaporation, 316–317
  sources, 316
Sound deadener, removing, 72
Space body shell construction,
  252–253
Special fasteners, 59–61
Speed clips, 59–60
Speed nuts, 60
Split parts, repairing, 138
Spoons, 49
SSpot-in,S 364
Spot spraying, 364
Spot welding, 183
  controls, 184
  nozzles, 183–184
  procedure, 184–185
Spray booth, 351
Spray guns, 332–343
  adjustments,, 335-336, 356
  cleaning, 340
  maintenance, 341
  parts of, 333–335
  problems and causes, 341–342
  speed, 358
  setting, 356
  techniques, 357–359
  types, 337–340
  using, 356–359
Spray painting control, problems,
  and causes, 359
Spray pattern adjustment valve,
  335
  correcting an improper, 359
Spraying procedure, 353–354,
  363–364
Spreader adjustment valve, 335
Spreader attachment, 95
Spring leaves, 286
Spring lock washers, 62

Springs, 286
  underslung and overslung,
  287
Square-faced hammers, 47
Square nut, 58
Stabilizer shaft, 291
Staining of body filler, 119
Standard drive, 40
Starter punch, 44
Steel beam, 20
Steering-axis inclination, 295–296
Steering linkage, 291
Stirring paint, 355
Stone shield, 18
Storage battery, 371–373
Stove bolts, 54
Straight polarity, 172
Straight ridges forming in sheet
  metal, 213–214
Straightening, 221
  deck lid-to-hinge mounting
  panel, 224–226
Strap-type hinge, 234, 241
Strength of panels, 7–8, 82
Stress relieving, 283
Stretched sheet metal, 103–104
Striking the arc, 173
Structural members, 247
Studs, 54, 63
Surface imperfections, feeling
  for, 74
Surface preparation for painting,
  307–310
Surface preparation for plastic
  filling, 109–110
Surface sanding, 301–302
Surform file, 51
Suspension systems, 285–291
Sway, 255
Sway bar, 291
Synthetic enamels, 318, 321

Tacking a patch, 198
Tack rag, 330
Tack weld, 154, 185
Talc, 107–108
Taper punch, 44
Tapering, 299
Tapping to obtain an arc, 173
Tee joint, 153
Temperature of spray booth and
  vehicle, 351–352
Tempered safety glass, 30

Tension, 97, 100
Terminal connectors, 377
Terminals, 377
Testing electric circuit, 385
Thermoplastic plastics, 121
Thermosetting resin, 121, 122
Thinners, 316
Thread pitch, 55
Threads, 55–56
  coarse, 55
  fine, 55
  identification of, 55–56
  pipe, 56
Through-centre point, 99
Tie bar, 18
Toe-in and toe-out, 295
Topcoats, 298, 318
Torn parts, repairing, 138
Torsion bar, 131, 287
Torque wrenches, 40–41
Torx screwdrivers, 36
Tracking, 296
Tramming gauge, 262–263
Transformers, spray gun air,344
Trigger, 336
Triggering the spray gun, 358
Troubles, spray painting, 359
Tubular speed clips, 59–60
Turning radius, 295
Twist drills, 45
Twist, 257
  checking for, 267–268
Two-stage air compressor,
  346–347
Two-stage regulator, 148
Two-tone masking, 306–307

Undercoats, 324–328
Underseal, removing, 72
Underslung springs, 287
Unintentional ground circuit,
  376
Unitized vehicle design, 5, 6–7
Unitized vehicle frames, 247,
  250
  repair procedures, 281–282
Universal systems, 276
Upper body measuring points,
  264
Urethanes, 322–323
Uses of the disc grinder, 80–81
Using jumper cables, 373

Ventilator window, 23
Vertical position joints, 181
Vertical welds, 159
Vibrators, 299, 309
Vinyl wash, 325
Viscosity, 354
Vise grips, 42
Volt, 171
Voltage, 373

Warping, removing, 219
Washers, 61–62
  flat, 61
  lock, 61
  sizes, 62
  spring lock, 62
  fender, 62
  finishing, 62
Watersanding, 304
Wax removal, 328–329
Weatherstrip, 13, 31
  checking the seal of, 244–245
Wedgy attachment, 95
Welders, ac and dc, 171
Welding
  crack or rip, 199–200
  galvanized iron,145
  gas metal arc, 144
  natural gas, 145

oxy-acetylene, 144
patches, 199
plasma arc, 144
propane, 144
repair panels, 199
safety, 144–145
sheet metal, 159
spot, 144
types of, 144
with welding rod, 156
without welding rod, 154
Welding flames, 151–152
Welding gun, 170
Welding joints, 153–154
Welding positions,
  horizontal, 153
  vertical, 153
Welding precautions, 147
Welding procedure, 150–151,
  155, 157
Welding speed, 176
Welding tips, 150
  cutting with, 161–162
Welds
  fillet, 153–154
  horizontal, 159
  plug, 154
  tack, 154
  vertical, 159

Wheel alignment principles,
  292–296
  settings, 293
Window regulator, 23–24
Window run channel, 24
Windows, masking, 305–306
Windshield, 31–32
Wire resistance, 377
Wires, 376–378
Wooden body construction, 2
Work hardening, theory of,
  66–67
Wrenches, 37–41
  box, 38
  combination, 39
  flare nut, 39
  hex key, 41
  open end, 38
  ratcheting box, 39
  sizes, 38
  socket, 39–40
  torque, 40–41
Wrinkling, 369

X filing, 76–77

Yield point, 104

Zero point, 99
Zinc chromate primer, 325